D0340592

NUTATION AND FORCED MOTION OF THE EARTH'S POLE

Е. П. ФЕДОРОВ

НУТАЦИЯ И ВЫНУЖДЕННОЕ ДВИЖЕНИЕ ПОЛЮСОВ ЗЕМЛИ

ПО ДАННЫМ ШИРОТНЫХ НАБЛЮДЕНИЙ

NUTATION AND FORCED MOTION OF THE EARTH'S POLE

From the Data of Latitude Observations

BY

YE. P. FEDOROV

ASTRONOMICAL OBSERVATORY
UKRAINIAN ACADEMY OF SCIENCES, KIEV

TRANSLATED FROM THE RUSSIAN BY

BERTHA SWIRLES JEFFREYS, M.A., PH.D.

FELLOW OF GIRTON COLLEGE, CAMBRIDGE

WITH A FOREWORD BY

SIR HAROLD JEFFREYS, F.R.S.

FORMERLY PLUMIAN PROFESSOR OF ASTRONOMY
IN THE UNIVERSITY OF CAMBRIDGE

A Pergamon Press Book

THE MACMILLAN COMPANY
NEW YORK
1963

This book is distributed by
THE MACMILLAN COMPANY · NEW YORK
pursuant to a special arrangement with
PERGAMON PRESS LTD
Oxford, England

Library of Congress Card Number: 61-11525

A translation of the original volume
Nutatsiya i Vynuzhdennoye Dvizheniye Polyusov Zemli po Dannym Shirotnykh Hablyudenii
(Izdatel'stvo Akademii Nauk Ukrainskoi SSR Kiev–1958)

The text of this book has been corrected
with the knowledge of the author

Printed in Great Britain at Compton Printing Works, London

CONTENTS

CONTENTS

F O R E W O R D

by Sir Harold Jeffreys, F.R.S.

1. The easiest way of deriving theoretical expressions is by use of Lagrange's theory of small oscillations. The Earth is treated as a rigid body with moments of inertia A, A, C. We take the effect of the Sun first and treat the orbit as circular.*

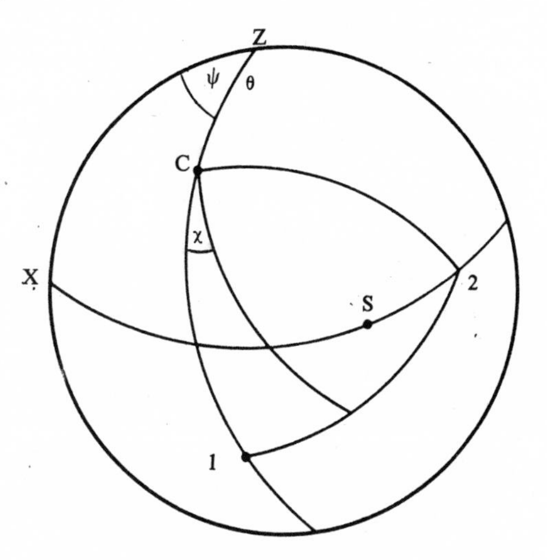

Fig. 1

Z is the pole of the ecliptic, C that of the Earth. The work function due to the Sun, so far as it involves the

*It should be noticed that the notation used in the foreword is independent of that in the Memoir.

orientation of the Earth, is

$$W = \frac{3f\,S(C - A)}{2r^3}\left(\tfrac{1}{3} - \cos^2 CS\right). \tag{1}$$

The direction 2 is the Sun's descending node on the equator. Longitudes are measured from a fixed point X in the ecliptic. The longitude of S is $\odot$. That of 2 is $S2 = \frac{1}{2}\pi + \psi$ Hence

$$S2 = \tfrac{1}{2}\pi + \psi - \odot\ . \tag{2}$$

Also $12\,S = \theta$. Hence from the triangle $C2S$, since $C2 = \frac{1}{2}\pi$,

$$\cos CS = \sin\theta\cos(\psi - \odot). \tag{3}$$

Also

$$f(S + E + M)/r^3 = n'^2, \tag{4}$$

where n' is the Earth's mean motion about the Sun. We can neglect E and M in comparison with S. Then

$$\begin{aligned} W &= \tfrac{3}{2}(C - A)n'^2\left(\tfrac{1}{3} - \sin^2\theta\cos^2(\psi - \odot)\right) = \\ &= -\tfrac{3}{4}n'^2(C - A)\sin^2\theta\{1 + \cos 2(\psi - \odot)\} \end{aligned} \tag{5}$$

+ terms independent of θ and ψ + terms containing the eccentricity of the Earth's orbit.

$$2T = A(\dot\theta^2 + \sin^2\theta\,\dot\psi^2) + C(\dot\chi + \dot\psi\cos\theta)^2. \tag{6}$$

The equations of motion are

$$\dot\chi + \dot\psi\cos\theta = \omega = \text{constant} \tag{7}$$

$$\begin{aligned} A(\ddot\theta - \sin\theta\cos\theta\,\dot\psi^2) + C\omega\dot\psi\sin\theta = -\tfrac{3}{2}n'^2(C - A)\sin\theta\cos\theta\,\times \\ \times\{1 + \cos 2(\psi - \odot)\} \end{aligned} \tag{8}$$

$$\frac{d}{dt}(A\sin^2\theta\,\dot\psi + C\omega\cos\theta) = \tfrac{3}{2}n'^2(C - A)\sin^2\theta\sin 2(\psi - \odot). \tag{9}$$

If we neglect $\dot\psi^2$ the constant term in (8) gives a steady motion with $\dot\theta = 0$,

$$\dot{\psi} = -\frac{3}{2}\frac{n'^2}{\omega}\frac{C-A}{C}\cos\theta\,. \tag{10}$$

This is the Sun's contribution to the precession and is retrograde. The terms in $2(\psi' - \odot)$ give a motion with argument $2\odot$ and therefore semiannual.

In general, if we neglect squares of small quantities the equations can be put in the form

$$\left.\begin{aligned} A\ddot{\theta} + C\omega \sin\theta\dot{\psi} &= \alpha\cos\sigma t \\ C\omega\dot{\theta} - A\sin\theta\ddot{\psi} &= \beta\sin\sigma t \end{aligned}\right\} \tag{11}$$

and if for a periodic motion we write

$$\theta = \varepsilon + \lambda\cos\sigma t, \quad \sin\varepsilon\delta\psi = \mu\sin\sigma t \tag{12}$$

we have

$$-A\sigma^2\lambda + C\omega\sigma\mu = \alpha$$
$$-C\omega\sigma\lambda + A\sigma^2\mu = \beta,$$

whence

$$\lambda = -\frac{C\omega\beta - A\sigma\alpha}{C^2\omega^2\sigma - A^2\sigma^3}, \qquad \mu = \frac{C\omega\alpha - A\sigma\beta}{C^2\omega^2\sigma - A^2\sigma^3}\,. \tag{13}$$

In the earlier works on the subject it was considered that since σ is much smaller than ω in all nutations, $\ddot{\theta}$ and $\ddot{\psi}$ could be neglected; this led to

$$\lambda = -\frac{\beta}{C\omega\sigma}, \qquad \mu = \frac{\alpha}{C\omega\sigma}\,. \tag{14}$$

$\delta\theta$, $\sin\varepsilon\,\delta\psi$ represent displacements of the axis of figure relative to inertial axes. The usual astronomical practice is to give displacements of the instantaneous axis of rotation, the direction of which is given with respect to the axes 12 by

$$\left(\frac{\omega_1}{\omega}, \frac{\omega_2}{\omega}\right) = \left(-\frac{\sin\theta\dot{\psi}}{\omega}, \frac{\dot{\theta}}{\omega}\right) = \left(-\frac{\mu\sigma\cos\sigma t}{\omega}, -\frac{\lambda\sigma\sin\sigma t}{\omega}\right).$$

Thus if λ', μ' refer to the instantaneous axis

$$\left.\begin{aligned} (C^2\omega^2\sigma - A^2\sigma^3)\lambda' &= -C\omega\beta - (C-A)\sigma\alpha + A\beta\sigma^2/\omega \\ (C^2\omega^2\sigma - A^2\sigma^3)\mu' &= C\omega\alpha - (C-A)\sigma\beta - A\alpha\sigma^2/\omega \end{aligned}\right\} \tag{15}$$

On account of the smallness of $C-A$ the terms in σ on the right are small, and even the terms in σ^2 approximately cancel the terms in σ^2 on the left. Thus the first approximation (14) is a much better approximation to the displacement of the instantaneous axis than to that of the axis of figure. This is pointed out by Woolard.

The displacements of the axis of angular momentum relative to C 12 are $A\mu\sigma \cos \sigma t/C\omega$, $A\lambda\sigma \sin \sigma t/C\omega$; if λ'', μ'' refer to the whole displacement of the axis of angular momentum,
$(C^2\omega^2\sigma - A^2\sigma^3)\lambda'' = -C\omega\beta + A^2\sigma^2\beta/C\omega$,

that is,

$$\lambda'' = -\beta/C\omega\sigma, \tag{16}$$

and similarly

$$\mu'' = \alpha/C\omega\sigma. \tag{17}$$

Thus the first approximation gives the motion of the axis of angular momentum, irrespective of the value of σ/ω. It has other important properties pointed out by Fedorov. If the forcing couples are of the form $f(t, \theta, \psi)$ and are of the first order of small quantities, then making any first order change in θ and ψ makes a second order change in the couples, which can be neglected. But the displacements are all of the first order, and hence in the calculation of the couples the axis of figure can be replaced by that of angular momentum, and the equations of motion therefore determine the changes of angular momentum. Now since any internal reactions give no resultant couple it follows that to the first order of small quantities the angular momentum, even for a deformable body, depends only on the initial conditions and the forcing couples. It is independent of all deformations, elastic or inelastic; and it is totally unaffected by the free and annual nutations commonly known as the variation of latitude. Fedorov is certainly right in maintaining that if we want an intermediate standard of reference independent of all properties of the Earth other than its moments of inertia, that standard must be the axis of angular momentum.

On the other hand, I do not agree with him that we need any

intermediate standard at all. Astronomical observations give the direction of a star with respect to a frame determined by the local vertical and a fixed azimuth. This, for a rigid Earth, would be a frame fixed relatively to the Earth, and in particular to a frame determined by the axis of greatest moment of inertia and a fixed meridian. There is apparently a widespread belief among astronomers that it is possible to observe the instantaneous axis of rotation by, for instance, observing zenith distances of a circumpolar star when it crosses the meridian above and below the pole. But in half a day some of the nutations vary by as much as the standard errors of the solutions and more than the error tolerated in the calculation. There is no way at all of observing the axis of angular momentum. In all cases an observation gives the direction of the star relative to the Earth, and the only possible standard is the axis of figure.

In fact, what Fedorov does is to treat the predicted motion of the instantaneous axis as a first approximation to that of the axis of figure and analyse the residuals. Thus his final results are displacements of the axis of figure.

Oppolzer's contribution was to recognize that as accuracy had improved the first approximation derived for a displacement of the axis of figure was not quite good enough, and he took into account the correction of order σ/ω of the main part. But he introduced confusion by defining the nutation as the motion of the instantaneous axis, which is of no observational and very little theoretical interest, and then referring the additional part of the displacement of the axis of figure to axes fixed in the Earth and calling it the diurnal variation of latitude. This procedure separates the observed phenomenon arbitrarily into two parts, and by representing them in different ways makes them look different in form. As it puzzled H.R.Morgan, I do not feel in the least ashamed of having found it difficult to understand.

The origin of the principal terms due to the Moon may be sketched as follows. We write n for the Moon's mean motion and k for the mass-ratio of the Earth and Moon. The factor n'^2 is thus replaced by $n^2\kappa/(1+\kappa)$.

We take axes in the plane of the lunar orbit, with pole **K**. In this frame the direction cosines of C are (l, m, n) (not of course the same n), those of the Moon (cos ☾, sin ☾, 0). Then

$$\cos CM = l \cos ☾ + m \sin ☾ \tag{18}$$

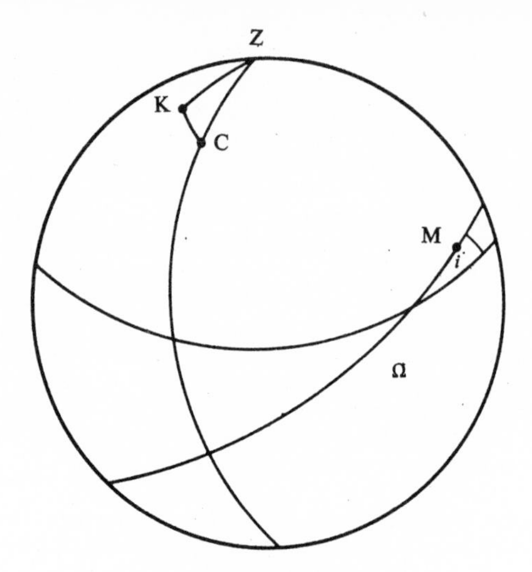

Fig. 2

and its mean over a month is

$$\tfrac{1}{2}(l^2 + m^2) = \tfrac{1}{2} - \tfrac{1}{2}n^2 = \tfrac{1}{2} - \tfrac{1}{2}\cos^2 CK = \tfrac{1}{2}\sin^2 CK. \tag{19}$$

Now

$$XZK = -pt, \tag{20}$$

where p is the mean motion of the Moon's node on the ecliptic, and XZC = ψ (the additive constant can be restored when required.) Thus

$$\cos CK = \cos i \cos\theta + \sin i \sin\theta \cos(\psi + pt), \tag{21}$$

and

$$W = \frac{3}{4}\frac{n^2\kappa}{1+\kappa}(C-A)\cos^2 CK + \text{constant}$$

$$= \frac{3}{4}\frac{n^2\kappa}{1+\kappa}(C-A)[\cos^2 i\cos^2\theta + \tfrac{1}{2}\sin 2i \sin 2\theta\cos(\psi + pt) + + \tfrac{1}{2}\sin^2 i \sin^2\theta\{1 + \cos 2(\psi + pt)\}]. \tag{22}$$

Then

$$\frac{\partial W}{\partial\theta} = \frac{3}{4}\frac{n^2\kappa}{1+\kappa}(C-A)\{-(\tfrac{3}{2}\cos^2 i - \tfrac{1}{2})\sin 2\theta + \sin 2i \cos 2\theta \cos(\psi + pt) + \\ + \tfrac{1}{2}\sin^2 i \sin 2\theta \cos 2(\psi + pt)\}, \quad (23)$$

$$\frac{\partial W}{\partial\psi} = \frac{3}{4}\frac{n^2\kappa}{1+\kappa}(C-A)\{-\tfrac{1}{2}\sin 2i \sin 2\theta \sin(\psi + pt) - \\ - \sin^2 i \sin^2\theta \sin 2(\psi + pt)\}. \quad (24)$$

The constant part of $\partial W/\partial\theta$ gives a steady decrease of $\dot{\psi}$, which is the lunar contribution to the precession. It is rather more than twice the solar part. The parts of $\partial W/\partial\theta$ and $\partial W/\partial\psi$ with argument ψ +pt give a motion of period equal to the period of revolution of the Moon's node, 18.6 years. This is the principal nutation. The terms of argument 2(ψ +pt) give a much smaller nutation of period 9.3 years. In addition the variation of cos CM within a month gives terms of period half a lunar (nodal) month, analogous to the solar semi-annual terms, but more complicated in form.

In a full treatment it is necessary to allow also for the eccentricities of the orbits and for various perturbations of the Moon by the Sun. This has been carried out most fully by Woolard. Fedorov's paper is, however, concerned entirely with the terms of arguments ☊ = -pt + constant and 2☾, and it is considered sufficient here to give only a brief account of how these terms arise.

2. The theoretical values are obtained as follows. If a is the Moon's mean distance, the Moon's attraction on the Earth produces a monthly movement of the Earth, of radius $\kappa a/(1+\kappa)$. This affects the direction of a neighbouring planet, especially Eros near opposition, as seen from the Earth. The ratios of planetary distances being known, the effect is expressed as a monthly displacement of the Sun, known as the lunar inequality. Thus if the distance of the Sun is known the absolute magnitude of the Earth's monthly displacement is known, and hence κ, since a is known. Thus the mass of the Moon is found.

The solar parallax has been determined optically many times. The most recent, and apparently the most accurate determination, is by H.Spencer Jones. It can also be determined indirectly. If we can measure the perturbations of another planet due to the Earth and Moon together, this gives the ratio $(E+M)/S$. But we have also

$$f(S+M+E)/a'^3 = n'^2 \quad (1)$$

where a' is the Sun's distance, and

$$f(E+M)/a^3 = n^2 , \quad (2)$$

apart from small known corrections. These equations determine a/a' and hence the Sun's distance. Unfortunately, the best determination on these lines, due to E.Rabe, is apparently inconsistent with Spencer Jones's, and has a much smaller apparent uncertainty. No systematic error has been detected in either determination, but several other analyses have confirmed Rabe.

The rate of precession is of the form

$$\frac{C-A}{C}\left(\alpha+\beta\frac{\kappa}{1+\kappa}\right), \quad (3)$$

where α and β are known. Hence, if κ is known we can find $(C-A)/C$, the dynamical ellipticity, also called the precessional constant. The principal nutation, for a rigid body, has amplitude in obliquity

$$N = \gamma\frac{\kappa}{1+\kappa}\frac{C-A}{C} . \quad (4)$$

Up till 1901 it was customary to use (3) and (4) as a pair of equations to determine both κ and $(C-A)/C$. Hinks determined the lunar inequality directly from observations of Eros near opposition, and derived an apparently much more accurate determination of κ. Thus the use of the observed nutation constant for this purpose was considered superseded. However, the observed values were systematically smaller than that derived from the lunar inequality and the rate of precession. J.Jackson was the first to insist that the difference was genuine. (It should be noted that he applied the correction to Newcomb's nutation with the wrong sign, and in this respect he was followed by Spencer Jones. The mistake was pointed out by G.M.Clemence (A.J.53, 1948, 179); thus the values 9".2066 ± 0".0082 and 9".2134 ± 0".0063 attributed to them on p. 71 should read 9".2134 ± 0".0082 and 9".2066 ±

0".0063). For a rigid Earth the coefficient would be 9".2272 or 9".2242 according as Spencer Jones's or Rabe's solar parallax is adopted. The effect of elasticity on the principal nutation had been shown to be small. The dynamics of a rigid shell filled with liquid had been studied by Kelvin, Hough, Greenhill and Poincaré; Fedorov calls attention also to Sloudsky and Joukowsky. Poincaré gave two different methods, one of which is reproduced in Lamb's Hydrodynamics, but the other is more readily capable of being generalized to an elastic shell and a non-uniform core. Bondi and Lyttleton called my attention to the passage in Lamb's book, and using Bullen's value of the moment of inertia of the core I found that a liquid core would reduce the amplitude by about 1 part in 150, which was too much. Allowance for elasticity of the shell reduced the effect, but it was only when Takeuchi gave a complete solution for an elastic shell with properties found from seismological data that a solution for the actual Earth became possible. This was carried out by R.O.Vicente and myself. The most convenient method was to refer the Earth to axes rotating with the mean angular velocity, introduce suitable functions to represent additional displacements, and treat their coefficients as Lagrangian coordinates.

For a rigid Earth the ratio of the amplitudes in θ and ψ (obliquity and longitude) is fixed. Consequently in all analyses of observations before Fedorov's the two components have been assumed to be in the ratio for a rigid body. But the theoretical ratio is slightly affected by allowance for elasticity, and much more by allowance for fluidity of the Earth's central core. This arises in the following way. For any constitution of the Earth the precession remains the same. That is, if σ, the speed of an oscillation referred to inertial axes, is zero, the constitution gives no change of the forced motion; and for small changes of σ the changes will be proportional to σ. Now a nutation is in an ellipse, and can be regarded as the resultant of two circular motions of equal and opposite speeds. If one of these has its amplitude reduced by some change in the supposed constitution of the Earth, the other will be correspondingly increased, and the result will be a change of the ratio of the axes of the ellipse. Hence in particular I think it impossible to reduce the theoretical amplitude of the principal nutation in obliquity without reducing that in longitude by a larger fraction.

I formerly thought that the nutations might have measurable lags in phase, on account of possible imperfections of elasticity in the Earth. However, any couples arising in this way would arise only from the attraction of the Moon on the bodily tides, which are of the order of 10^{-5} of the differences of elevation corresponding to the ellipticity of figure. Thus even if the bodily tides lagged by 90°, the lags in the nutations could only be of order 10^{-3} in circular measure. Further, if the lag of the tides reached even 1° it would lead to other consequences that are not verified. Hence it seems impossible that the lags can really be more than a few minutes of arc in phase, and very unlikely that they are more than a few seconds.

3. The estimation of the observed values can be described as follows. We denote the zenith by J as we have already used Z for the pole of the ecliptic. Consider a star of

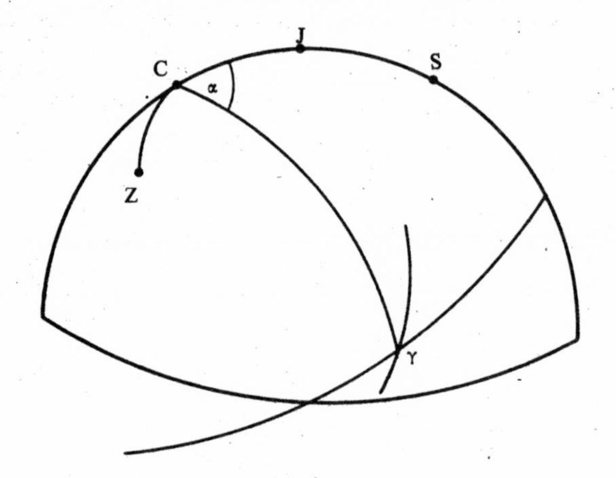

Fig. 3

right ascension α crossing the meridian. The displacements of the pole of figure, C, are $\delta\theta$ along ZC and $\sin\varepsilon\delta\psi$ positively perpendicular to ZC. Then the two increase CS by

$$\delta CS = -\delta\theta\cos(\tfrac{1}{2}\pi - \alpha) + \sin\varepsilon\delta\psi\sin(\tfrac{1}{2}\pi - \alpha) =$$

$$= -\lambda\cos\sigma t\sin\alpha + \mu\sin\sigma t\cos\alpha\ .$$

When the star crosses the meridian, the local sidereal time is equal to α. Since CJ is constant for a rigid Earth,

$\delta CS = \delta JS$. Hence analysis of zenith distances of stars when they cross the meridian determines both λ and μ.

The observations of the ILS are made visually with a fixed telescope with a vertical axis, and the zenith distance of the star on meridian passage is measured with a micrometer. The principal advantage of a vertical telescope is that atmospheric refraction is small. The characteristic feature of the Talcott method is that instead of observing one star that passes close to the zenith, two are taken that pass the zenith at nearly equal distances on opposite sides. The algebraic mean of the zenith distances is taken, and treated as if it was an observation of a single star. This method makes many more stars available, since the refractions cancel from the mean and it is not necessary, for equal accuracy, to use stars that pass extremely close to the zenith.

I think that the rigid use of the equation

$$\varphi = z + \delta$$

makes for additional confusion. φ , the latitude, would be regarded in geodesy as a coordinate of the place and constant with regard to time except possibly for tectonic disturbances of the Earth's surface. δ , the declination of the star, is expressed in astronomical catalogues in the form a $+bt$, a representing the value at a standard epoch and b the proper motion. It seems undesirable to include periodic terms in either φ or δ. The 14-monthly and annual terms in the motion of the Earth's axis are ordinarily spoken of as the 'variation of latitude', but it had never occurred to me until recently that this was anything but an ellipsis, in which the crucial word 'apparent' had been suppressed. It would, I think, add clarity if the equation was written

$$z = \varphi - \delta + \text{periodic terms},$$

where φ is a constant and δ is of the form a +bt.

To economize labour the observations at the three stations have been combined before analysis, but a large part of the work is devoted to detecting systematic errors in the micrometers. Now it is very unlikely that there were simultaneous sudden changes at all the three stations. Also two of the stations, Mizusawa and Ukiah, are in earthquake regions, and a definite change in the latitude of Ukiah was detected by W.D.Lambert. For both these reasons it would have been better to study the stations separately. Again, the stars fall into three groups according to the intervals of time when they were observed. These were combined into two, and the results were combined by least squares. The data overlap, and the estimates are not wholly independent. I have combined them by a method used previously in a similar case* and find that the changes are only by one or two units in the fourth decimal. I am sorry to criticize a work of such magnitude on account of omissions: I am unable to forget that the number of observations treated is between 5 and 10 times what I (with help) handled in the construction of the seismological tables.

4. Comparison of theory and observation. Major errors in the mechanical properties adopted for the Earth's shell in the theory are out of the question. Those of the core are in some doubt, for though its mean density and compressibility are well known, the velocity of longitudinal elastic waves changes discontinuously at the boundary of a region known as the inner core. The density of the inner core is doubtful, and it is not clear even whether it is liquid or solid. In any case, full treatment of the effects of the inner core on the nutations would introduce prohibitive mathematical difficulties. Vicente and I therefore considered two models for the core, both adjusted to have the right mass and moment of inertia, and with ellipticity given by Bullard's theory of the figure of the Earth. In one model the core was taken as homegeneous and incompressible, with an extra particle at the centre. In the other it was taken as having a quadratic law of density, the whole variation being due to compression. Actually the known compressibility would account for about half the departure from uniformity of density.

Since in a statistical work there is nearly always a possibility that uncertainties may be underestimated on account of correlation between the errors, and since Fedorov's lags seemed theoretically impossible, I used these to re-estimate the uncertainties.

In the abstract communicated to the IAU at Moscow, 1958, and since published**, Fedorov quotes also an estimate by N.A.Popov of the semi-annual nutation, from two bright zenith stars observed at Poltava. This is not mentioned in the present memoir, but I give the results in the following

*MNRAS 99, 1939, 206-10.
**A.J. 64, 1959, 81-84.

comparison, with the revised uncertainties.*

Obliquity observed	Central particle model	Quadratic law of density
cos ☊ 9".198 ± 0".004	9".2015	9".2187
cos 2☾ 0".0949 ± 0".0027	0".0972	0".0971
cos 2☉ 0".578 ± 0".004	0".5734	0".5403
Longitude (sin $\varepsilon\delta\psi$)		
sin ☊ 6".853 ± 0".004	6".826	6".8491
sin 2☾ 0".0918 ± 0".0027	0".0896	0".0897
sin 2☉ 0".533 ± 0".004	0".5232	0".4883

Fedorov's ratio of amplitudes in the two components for the ☊ terms agrees with the rigid body value; neither theoretical ratio does. In fact, one component agrees well with the central particle model, the other with the Roche model. The 2☾ terms agree with both models. The 2☉ terms agree better with the central particle model. The differences are surprising, particularly since compressibility of the core is certainly important. An intermediate law of density, which would be more plausible geophysically, would disagree with the observations for both the ☊ and the 2☉ terms. But this is not quite obvious for the 2☉ terms because there are resonances in the neighbourhood of period 6 months, and a simple interpolation may not be valid.

In any case the discrepancies between theory and observation have been greatly reduced, though the position still cannot be considered perfectly satisfactory.

Harold Jeffreys

*H.Jeffreys, MNRAS 119, 1959, 75-80.

INTRODUCTION

The classical theory of rotatory motion, that is, the theory based on the assumption that the Earth is an absolutely rigid body, was complete at the end of the last century. In 1882 Oppolzer obtained the formulae for precession and nutation in the form in which they are applied today. Subsequent revisions produced only improvements of the calculated values of certain constants appearing in the formulae. In this theory certain notable inexactitudes and omissions were not discovered. It was also not noticed that its conclusions differed in some ways from the observed data. It was recognized that the Earth is not an absolutely rigid spheroid; however, at that time there seemed to be no need to replace the existing theory by one based on different assumptions about the mechanical properties of the Earth.

The position changed when the 14-monthly variation of latitude was discovered. In undertaking the harmonic analysis of the results of latitude observations Chandler's first object was not to make an exact check on Euler's theory of the motion of the pole. However, his work played an important role in the history of the problem, just because the results did not agree with the conclusions of the theory. They showed that it was necessary to revise the central assumption of the absolute rigidity of the Earth. At the same time scientists had a criterion of the truth of any other hypothesis about the properties of the Earth, that it should give a theoretical value of the free nutation equal to the observed one, that is, 14 months.

Hough used this criterion to test the hypothesis of a liquid core of the Earth, and finding that the dynamical effect of the core led to a decrease of the free period [28] took this hypothesis to be wrong. Newcomb considered the effect of elastic deformation of the Earth on its rotation, and by means of simple considerations showed that such deformation actually increased the free period. It appeared from the work of Schweydar that this increase of period was the only manifestation of the effect of elasticity that could be detected in the analysis of astronomical observations. In other respects the rotation of the elastically deformed Earth proceeds practically as if it was absolutely rigid. Although the formulae for precession and nutation were originally obtained on just this assumption, they can be applied equally well when we take the Earth to be an elastic body.

New consideration of the basis of the theory of the rotation of the Earth would be necessary if some formerly unknown discrepancies were found between theory and observation. Then theoretical investigations would have a definite aim and would not appear to be only the solution of abstract mechanical problems. Consequently it is desirable to have as complete a comparison as possible between the results of the theory of the rotation of an ideally elastic Earth and the astronomical observations. The present work is an attempt at such a comparison.

In Chapter I an account of the theory is given; use is made of the vector and tensor method. In justification of such a departure from the traditional way of deducing the equations for precession and nutation it is sufficient to point out that the vector notation is now universally adopted in courses on the mechanics of rigid bodies.

We know of only two works that discuss the theoretical question of the effect of an external disturbing force on the rotation of an elastic Earth, namely those of Schweydar [48] and Sekiguchi [51]. The work of Sekiguchi is based on the results of his previous work [49], in which Woolard [59] pointed out that there is a mistake in principle. We made use of the work of Schweydar mainly as a check on the results that we obtained in another way.

We had to decide just which of the theoretical results presented most interest for comparison with observation. We first considered the constant of nutation N. In a short account of the history of this question Idelson [20] explained its importance in the following passage: "In 1930 de Sitter took as a mean of all determinations

$$N = 9''.2075 \pm 0''.0055.$$

However, the value obtained by his method* is

* This value was chosen for consistency, on a rigid Earth theory, with the rate of precession, and Hinks's determinations of the solar parallax and the lunar inequality. It is

$$N = 9''.2181.$$

"In relation to this, Jackson pointed out this discrepancy as 'one of the outstanding discordances of the constants of the Solar System', and suggested that the relativistic effect on the precession might not exhaust the effect of relativity on the relations between the constants. Brouwer remarks that de Sitter vainly searched for the solution of this problem during the last years of his life."

And further: "From the preceding summary it may be seen that the question of the constant of nutation has not yet reached a final solution: the analysis of the enormous amount of material of the ILS undoubtedly makes N less than the theoretical value."

Recently Jeffreys has attempted to explain the discrepancy by assuming a liquid core, and as far as we know is continuing his investigations on this subject.

The results of Przybyllok, to which Idelson gives great weight, are derived from the data of the ILS from 1900 to 1915. At the present time we have far more material; the results of the ILS published hitherto cover almost two cycles of nutation. It seems to us important to determine the constant of nutation first of all, in order to see whether the new result for N approximates to the theoretical one or departs even more significantly.

If the adopted value of N is erroneous, the 19-year period should be discovered in the non-polar variation of latitude, but it may arise from causes that are indicated in [19] (Fedorov, 1954). Our problem was to make as complete a test as possible of the theory of the rotation of the Earth; it was not limited to a determination of N alone (the coefficient of the term in obliquity) but to examine whether there is a phase lag and whether the observations confirmed the theoretical ratio of the axes of the nutation ellipse. Up to the present time there have been hardly any attempts to investigate these questions, and a definite answer has not been obtained.

The theory of precession and nutation leads to certain relations between the constants of precession and nutation and

---

thus a theoretical value. Later determinations make it a little larger. - Translator.

the coefficients of all the other terms in the formulae for the nutations in right ascension and declination. Thus if the constants of precession and nutation are known from observation all the other coefficients are determined by a strict calculation. So long as there were no doubts about the correctness of the theory there was no point in trying to determine these other coefficients directly from the observations. But such determinations, as we have noted previously [15], gain in interest if they are regarded as a means of checking the theory.

Recently Sekiguchi [50], Morgan [35] and Popov [12] almost simultaneously and quite independently tried to determine the amplitude of the fortnightly term from various sets of latitude observations. The basis of such a determination is as follows. If the amplitude of the fortnightly term obtained from the theory differs from the right one, a term

$$a \sin(2☾ - \alpha),$$

appears in the variation of latitude, where ☾ is the Moon's mean longitude and α the mean right ascension of the pair of stars (or right ascension of a zenith star). It should be noticed, however, that the lunar diurnal term in the expression of Oppolzer for the forced variation of latitude has just this form. This leads to an uncertainty in the interpretation of the results of analysis of the observations. One might suppose, as Morgan has done, that the theoretical value of the coefficient of this term is not subject to correction, and might consider the difference between it and the observed value as a correction to the fortnightly term. However, we may not do this. Oppolzer obtained the expression for the forced variation of latitude as one of the results of the theory of rotation of an absolutely rigid Earth. In Chapter I we solve the analogous problem, starting from the assumption that the Earth is a perfectly elastic body, but since our intention is to test this assumption, we may use the theoretical expression for the forced variation of latitude only for comparison with the results of observation, and not for the correction of these results.

The uncertainty mentioned above may be removed in the following way. The formulae for precession and nutation describe the motion in space of the angular momentum of the Earth. In Chapter I we show that these formulae are not changed with any reasonable assumption about the mechanical properties of the Earth. This means that if a term $a \sin(2☾ - \alpha)$ is discovered in the analysis of the latitude observations it can only be identified with the lunar diurnal term. Thus the observations must answer the following question: does the forced motion of the pole take place in agreement with the theory of an elastic Earth? This question we consider in Chapter III of the present work.

We do not attempt to construct a theory of the rotation of the Earth on the basis of any other assumption about its mechanical properties. However we touch upon the hypothesis of a liquid core in the last chapter, where we use the results of previous chapters to derive some results on the interaction of the core and the shell.

Our initial data for all our further calculations will be the results of observations of pairs of stars by the Talcott method. We call the centre of the arc of a great circle connecting a pair of stars the centre of the pair. When we say "declination of the pair" we mean the declination of this centre (as in the expression "declination of the Sun" or "declination of the Moon"). Evidently it is equal to the half sum of the declinations of the stars forming the pair. We define similarly the terms "zenith distance" and "right ascension" of a pair. Further we shall sometimes use abbreviations when in the context they cannot lead to misunderstanding.

CHAPTER I

THEORY OF THE ROTATIONAL MOTION OF A PERFECTLY ELASTIC EARTH

1. Derivation of the Equations of Motion of the Angular Momentum of the Earth

$X'Y'Z'$ are a fixed system of coordinates. The plane $X'OY'$ coincides with the plane of the ecliptic at some initial epoch and the axis OX' goes through the vernal equinox at that epoch (Fig. 1).

We denote the unit vectors of this system by $\mathbf{i}'$, $\mathbf{j}'$, $\mathbf{k}$. Further take a unit vector $\mathbf{k}$ and define a second coordinate system in the following way: the axis OZ is in the direction of the vector $\mathbf{k}$ and the axis OX in that of the vector $\mathbf{i}$, where

$$\mathbf{i} = \frac{\mathbf{k} \wedge \mathbf{k}'}{\sin \Theta},$$

and Θ is the angle between $\mathbf{k}$ and $\mathbf{k}'$. We denote the angle between OX' and OX by ψ.

Any vector may be written as

$$\mathbf{a} = \mathbf{i}'x' + \mathbf{j}'y' + \mathbf{k}'z' = \mathbf{i}x + \mathbf{j}y + \mathbf{k}z = \mathbf{k}a_\varphi + \mathbf{k}'a_\psi - \mathbf{i}a_\Theta, \tag{1.1}$$

where x', y', z' and x, y, z are the projections of the vector $\mathbf{a}$ on the axes of the two coordinate systems and a_φ, a_ψ, $-a_\Theta$ are the components of the vector in the three directions $\mathbf{k}$, $\mathbf{k}'$, $\mathbf{i}$.

From (1.1) it is easy to obtain the expressions for the projections of the vector on the axes of one system in terms of those on the other, or in terms of a_φ, a_ψ, $-a_\Theta$. For this we use the following table of the cosines between the directions of the axes of the two systems.

	$\mathbf{i}'$	$\mathbf{j}'$	$\mathbf{k}$
$\mathbf{i}$	$\cos\psi$	$\sin\psi$	0
$\mathbf{j}$	$-\cos\Theta\sin\psi$	$\cos\Theta\cos\psi$	$-\sin\Theta$
$\mathbf{k}$	$-\sin\Theta\sin\psi$	$\sin\Theta\cos\psi$	$\cos\Theta$

Then for example to find the expression for x' in terms of a_φ, a_ψ, $-a_\Theta$, we find the scalar product of (1.1) with $\mathbf{i}'$, namely

$$x' = \mathbf{i}'\cdot\mathbf{a} = \mathbf{i}'\cdot\mathbf{k}a_\varphi + \mathbf{i}'\cdot\mathbf{k}'a_\psi - \mathbf{i}\cdot\mathbf{i}'a_\Theta = -\sin\Theta\sin\psi a_\varphi - \cos\psi a_\Theta .$$

We denote by $\mathbf{G}$ the moment of momentum of the Earth and take $\mathbf{k}$ in the direction of $\mathbf{G}$. Then

$$\mathbf{G} = \mathbf{k}G.$$

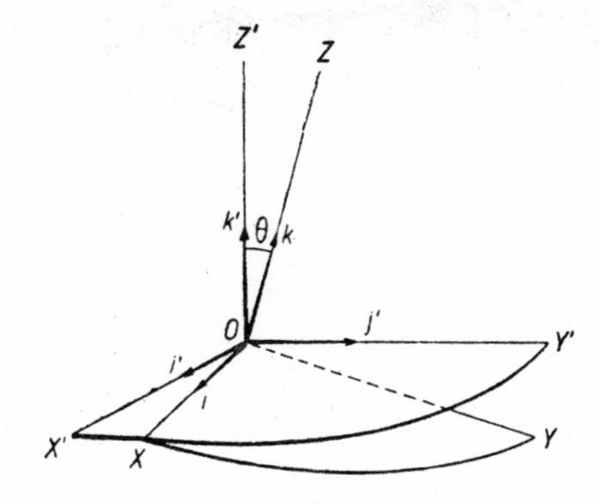

Fig. 1

Then the projections of $\mathbf{G}$ on the fixed axes are given by

$$X' = -G\sin\Theta\sin\psi, \quad Y' = G\sin\Theta\cos\psi, \quad Z' = G\cos\Theta . \quad (1.2)$$

We denote the angular velocity of rotation of the vector $\mathbf{G}$ by Ω. Then from the rate of change of angular momentum we have

$$\mathbf{k}\dot{G} + \Omega \wedge \mathbf{G} = \mathbf{L} \quad (1.3)$$

where $\mathbf{L}$ is the moment of the external forces.

Let

$$\mathbf{r} = \mathbf{i}'x' + \mathbf{j}'y' + \mathbf{k}'z'$$

be the radius vector of the heavenly body (Sun or Moon). The force due to the Earth on this body is equal to grad V, where V is that part of the Earth's gravitational potential which depends on the directions of the principal axes of inertia. Then the couple can evidently be written as

$$\mathbf{L} = -\mathbf{r} \wedge \operatorname{grad} V, \tag{1.4}$$

where

$$V = -\frac{3}{2}\frac{fM}{r^5}\mathbf{r}\cdot I\mathbf{r}$$

in which M is the mass of the heavenly body, f the constant of gravitation and I the inertia tensor of the Earth.

Further

$$\operatorname{grad} V = -\frac{3}{2} fM\left[\frac{1}{r^5}\operatorname{grad}(\mathbf{r}\cdot I\mathbf{r}) + \mathbf{r}\cdot I\mathbf{r}\operatorname{grad}\frac{1}{r^5}\right]. \tag{1.5}$$

Since grad r^{-5} is in the direction of $\mathbf{r}$, we can omit the second term on the right in forming the vector product $\mathbf{r} \wedge \operatorname{grad} V$. It is easy to show that

$$\operatorname{grad}(\mathbf{r}\cdot I\mathbf{r}) = 2I\mathbf{r}$$

Then we can write equation (1.3) in the following form:

$$\mathbf{k}\dot{G} + \Omega \wedge \mathbf{G} = \frac{3fM}{r^5}\mathbf{r} \wedge I\mathbf{r}. \tag{1.6}$$

As the system XYZ rotates, the angles ψ and θ vary; hence we can write the angular velocity of this frame as the vector sum of two angular velocities

$$\Omega = \mathbf{k}'\dot{\psi} - \mathbf{i}\dot{\theta}$$

whence

$$\Omega \wedge \mathbf{G} = G(\mathbf{k}' \wedge \mathbf{k}\dot{\psi} - \mathbf{i} \wedge \mathbf{k}\dot{\theta}) = G(-\mathbf{i}\sin\theta\dot{\psi} + \mathbf{j}\dot{\theta}).$$

Using this result we form the scalar product of both sides of equation (1.6) with the vectors $-\mathbf{i}$, $\mathbf{k}$ and $\mathbf{k}'$ in turn; then we obtain

$$\left.\begin{aligned} G\sin\Theta\dot{\psi} &= -\frac{3fM}{r^5}\mathbf{i}\cdot(\mathbf{r}\wedge I\mathbf{r}) = -\frac{3fM}{r^5}I\mathbf{r}\cdot(\mathbf{i}\wedge\mathbf{r}) \\ \dot{G} &= \frac{3fM}{r^5}\mathbf{k}\cdot(\mathbf{r}\wedge I\mathbf{r}) = \frac{3fM}{r^5}I\mathbf{r}\cdot(\mathbf{k}\wedge\mathbf{r}) \\ G\cos\Theta - G\sin\Theta\dot{\Theta} &= \frac{3fM}{r^5}\mathbf{k}'\cdot(\mathbf{r}\wedge I\mathbf{r}) = \frac{3fM}{r^5}I\mathbf{r}\cdot(\mathbf{k}'\wedge\mathbf{r}) \end{aligned}\right\} \quad (1.7)$$

The last of these expressions is found by using the law of transposition in the triple scalar product.

2. Variation of the Inertia Tensor with the Deformation of the Earth

We now find the expressions for the elements of the inertia tensor of the Earth as it changes its form under the influence of a force of a tidal nature. We shall take the ellipsoid of inertia of the undeformed Earth to be bi-axial, that is, we assume that the moment of inertia of the Earth about any equatorial axis is A. We take the principal axes of this ellipsoid as axes of an auxiliary coordinate system and denote by α, β, γ the cosines of the angles which the axis OZ^* of this system makes with the axes of the basic system. The inertia tensor of the Earth in the auxiliary system is diagonal of the form

$$\begin{Bmatrix} A & 0 & 0 \\ 0 & A & 0 \\ 0 & 0 & C \end{Bmatrix},$$

and in the system XOY it may be easily shown to be

$$AE + (C - A)P\,, \quad (1.8)$$

where E is the unit tensor and P is given by

$$P = \begin{Bmatrix} \alpha\alpha & \alpha\beta & \alpha\gamma \\ \beta\alpha & \beta\beta & \beta\gamma \\ \gamma\alpha & \gamma\beta & \gamma\gamma \end{Bmatrix}. \quad (1.9)$$

Now let us suppose that the motion of the Earth ceases. If the Earth were really a liquid body (an assumption ordinarily made in the theory of the figure of the Earth) it would take, clearly, a spherical form, but since as a matter of fact the Earth, or at least its shell, is an elastic body, it would, even in the absence of rotation, remain a spheroid, but having less compression than it actually does. In this case we call the inertia tensor I_0 and the difference between the polar and the equatorial moment of inertia

$$(1-\varkappa)(C-A).$$

In fact the Earth rotates not around the polar axis of the tensor I_0 but around the instantaneous axis, which is continually changing its position. It is along this axis that the elastic Earth contracts owing to centrifugal force. We shall therefore write the whole inertia tensor in the form

$$I=I_0+I_\omega,$$

where the tensor I_ω takes diagonal form in the auxiliary coordinate system, the axis OZ^* of which coincides with the vector angular velocity $\boldsymbol{\omega}$; the difference between the diagonal elements of this tensor is

$$\varkappa(C-A).$$

If the density and elastic properties of the interior of the Earth are functions of the distance from the centre only, then it follows from the theory of the tidal deformation of the Earth that this difference is proportional to the potential of the centrifugal force

$$V_\omega=-\frac{1}{2}n^2W_2,$$

where n is the modulus of the angular velocity of rotation of the Earth and W_2 a spherical harmonic of the second order. We can now write the angular momentum $\mathbf{G}$ as

$$\mathbf{G}=(I_0+I_\omega)\boldsymbol{\omega},$$

and using (1.8) we obtain

$$\mathbf{G}=\{(1-\varkappa)[AE+(C-A)P_0]+\varkappa[AE+(C-A)P_\omega]\}\boldsymbol{\omega}. \quad (1.10)$$

We denote the direction cosines of the polar axis of the tensor I_0 in this system by $\alpha_0, \beta_0, \gamma_0$. In the whole period for which we have data on the motion of the pole α_0 and β_0 have never exceeded 2×10^{-6} and γ_0 has not differed from 1 by more than 10^{-11}. Hence we shall neglect the squares and products of α_0 and β_0 and put γ_0 equal to unity. Then the tensor P_0 takes the following form

$$P_0 = \begin{Bmatrix} 0 & 0 & \alpha_0 \\ 0 & 0 & \beta_0 \\ \alpha_0 & \beta_0 & 1 \end{Bmatrix}.$$

We denote the cosines of the angles between $\boldsymbol{\omega}$ and the axes of the system XYZ by α', β', γ'. They have a form similar to that of α_0, β_0, γ_0, and we can write the matrix P_ω simply with a change of indices.

From (1.10) we obtain by projection on the X-axis

$$(1-\varkappa)[A\omega_x + (C-A)\alpha_0\omega_z] + \varkappa[A\omega_x + (C-A)\alpha'\omega_z] = 0 .$$

Denoting $\dfrac{C-A}{A}$ by a^2 and noticing that

$$\frac{\omega_x}{\omega_z} = \alpha',$$

we find after a simple rearrangement that

$$\alpha' = -\frac{(1-\varkappa)a^2}{1+\varkappa a^2}\alpha_0 . \tag{1.11}$$

Projection on the axis of Y gives an analogous relation between β' and β_0. In the denominators on the right we can neglect the second term; then we may write

$$\left.\begin{aligned} \alpha' &= -(1-\varkappa)a^2\alpha_0 \\ \beta' &= -(1-\varkappa)a^2\beta_0 \end{aligned}\right\} . \tag{1.12}$$

Hence the tensor P_ω may be written in the form

$$P_\omega = \begin{Bmatrix} 0 & 0 & -(1-\varkappa)a^2\alpha_0 \\ 0 & 0 & -(1-\varkappa)a^2\beta_0 \\ -(1-\varkappa)a^2\alpha_0 & -(1-\varkappa)a^2\beta_0 & 1 \end{Bmatrix}. \tag{1.13}$$

We now consider the deformation of the Earth which occurs under the action of the tidal force of the Sun and Moon. In the calculation of the variation of the elements of the tensor I caused by this deformation we take the initial form of the Earth spherical, that is, we suppose that the inertia tensor of the undeformed Earth is AE, where E is the unit tensor.

Then for any system of coordinates the axis OZ^* of which coincides with the line OO_1 through the centres of the Earth and the disturbing body the inertia tensor of the Earth takes a diagonal form, and the difference between the principal moments of inertia is

$$\varkappa_0 (C - A) \frac{V}{V_\omega},$$

where V is the potential of the tidal force. For the Sun we use the symbol V_1 and for the Moon V_2. The coefficient $\varkappa$ is replaced by the coefficient $\varkappa_0$ in the following considerations.

The ocean tide produced by changes in centrifugal force can be treated as static; hence the variation of the inertia tensor is related to both the ocean tide and the deformation of the solid spheroid. The semi-diurnal and diurnal tides of the Ocean arising from the gravitational action of the Sun and Moon cannot be treated as static and hence their amplitudes may not be taken simply proportional to the potential of the disturbing force. In the further work we shall have to do chiefly with the diurnal tides (since only they change the products of inertia of the Earth). It is known that the diurnal tide in the ocean is practically absent, and therefore in the calculation of the changes of moments of inertia in the case considered it is necessary to take account only of the bodily tide and to use the corrected coefficient which we obtained after excluding the effect of the oceanic tide. This coefficient we also denote by $\varkappa_0$. From the expressions

$$V_1 = \frac{3}{2} \frac{fM_1}{r_1^3} W_2, \qquad V_2 = \frac{3}{2} \cdot \frac{fM_2}{r_2^3} W_2$$

we obtain the following values for the differences between the principal moments of inertia of the deformed Earth

$$c_1 - a_1 = -\frac{3fM_1}{n^2 r_1^2} \varkappa_0 (C - A), \qquad c_2 - a_2 = -\frac{3fM}{n^2 r_2^3} \varkappa_0 (C - A). \quad (1.14)$$

Thus passing to the case of a rotating Earth subject to the tidal action of the Sun and Moon we must make two additions to the expression for the inertia tensor, that is, it takes the form

$$I = I_0 + I_\omega + I_1 + I_2. \quad (1.15)$$

Here

$$I_1 = (c_1 - a_1) P_1, \qquad I_2 = (c_2 - a_2) P_2 , \tag{1.16}$$

$$P_1 = \frac{1}{r_1^2} \begin{Bmatrix} x_1x_1 & x_1y_1 & x_1z_1 \\ y_1x_1 & y_1y_1 & y_1z_1 \\ z_1x_1 & z_1y_1 & z_1z_1 \end{Bmatrix}, \qquad P_2 = \frac{1}{r_2^2} \begin{Bmatrix} x_2x_2 & x_2y_2 & x_2z_2 \\ y_2x_2 & y_2y_2 & y_2z_2 \\ z_2x_2 & z_2y_2 & z_2z_2 \end{Bmatrix}, \tag{1.17}$$

where x_1, y_1, z_1 and x_2, y_2, z_2 are the coordinates of the Sun and Moon and r_1 and r_2 the corresponding distances from their centres to the centre of the Earth.

Now (1.15) may be written

$$I = (1 - \varkappa) [AE + (C - A) P_0] + \varkappa [AE + (C - A) P_{\omega}] - $$
$$- \frac{3fM_1}{n^2 r_1^3} \varkappa_0 (C - A) P_1 - \frac{3fM_2}{n^2 r_2^3} \varkappa_0 (C - A) P_2$$

or

$$I = AE + (C - A) \left[(1 - \varkappa) P_0 + \varkappa P_{\omega} - \frac{3f\varkappa_0}{n^2} \left(\frac{M_1}{r_1^3} P_1 + \frac{M_2}{r_2^3} P_2 \right) \right]. \tag{1.18}$$

3. Equations of Precession and Nutation

The expression for I obtained in section 2 must be substituted in (1.6), in which we write the right side as the sum of two terms

$$\frac{3fM_1}{r_1^5} \mathbf{r}_1 \wedge I\mathbf{r}_1 + \frac{3fM_2}{r_2^5} \mathbf{r}_2 \wedge I\mathbf{r}_2 .$$

After this substitution we get the following groups of terms (a common factor has been omitted):

$$\frac{M_1^2}{r_1^8} \mathbf{r}_1 \wedge P_1\mathbf{r}_1 + \frac{M_2^2}{r_2^8} \mathbf{r}_2 \wedge P_2\mathbf{r}_2 + \frac{M_1M_2}{r_1^5 r_2^5} (r_1^2\mathbf{r}_1 \wedge P_2\mathbf{r}_1 + r_2^2\mathbf{r}_2 \wedge P_1\mathbf{r}_2).$$

It is easily shown that

$$r_1^2\mathbf{r}_1 \wedge P_2\mathbf{r}_1 = (\mathbf{r}_1 \wedge \mathbf{r}_2)(\mathbf{r}_1 \cdot \mathbf{r}_2) .$$

If $\mathbf{r}_1 = \mathbf{r}_2$ the vector product $\mathbf{r}_1 \wedge \mathbf{r}_2 = 0$. Also $\mathbf{r}_1 \wedge \mathbf{r}_2 = - \mathbf{r}_2 \wedge \mathbf{r}_1$ and therefore the last sum of terms above is zero. From this it follows that the disturbing influences of the Sun and Moon may be considered separately, and to shorten the calculation we may again limit ourselves to one term on the right of (1.6).

Noticing that $\mathbf{r} \wedge E\mathbf{r} = 0$ we obtain

$$\frac{3fM}{r^5}\mathbf{r} \wedge J\mathbf{r} = \frac{3fM}{r^5}\mathbf{r} \wedge (I_0 + I_\omega + I_1)\mathbf{r} = \tag{1.19}$$
$$= \frac{3fM}{r^5}(C - A)[(1 - \varkappa)\mathbf{r} \wedge P_0\mathbf{r} + \varkappa\mathbf{r} \wedge P_\omega\mathbf{r}] .$$

Using this expression we may transform the right side of equation (1.8), first noticing that

$$\mathbf{i} \wedge \mathbf{r} = -\mathbf{j}z + \mathbf{k}y, \quad \mathbf{k} \wedge \mathbf{r} = -\mathbf{i}y + \mathbf{j}x,$$
$$\mathbf{k}' \wedge \mathbf{r} = -\mathbf{i}(z\sin\Theta + y\cos\Theta) + \mathbf{j}x\cos\Theta + \mathbf{k}x\sin\Theta$$

On the other hand

$$P_0\mathbf{r} = \mathbf{i}\alpha_0 z + \mathbf{j}\beta_0 z + \mathbf{k}(\alpha_0 x + \beta_0 y + z) ;$$

hence

$$P_0\mathbf{r}(\mathbf{i} \wedge \mathbf{r}) = yz + \alpha_0 xy + \beta_0(y^2 - z^2) = yz + \varepsilon,$$
$$P_0\mathbf{r}(\mathbf{k} \wedge \mathbf{r}) = \beta_0 xz - \alpha_0 yz = \varepsilon',$$
$$P_0\mathbf{r}(\mathbf{k}' \wedge \mathbf{r}) = xz\sin\Theta + z\cos\Theta(\beta_0 x - \alpha_0 y) +$$
$$+ \sin\Theta(\alpha_0 x^2 - \alpha_0 z^2 + \beta_0 xy) = xz\sin\Theta + \varepsilon'' .$$

We denote by ε, ε', ε'' the sums of terms containing α_0 or β_0 and therefore of the order 10^{-6}.

Similarly we obtain

$$P_\omega\mathbf{r}(\mathbf{i} \wedge \mathbf{r}) = yz - (1 - \varkappa)a^2\varepsilon,$$
$$P_\omega\mathbf{r}(\mathbf{k} \wedge \mathbf{r}) = -(1 - \varkappa)a^2\varepsilon',$$
$$P_\omega\mathbf{r}(\mathbf{k}' \wedge \mathbf{r}) = xz\sin\Theta - (1 - \varkappa)a^2\varepsilon''$$

Here the terms containing ε, ε', ε'' may certainly be neglected. Then equations (1.7) can be written as

$$G\sin\Theta\dot{\psi} = -\frac{3fM}{r^5}(C - A)[yz + (1 - \varkappa)\varepsilon],$$

$$\dot{G} = \frac{3fM}{r^5}(C - A)(1 - \varkappa)\varepsilon',$$

$$\dot{G}\cos\Theta - G\sin\Theta\dot{\Theta} = \frac{3fM}{r^5}(C - A)[xz\sin\Theta + (1 - \varkappa)\varepsilon''] .$$

To make an approximate estimate of the variation of the angular velocity we replace G by Cn. Then

$$\left.\begin{aligned} n\dot{\psi} &= -\frac{3fM}{r^5}\cdot\frac{C-A}{C}\cdot\frac{1}{\sin\Theta}\,[yz+(1-\varkappa)\varepsilon] \\ \dot{n} &= \frac{3fM}{r^5}\cdot\frac{C-A}{C}\cdot(1-\varkappa)\,\varepsilon' = n\,(1-\varkappa)\,(\alpha_0\sin\Theta\dot{\psi}-\beta_0\dot{\Theta}) \\ n\dot{\Theta} &= -\frac{3fM}{r^5}\cdot\frac{C-A}{A}\left[xz+\frac{1-\varkappa}{\sin\Theta}\,(\varepsilon''-\varepsilon'\cos\Theta)\right] \end{aligned}\right\}. \quad (1.20)$$

We remember that α_0 and β_0 are essentially the direction cosines of the polar axis of the Earth referred to the system XYZ. These axes have the angular velocity of the Earth about the instantaneous axis of rotation, which almost coincides with the direction of **G**. Hence we may take approximately (with an appropriate choice of the epoch from which time is measured)

$$\alpha_0 = \sigma\cos nt, \qquad \beta_0 = \sigma\sin nt,$$

and then

$$\Delta n = (1-\varkappa)\,n\sigma\int(\dot{\psi}\sin\Theta\cos nt-\dot{\Theta}\sin nt)\,dt.$$

Since $\dot{\Theta}$ and $\dot{\psi}$ vary slowly compared with nt, we shall take them to be constant in the solution of this integral equation. Then we get

$$\Delta n = (1-\varkappa)\,\sigma\,(\dot{\psi}\sin\Theta\sin nt+\dot{\Theta}\cos nt).$$

Of the terms in the expressions for $\dot{\psi}$ and $\dot{\Theta}$ the largest appears to be the constant term $\dot{\psi}$, that is, the luni-solar precession. In calculating this term we restrict ourselves to an estimate of the amplitude of the oscillation of Δn. We use the following numerical values:

$$1-\varkappa = 0.7, \quad \sigma = 10^{-6}, \quad \sin\Theta = 0.4,$$

$\dot{\psi} = 50''$ per annum, or 6.8×10^{-7} radians per day. We get $\Delta n = 1.9 \times 10^{-13}$ radians per day.

On this estimate we may base the following conclusions:

1. The angular velocity of the daily rotation of the Earth and the magnitude of **G** may be taken as constant.

2. ε, ε' and ε'' are small quantities all of the same order and therefore we may with sufficient accuracy replace equation (1.20) by the following:

$$\left.\begin{aligned}\dot{\psi} &= -\frac{3fM}{nr^5}\cdot\frac{C-A}{C}\cdot\frac{1}{\sin\Theta}yz \\ \dot{\Theta} &= \frac{3fM}{nr^5}\cdot\frac{C-A}{C}xz\end{aligned}\right\} . \qquad (1.21)$$

These are the usual equations of precession and nutation; the method of integration is well known.

We see that the elastic deformation of the Earth does not affect the motion in space of the vector **G**, the angular momentum of the Earth. Moreover the equations for its motion are practically unchanged for any assumptions about the interior of the Earth, since for all admissible assumptions the tidal deformation of the Earth has so little effect on the form of the ellipsoid of inertia that its effect may always be omitted from the moments of the external forces.

4. Differential Equations for the Motion of the Angular Momentum Vector Relative to the Earth

To complete the solution of the problem of the motion of the elastically deformed Earth we must find the motion of the principal axes of the tensor I_0 relative to the system XYZ, or, contrariwise, the motion of the system XYZ relative to the principal axes of the tensor I_0, which we denote by OX_0, OY_0, OZ_0. These axes rotate with angular velocity $\boldsymbol{\omega}$ and hence we may write

$$\dot{\mathbf{G}} + \boldsymbol{\omega} \wedge \mathbf{G} = \mathbf{L} \ ;$$

but

$$\mathbf{L} = \Omega \wedge \mathbf{G} \ ;$$

Hence

$$\dot{\mathbf{G}} + (\boldsymbol{\omega} - \Omega) \wedge \mathbf{G} = 0 \ . \qquad (1.22)$$

The angular velocity is equal to

$$\boldsymbol{\omega} = I^{-1}\mathbf{G} \ ,$$

where I^{-1} is the tensor reciprocal to I. To calculate the elements of this tensor, we use the formula

$$(I_{kl}^{-1}) = \frac{Q_{lk}}{D}$$

in which the indices k and l denote the columns and rows of matrices, Q_{lk} = minor of (I_{lk}) multiplied by $(-1)^{k+l}$, and D is the determinant of the matrix.

In this formula to the first order of small quantities

$$I^{-1} = \frac{E}{A} - (1-\varkappa)\frac{C-A}{CA}P_0 - \frac{1}{AC}(I_\omega + I) =$$
$$= \frac{E}{A} - (1-\varkappa)\frac{C-A}{CA}P_0 - \frac{\varkappa(C-A)}{CA}P_\omega + \frac{3fM\varkappa_0}{n^2r^3}\cdot\frac{C-A}{CA}P_1. \quad (1.23)$$

We now project the vectors in equation (1.22) on the axes of the system $X_0Y_0Z_0$, and hence we write the tensors in the form

$$P_0 = \begin{Bmatrix} 0 & 0 & 0 \\ 0 & 0 & 0 \\ 0 & 0 & 1 \end{Bmatrix}, \qquad P_\omega = \frac{1}{n}\begin{Bmatrix} 0 & 0 & \omega_x \\ 0 & 0 & \omega_y \\ \omega_x & \omega_y & \omega_z \end{Bmatrix}.$$

The tensor I takes the same form as in the system XYZ, but it must now be understood in calculating its elements that we use the coordinates of the heavenly body in the system $X_0Y_0Z_0$. We write equation (1.22) as

$$\dot{\mathbf{G}} + I^{-1}\mathbf{G} \wedge \mathbf{G} - \Omega \wedge \mathbf{G} = 0. \quad (1.24)$$

We consider separately the sum of the terms

$$\frac{3fM\varkappa_0}{n^2r^3}\cdot\frac{C-A}{AC}P_1\mathbf{G} \wedge \mathbf{G} - \Omega \wedge \mathbf{G} = \mathbf{F},$$

and we notice that

$$\Omega \wedge \mathbf{G} = \mathbf{L} = \frac{3fM}{r^5}\mathbf{r} \wedge I\mathbf{r},$$

where approximately

$$\Omega \wedge \mathbf{G} = \frac{3fM}{r^5}(C-A)(\mathbf{i}_0 z_0 y_0 - \mathbf{j}_0 x_0 z_0).$$

On the other hand we have the following approximate expression

$$P_1\mathbf{G} \wedge \mathbf{G} = \frac{C^2n^2}{r^2}(\mathbf{i}_0 z_0 y_0 - \mathbf{j}_0 x_0 z_0),$$

and hence

$$\mathbf{F}=\frac{3fM}{r^5}(C-A)\left(\frac{C}{A}\varkappa_0-1\right)(\mathbf{i}_0z_0y_0-\mathbf{j}_0x_0z_0)=-\left(1-\frac{C}{A}\varkappa_0\right)\Omega\wedge\mathbf{G}\ .$$

Since $\frac{C}{A}$ is approximately unity we write

$$\mathbf{F}=-(1-\varkappa_0)\Omega\wedge\mathbf{G}. \qquad (1.25)$$

The vector $P_\omega\mathbf{G}$ is sufficiently near to the direction of $\mathbf{G}$ for us to take to the first order of small quantities

$$P_\omega\mathbf{G}\wedge\mathbf{G}=0.$$

Then in the expression for the tensor I^{-1} we may neglect the third term and certainly the first, since

$$E\mathbf{G}=\mathbf{G}.$$

Taking all this into account we may write equation (1.22) in the form

$$\dot{\mathbf{G}}-(1-\varkappa)\frac{C-A}{CA}P_0\mathbf{G}\wedge\mathbf{G}-(1-\varkappa_0)\Omega\wedge\mathbf{G}=0. \qquad (1.26)$$

We write the equations obtained by projecting on the axes of the system $X_0Y_0Z_0$ as

$$\left.\begin{array}{l}\dot{X}+(1-\varkappa)a^2nY-(1-\varkappa_0)Cn\Omega_y=0\\ \dot{Y}-(1-\varkappa)a^2nX+(1-\varkappa_0)Cn\Omega_x=0\\ \dot{Z}=0\end{array}\right\}. \qquad (1.27)$$

X, Y, Z denote the projections of the vector $\mathbf{G}$ on the axes of this system.

It remains to express Ω_x and Ω_y in terms of $\dot{\psi}$ and $\dot{\Theta}$, that is, the projections of the angular velocity on the axes OZ' and OX. The position of the system of axes $X_0Y_0Z_0$ relative to XYZ is defined by a set of Euler angles, u, v and Θ_0 (see Fig. 2). The angle $u=XOM$ is measured in the plane XOY,

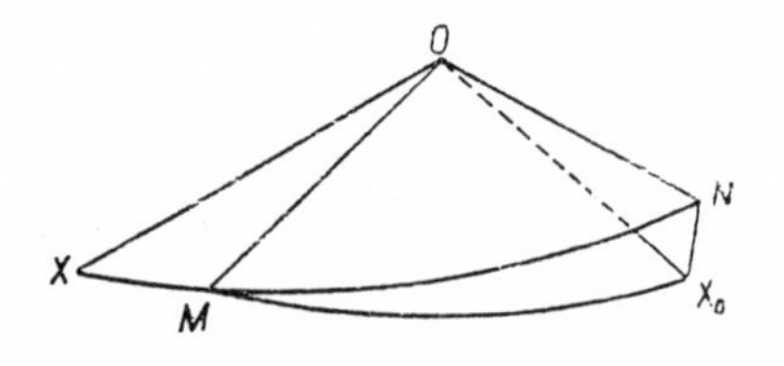

Fig. 2

the angle $v = MOX_0$ in the plane X_0OY_0. Since the angle Θ_0 is small, we may, constructing in the plane XOY the angle

$$\varphi = XON = u + v,$$

take

$$XOX_0 = YOY_0 = \varphi, \quad X_0OY = 90^\circ - \varphi, \quad XOY_0 = 90^\circ + \varphi.$$

Then

$$\Omega_x = \sin\Theta \sin\varphi\dot{\psi} - \cos\varphi\dot{\Theta}, \quad \Omega_y = -\sin\Theta\cos\varphi\dot{\psi} + \sin\varphi\dot{\Theta}.$$

Putting these values in (1.27) we find finally

$$\left.\begin{aligned} \dot{X} + (1-\varkappa)a^2nY &= Cn(1-\varkappa_0)(-\sin\Theta\cos\varphi\dot{\psi} + \sin\varphi\dot{\Theta}) \\ \dot{Y} - (1-\varkappa)a^2nX &= Cn(1-\varkappa_0)(\sin\Theta\sin\varphi\dot{\psi} + \cos\varphi\dot{\Theta}) \end{aligned}\right\}. \quad (1.28)$$

5. Integration of the Equations of Relative Motion of the Angular Momentum Vector

In the integration of the equations of relative motion of the angular momentum we make use of the expressions for ψ and Θ that are given by the theory of precession and nutation, based on the assumption that the Earth is absolutely rigid. We write the complete angular velocity as the sum of the relative angular velocities

$$\boldsymbol{\omega} = \boldsymbol{\omega}' + \Omega.$$

Projecting on the direction of **G** we have

$$n = \dot{\varphi} + \dot{\psi}\cos\Theta,$$

whence we get

$$\varphi = nt - \int \dot{\psi}\cos\Theta\, dt = n_1 t. \quad (1.29)$$

The most important term in the expression for ψ is the luni-solar precession. The variation of Θ is unimportant; hence n_1 is practically constant. Using this in (1.28) we have

$$\left.\begin{aligned} \dot{X} + (1-\varkappa)a^2nY &= Cn(1-\varkappa_0)(-\sin\Theta\cos n_1t\dot{\psi} + \sin n_1t\dot{\Theta}) \\ \dot{Y} - (1-\varkappa)a^2nX &= Cn(1-\varkappa_0)(\sin\Theta\sin n_1t\dot{\psi} + \cos n_1t\dot{\Theta}) \end{aligned}\right\}. \quad (1.30)$$

The expressions for precession and nutation in longitude and obliquity are

$$\psi = pt + \sum N_i \sin \mu_i t, \qquad \Theta = \Theta_0 + \sum M_i \cos \mu_i t.$$

Hence

$$\dot{\psi} = p + \sum N_i \mu_i \cos \mu_i t, \qquad \dot{\Theta} = \quad \sum M_i \mu_i \sin \mu_i t. \tag{1.31}$$

We write

$$-M_i \mu_i = B_i + B_i', \qquad N_i \mu_i \sin \Theta = B_i - B_i'. \tag{1.32}$$

Then (1.30) may be written as

$$\left.\begin{aligned} \dot{X} + (1-\varkappa) a^2 n Y = Cn(1-\varkappa_0)[&-p \sin \Theta \cos n_1 t - \\ &-\sum B_i \cos (n_1 + \mu_i) t + \sum B_i' \cos (n_1 - \mu_i) t] \\ \dot{Y} - (1-\varkappa) a^2 n X = Cn(1-\varkappa_0)[&p \sin \Theta \sin n_1 t + \\ &+ \sum B_i \sin (n_1 + \mu_i) t - \sum B_i' \sin (n_1 - \mu_i) t] \end{aligned}\right\} . \tag{1.33}$$

The solution of these equations without the right sides is

$$\left.\begin{aligned} X &= U \cos (1-\varkappa) a^2 nt + V \sin (1-\varkappa) a^2 nt \\ Y &= U \sin (1-\varkappa) a^2 nt - V \cos (1-\varkappa) a^2 nt \end{aligned}\right\} \tag{1.34}$$

where U and V are constants. In order to get the solution with the right sides present we treat U and V as functions of the time. Then

$$\dot{X} = \dot{U} \cos (1-\varkappa) a^2 nt + \dot{V} \sin (1-\varkappa) a^2 nt - (1-\varkappa) a^2 n Y,$$

$$\dot{Y} = \dot{U} \sin (1-\varkappa) a^2 nt - \dot{V} \cos (1-\varkappa) a^2 nt + (1-\varkappa) a^2 n X,$$

and substituting in (1.33) we get

$$\begin{aligned} \dot{U} = Cn(1-\varkappa_0)\{&-p \sin \Theta \cos [n_1 + (1-\varkappa) a^2 n] t - \\ &-\sum B_i \cos [n_1 + \mu_i + (1-\varkappa) a^2 n] t + \sum B_i' \cos [n_1 - \mu_i + (1-\varkappa) a^2 n] t\}, \\ \dot{V} = Cn(1-\varkappa_0)\{&-p \sin \Theta \sin [n_1 + (1-\varkappa) a^2 n] t - \\ &-\sum B_i \sin [n_1 + \mu_i + (1-\varkappa) a^2 n] t + \sum B_i' \sin [n_1 - \mu_i + (1-\varkappa) a^2 n] t\}. \end{aligned}$$

In integrating these expressions we shall take $\sin\Theta$ as constant. Carrying out the integration, with some rearrangement, we get

$$\left.\begin{aligned}
X = {} & U_0 \cos(1-\varkappa)\,a^2nt + \\
& + V_0 \sin(1-\varkappa)\,a^2nt - \frac{Cn(1-\varkappa_0)\,p \sin\Theta \sin n_1 t}{n_1+(1-\varkappa)\,a^2n} - \\
& - \frac{Cn(1-\varkappa_0)}{2}\sum \frac{N_i\mu_i \sin\Theta - M_i\mu_i}{n_1+\mu_i+(1-\varkappa)\,a^2n}\sin(n_1+\mu_i)\,t - \\
& - \frac{Cn(1-\varkappa_0)}{2}\sum \frac{N_i\mu_i \sin\Theta + M_i\mu_i}{n_1-\mu_i+(1-\varkappa)\,a^2n}\sin(n_1-\mu_i)\,t, \\
Y = {} & U_0 \sin(1-\varkappa)\,a^2nt - \\
& - V_0 \cos(1-\varkappa)\,a^2nt - \frac{Cn(1-\varkappa_0)\,p \sin\Theta \cos n_1 t}{n_1+(1-\varkappa)\,a^2n} - \\
& - \frac{Cn(1-\varkappa_0)}{2}\sum \frac{N_i\mu_i \sin\Theta - M_i\mu_i}{n_1+\mu_i+(1-\varkappa)\,a^2n}\cos(n_1+\mu_i)\,t - \\
& - \frac{Cn(1-\varkappa_0)}{2}\sum \frac{N_i\mu_i \sin\Theta + M_i\mu_i}{n_1-\mu_i+(1-\varkappa)\,a^2n}\cos(n_1-\mu_i)\,t
\end{aligned}\right\} \quad (1.35)$$

Here U_0 and V_0 are new arbitrary constants. Then equations (1.29) and (1.35) completely define the motion of the system XYZ relative to $X_0Y_0Z_0$, and since the motion of XYZ in space (i.e. relative to $X'Y'Z'$) was found earlier we may consider the problem of the rotation of an elastically deformed Earth as solved.

6. Motion of the Pole of an Elastically Deformed Earth

Using the formulae adopted in the reduction of observations we do not strictly speaking obtain the observed declinations of the stars, that is, their angular distance from the plane of the instantaneous equator perpendicular to the instantaneous axis of rotation of the Earth, since in the proof of these formulae we do not take into account the effect of the diurnal nutation on the observed coordinates.

Starting from (1.21) we describe the motion in space of $\mathbf{G}$ and not of the instantaneous axis of rotation of the Earth. It follows from this that the formula of nutation in declination gives us the variation of the angular distances of the stars from the plane perpendicular to $\mathbf{G}$ (we shall call this the plane of the dynamical equator). In the calculation of latitude according to observations in the meridian we use the formula

$$\varphi = \delta + z,$$

where z is the observed zenith distance of the star; hence we find the angle between the plumb line and the plane of the dynamical equator. When we determine the position of the pole from latitude observations we define the position of the pole as the point where a line coinciding with the vector **G**, not the axis of rotation, cuts the surface.

The difference is not substantial, since the angle between **G** and $\boldsymbol{\omega}$ does not amount to 0".002. The instantaneous axis moves around **G** on a conical surface with period approximately a sidereal day, in consequence of which the observed declination shows a diurnal term, which, however, is not taken into account in the calculation of apparent place.

The introduction of an auxiliary system related to the vector **G** (system XYZ) instead of the instantaneous axis certainly has advantages in the exposition of the theory of the rotation of the Earth. In the reduction of astronomical observations it matters little which system we use; however in this case also it is in principle more correct to use the system of the dynamical equator. Then we must define latitude and instantaneous pole as we have done above.

We denote the coordinates of the pole by x and y. In accordance with our definition we have

$$x=\frac{X}{Cn}, \quad y=\frac{Y}{Cn}. \tag{1.36}$$

We also write

$$\frac{U_0}{Cn}=u_0, \quad \frac{V_0}{Cn}=v_0 . \tag{1.37}$$

From (1.35) we obtain

$$\left.\begin{aligned} x &= u_0 \cos(1-\varkappa) a^2 nt + v_0 \sin(1-\varkappa) a^2 nt - \\ &\quad - (1-\varkappa_0) \frac{p \sin\Theta}{n_1 + (1-\varkappa) a^2 n} \sin n_1 t - \\ &\quad - (1-\varkappa_0) \left[\sum q_i \sin(n_1+\mu_i) t + \sum q_i' \sin(n_1-\mu_i) t \right] \\ y &= u_0 \sin(1-\varkappa) a^2 nt - v_0 \cos(1-\varkappa) a^2 nt - \\ &\quad - (1-\varkappa_0) \frac{p \sin\Theta}{n_1 + (1-\varkappa) a^2 n} \cos n_1 t - \\ &\quad - (1-\varkappa_0) \left[\sum q_i \cos(n_1+\mu_i) t + \sum q_i \cos(n_1-\mu_i) t \right] \end{aligned}\right\}, \tag{1.38}$$

where

$$\left.\begin{aligned} q_i &= \frac{N_i \sin\Theta - M_i}{2} \cdot \frac{\mu_i}{n_1 + \mu_i + (1-\varkappa)\,a^2 n} \\ q_i &= \frac{N_i \sin\Theta + M_i}{2} \cdot \frac{\mu_i}{n_1 - \mu_i + (1-\varkappa)\,a^2 n} \end{aligned}\right\}. \qquad (1.39)$$

If we take the sidereal day as unit of time, $n = 2\pi$. The period of the free motion may be found from

$$\frac{2\pi}{T} = (1-\varkappa)\,a^2 n = (1-\varkappa)\,\frac{C-A}{A}\,2\pi$$

and hence

$$1 - \varkappa = \frac{A}{C-A} \cdot \frac{1}{T}\,. \qquad (1.40)$$

We take

$$\frac{A}{C-A} = 304, \qquad T = 433, \qquad 1 - \varkappa = 0.72.$$

The motion of the oceanic waters diminishes the Love number k. According to Molodenskii the correction is -0.04 [7]. From the formula (14) of [14] we see that this diminishes the magnitude of $\varkappa$, hence

$$1 - \varkappa_0 = 0.76\,.$$

The data for the calculation of the coefficients q_i, q_i' are taken from Woolard [59]. The arguments are in the notation of the Astronomical Yearbook.

In Table 1 the values of those coefficients are given that are greater than 0".001. The q_i do not reach this value and hence only q_i' are given. These must be multiplied by $1 - \varkappa_0$ and put in (1.38).

If further we multiply the first of these equations by $\cos\lambda$ and the second by $\sin\lambda$ and add, we find the variation of latitude at a point of longitude λ. Since

$$n_1 t + \lambda = S$$

is the sidereal time, we obtain the following expression for the forced variation of latitude

$$\begin{aligned}\Delta\varphi = &- 0'',0066 \sin S - 0'',0051 \sin (S - 2☾) - \\ &- 0''.0022 \sin (S - 2L) - 0''.0010 \sin (S - 2☾ - ☊) - \\ &- 0''.0010 \sin (S - 3☾ + \Gamma') + 0''.0009 \sin (S - ☊).\end{aligned} \quad (1.41)$$

TABLE 1

Argument	$N_i \sin\Theta$	M_i	$\frac{\mu_i}{n_1 - \mu_i + (1-\varkappa) a^2 n}$	q_i
☊	+6''.8586	+9''.2100	−0.00015	−0.0012
$2L$	+0 .5066	+0 .5522	+0.00548	+0.0029
2☾	+0 .0811	+0 .0884	+0.07869	+0.0067
2☾ − ☊	+0 .0136	+0 .0183	+0.07884	+0.0013
3☾ − Γ'	+0 .0104	+0 .0113	+0.12246	+0.0013

We find in this way a combination of small variations of latitude of period near to a sidereal day. Oppolzer first pointed out that these appear as a necessary consequence of the motion of the axis of rotation in space, and he also found their expression for a perfectly rigid Earth.

The elastic deformation of the Earth leads to the same relative diminution of the coefficients of all the Oppolzer terms, inasmuch as in $\Delta\varphi$ the factor $1 - \varkappa_0$ appears throughout. This and the lengthening of the period of the free nutation are the only manifestations of the influence of the deformation of the Earth on its rotational motion, inasmuch as the deformation has practically no effect on the motion of the angular momentum in space.

CHAPTER II

THE PRINCIPAL NUTATION TERMS

7. Method of Investigation. Initial Data

In the determination of latitude by the method of Talcott the following relation is generally used:

$$\varphi_0 = z + \delta , \tag{2.1}$$

where z is the observed zenith distance, δ the apparent declination of the pair.

Keeping only the principal nutation terms, we may express the influence of nutation on declination by the following formula:

$$\Delta_0\delta = - N_0 (n_0 \cos\alpha \sin☊ - \sin\alpha \cos☊) \tag{2.2}$$

If the values of the constant of nutation N_0 and the ratio of the axes of the nutation ellipse n_0 are in error, and the nutation is retarded in phase, then the values of the latitude calculated from formula (2.1) will contain errors, depending on the right ascension of the pair, α, and the longitude, ☊, of the Moon's ascending node. Then in the variation of latitude there appears a 19-yearly nutation term whose amplitudes and phases will be different for pairs of different right ascensions.

We suppose, further, that in fact the effect of the principal nutation terms is expressed as

$$\Delta\delta = - (N_0 + \Delta N) [(n_0 + \Delta n) \cos\alpha \sin(☊ - \beta_1) - \\ - \sin\alpha \cos(☊ - \beta_2)] , \tag{2.3}$$

where ΔN = correction to the constant of nutation, Δn = correction to the ratio of the coefficients of the principal nutation terms, and β_1, β_2 are the phase lags. Then the nutation terms are no longer contained in the variation of latitude, calculated from the formula

$$\varphi = z + \delta - \Delta_0\delta + \Delta\delta. \tag{2.4}$$

This is a reason for putting the 19-yearly variation of latitude φ_0 in the following form:

$$\Delta\varphi = \Delta_0\delta - \Delta\delta. \tag{2.5}$$

We transform the difference of the right sides of (2.2) and (2.3) to

$$\Delta\varphi = A_1 \cos\alpha \cos\Omega + B_1 \sin\alpha \cos\Omega + A_2 \cos\alpha \sin\Omega + B_2 \sin\alpha \sin\Omega, \tag{2.6}$$

where

$$\left.\begin{array}{ll} A_1 = -N_0 n_0 \beta_1, & A_2 = N_0 \Delta n + \Delta N n_0 \\ B_1 = -\Delta N, & B_2 = -N_0 \beta_2 \end{array}\right\}, \tag{2.7}$$

or to

$$\Delta\varphi = a_1 \cos(\Omega - \alpha) + b_1 \sin(\Omega - \alpha) + a_2 \cos(\Omega + \alpha) + b_2 \sin(\Omega + \alpha), \tag{2.8}$$

where

$$\left.\begin{array}{ll} a_1 = -\frac{N_0}{2}(\beta_2 + n_0\beta_1), & a_2 = \frac{N_0}{2}(\beta_2 - n_0\beta_1), \\ b_1 = \frac{N_0}{2}\Delta n + \frac{1 + n_0}{2}\Delta N, & b_2 = \frac{N_0}{2}\Delta n - \frac{1 - n_0}{2}\Delta N \end{array}\right\}. \tag{2.9}$$

From equations (2.7) and (2.9) we have

$$\left.\begin{array}{l} \Delta N = -B_1 = b_1 - b_2 \\ \Delta n = \frac{A_2 + B_1 n_0}{N_0} = \frac{(1 - n_0) b_1 + (1 + n_0) b_2}{N_0} \\ \beta_1 = -\frac{A_1}{N_0 n_0} = -\frac{a_1 + a_2}{N_0 n_0} \\ \beta_2 = -\frac{B_2}{N_0} = \frac{a_2 - a_1}{N_0} \end{array}\right\}. \tag{2.10}$$

With the help of (2.10) the problem of the determination of the corrections ΔN and Δn and also of the phase lags β_1 and β_2 is reduced to the determination of the coefficients A_1, B_1, A_2, B_2 or a_1, b_1, a_2, b_2.

We can see at once that these coefficients are very small and that therefore for their determination only series of the most precise observations over a long period of years are suitable. This condition is best satisfied by the systematic observations of latitude, in particular those of the International Latitude Service (ILS). Unfortunately they are published only up to 1934.* It was not possible to use the whole of the material, since on account of changes in the programme some pairs of stars were observed over less than a nutation period. These we in general omitted, and retained the following:

A	26 pairs observed from		1900 to 1934
B	27 " " "		1900 to 1922
C	21 " " "		1906 to 1934

In column 1 of Table 2 we give the number that was assigned to the pair in the programmes of 1899-1905 and 1912-1922. For some of these pairs the number was increased by 1 in the programme of 1922-1934, so that, for example, pair 65 was, after 1922.7, called number 66. These pairs are shown in Table 2 with asterisks.

The letters *A*, *B*, *C* denote the cycles when the observations of the given pairs were made. The GC numbers of the stars composing the pair are given in column 3, and columns 4 and 5 give the declination and proper motion of the centre of the pair, calculated from the data of the catalogue. Pairs 42, 48 and 84 consist of stars not in Boss's catalogue; their declinations and proper motions were taken from the catalogues published in "Results of the ILS" [43].

As is well known, 96 pairs of the ILS programme (for which observations were made before 1935) are divided into 12 groups with 8 pairs in each. The approximate values of the right ascensions of the centres of these groups are given in column 2 of Table 3. Columns 4 and 5 of Table 3 show the fractions of the year in which the mean times of observation of the corresponding group fall. There are two values τ_1 and τ_2 because from the epoch 1922.7 the observations began to be taken

---

* **After** this computation was finished, volume 9 (1935-1941.0) of **the** "Results" of the ILS was published by L.Carnera. - Translator.

TABLE 2

Pair	Cycle of observations	GC Number of stars	$\delta_{1950.0}$	μ_δ	a'	b'
1	*C*	48 345	39° 16′33″.62	−0″.004	+1.00	+0.04
2	*B*	473 632	21 11 .15	− .013	+1.00	+ .10
3	*B*	735 894	20 38 .48	− .018	+0.99	+ .16
5	*B*	1437 1594	22 9 .70	− .005	+ .95	+ .30
8	*B*	2323 2497	21 30 .41	− .022	+ .88	+ .48
9	*B*	2552 2851	23 48 .28	− .070	+ .84	+ .54
10	*C*	2978 3139	14 33 .05	− .013	+ .79	+ .61
11	*A*	3273 3466	13 47 .26	− .017	+ .76	+ .69
13	*A*	3779 3883	11 33 .42	− .030	+ .69	+ .73
14	*B*	4007 4226	20 2 .48	− .014	+ .64	+ .77
15	*B*	4316 4464	21 42 .95	− .028	+ .59	+ .81
16	*C*	4603 4868	14 44 .94	− .046	+ .52	+ .85
17	*A*	4973 5103	8 5 .48	− .112	+ .48	+ .88
18	*A*	5253 5351	14 16 .33	− .020	+ .44	+ .90
19	*C*	5663 5812	10 2 .39	− .040	+ .34	+ .94
20	*B*	5932 6011	17 50 .30	+ .004	+ .31	+ .95
21	*A*	6265 6350	12 4 .65	− .023	+ .25	+ .97
22	*A*	6470 6550	11 46 .32	− .023	+ .20	+ .98
23	*A*	6723 7105	13 37 .24	+ .010	+ .14	+ .99
24	*C*	7248 7621	6 23 .32	− .007	+ .02	+1.00
25	*A*	7796 7971	3 36 .12	− .084	− .02	+1.00
26	*A*	8296 8549	3 4 .66	− .036	− .10	+ .99
27	*C*	8801 8993	10 35 .58	− .072	− .16	+ .99
28	*A*	9122 9297	4 51 .46	− .044	− .23	+ .97
29	*C*	9671 9801	1 47 .64	− .030	− .26	+ .97
30	*A*	9987 10168	5 20 .60	+ .066	− .37	+ .93
32	*A*	10809 10948	5 6 .47	+ .003	− .48	+ .88

TABLE 2 (contd.)

Pair	Cycle of observations	GC Number of stars	$\delta_{1950.0}$	μ_δ	a'	b'
34	*C*	11603 11810	39° 2′42″.05	—0″.026	—0.56	+0.83
35	*B*	12226 12417	3 28 .24	— .042	— .67	+ .74
36	*B*	12534 12615	38 55 51 .14	— .224	— .71	+ .71
37	*B*	12737 12856	56 29 .59	— .028	— .74	+ .67
38	*C*	13004 13183	58 32 .44	— .057	— .77	+ .64
39	*B*	13369 13497	52 49 .95	— .054	— .82	+ .58
40	*B*	13827 14096	56 36 .26	+ .008	— .88	+ .48
41	*B*	14194 14312	53 27 .26	— .037	— .90	+ .43
42	*C*		56 8 .42	— .040	— .91	+ .42
44	*A*	15128 15215	59 45 .88	— .014	.96	+ .27
47	*B*	16053 16127	50 36 .44	— .018	—1.00	+ .09
48	*C*		39 0 3 .49	— .008	—1.00	+ .04
50	*B*	17127 17231	38 55 39 .42	+ .136	— .99	— .14
51	*B*	17305 17469	54 41 .14	— .003	— .98	— .19
52	*C*	17664 17767	39 1 42 .25	— .029	— .98	— .20
56	*C*	18860 19031	38 58 41 .01	— .016	— .89	— .45
57	*B*	19297 19385	54 53 .61	— .043	— .83	— .56
58	*A*	19501 19662	39 2 24 .58	— .044	— .80	— .60
61	*B*	20740 20849	38 56 10 .92	— .012	— .63	— .78
62	*B*	20983 21246	39 0 34 .19	— .030	— .58	— .82
64	*B*	21678 21756	38 57 24 .82	— .015	— .48	— .88
65*	*C*	21995 22130	39 0 28 .32	— .046	— .48	— .87
67*	*A*	22882 23029	2 9 .42	— .050	— .27	— .96
68*	*C*	23172 23374	5 26 .24	+ .030	— .28	— .96
69*	*C*	23571 23807	8 11 .25	— .014	— .23	— .97
70*	*A*	23989 24093	10 45 .62	+ .017	— .09	—1.00
71*	*A*	24251 24410	9 8 .34	+ .048	— .04	—1.00

TABLE 2 (contd.)

Pair	Cycle of obser-vations	GC Number of stars	$\delta_{1950.0}$	μ_δ	a'	b'
72*	*A*	24658 24787	11 50 .93	+ .056	+ .02	−1.00
73*	*A*	24903 25085	39° 8′40″.60	−0″.102	+0.06	−1.00
74*	*A*	25352 25502	12 33 .34	− .042	+ .14	−0.99
75*	*C*	25698 26049	7 20 .91	− .204	+ .17	− .99
76*	*A*	26454 26585	11 39 .50	− .012	+0.30	− .95
77*	*A*	26748 26893	11 29 .35	− .019	+ .35	− .94
78*	*A*	27146 27275	12 9 .43	+ .011	+ .41	− .91
80	*B*	27980 28123	19 15 .84	− .004	+ .53	+ .85
82	*A*	28551 28669	14 28 .48	+ .004	+ .61	− .79
83	*B*	28997 29159	19 15 .41	+ .002	+ .67	− .75
84	*C*		14 24 .07	− .011	+ .68	− .73
85	*A*	29616 29791	17 0 .48	− .012	+ .74	− .67
86	*C*	30016 30173	15 44 .66	− .030	+ .76	− .66
87	*B*	30338 30475	20 9 .52	+ .012	+ .82	− .58
88	*B*	30580 30728	23 20 .08	− .014	+ .84	− .54
89	*B*	30848 31081	22 57 .92	− .040	+ .87	− .49
90	*C*	31252 31430	18 0 .61	− .004	+ .92	− .39
91	*C*	31520 31749	17 47 .80	+ .003	+ .95	− .32
92	*B*	31854 32101	21 14 .90	+ .023	+ .96	− .29
96	*A*	33021 33253	19 44 .85	0	+1.00	− .05

symmetrically relative to midnight, which had not been done previously. Consequently the mean time of observation for each group changed.

In future we shall denote by k the whole number of years that have elapsed from the epoch 1900.0 to the beginning of the year of observation; hence the epoch corresponding to the mean time of observation of a given group will be expressed as

$$1900.0 + k + \tau_1 \text{ before } 1922.7$$

$$1900.0 + k + \tau_2 \text{ after } 1922.7.$$

TABLE 3

Group	$\bar{\alpha}$	Pair	Mean time of observation		Value of ☊ at the mean time of observation of the group		$\Delta_\tau\delta$
			τ_1	τ_2	1900	1922.7	
I	1^h	1- 8	0.83	0.76	243°.1	179°.0	+10"
II	3	9-16	0.93	0.85	241 .2	177 .2	+ 8
III	5	17-24	0.01	-0.07	259 .0	195 .0	+ 2
IV	7	25-32	0.08	0.02	257 .6	193 .3	+ 1
V	9	33-40	0.15	0.10	256 .3	191 .2	- 2
VI	11	41-48	0.22	0.18	254 .9	190 .2	- 3
VII	13	49-56	0.29	0.26	253 .4	188 .6	- 3
VIII	15	57-64	0.36	0.35	252 .2	186 .9	- 2
IX	17	65-72	0.44	0.43	250 .7	185 .4	0
X	19	73-80	0.52	0.51	249 .1	183 .8	+ 3
XI	21	81-88	0.62	0.60	247 .2	182 .1	+ 6
XII	23	89-96	0.73	0.68	245 .1	180 .5	+ 9

Notes. 1. Pairs observed up to 1922 under the number 72 were in 1922 given the number 73; hence they changed from Group IX to Group X.

2. The negative value of τ_2 for the group III must be understood in the sense that from 1923 the mean time of observation of this group changed to 0.93 of the preceding calendar year.

3. $\Delta_\tau\delta$ is the reduction to apparent place (see section 11).

8. Reduction of the Initial Data to a Common System of Declinations and Proper Motions

The initial data for the further calculations were taken from the following sources.

1. 1900-1905. "Results of the ILS", Vol. 3, pp. 66-185

[42]. The declinations and proper motions with which the latitude is calculated are published on pp. 64-65 of this volume, initial epoch 1903.0.

2. 1906-1908. "Results of the ILS", Vol. 4, pp. 162-220 [43]. Corrections published in Vol. 5, pp. 78-89 [44].

3. 1909-12. "Results of the ILS", Vol. 5, pp. 90-146 [44]. Declinations and proper motions given on pp. 76-77 for epoch 1909.0.

4. 1912-22. "Results of the ILS", Vol. 6, pp. 65-215 [24]. Declinations and proper motions given on pp. 26-7 of the same volume for the epoch 1915.0.

5. 1922.7-1934. "Results of the ILS", Vol. 8, pp.31-131 [35]. Declinations and proper motions given on pp. 29-30 for epoch 1928.0.

Thus the instantaneous latitudes published by the ILS had been calculated for the different cycles with different initial declinations and proper motions of the pairs.

We take four systems for the following initial epochs: 1903.0, 1909.0, 1915.0, and 1928.0. The mean date of observation of a pair in different years will not be exactly the same, but the limits for t_1 and t_2 will all remain sufficiently narrow; thus we found it possible not to calculate these magnitudes for each year separately, but simply to use their means calculated for the first period (up to 1922.7) and the second (after 1922.7) respectively.

During the time considered only three stations of the ILS, Carloforte, Mizusawa and Ukiah, carried out observations without interruption. As initial data we used results of observations from these stations alone. First of all, for each year and each pair we formed the mean of the instantaneous latitudes; we took away whole degrees, minutes and seconds, and denoted the remainder by the initial of the corresponding station. Further we obtained the value of the magnitude

$$F_1 = 0.402C + 0.302M + 0.296U. \qquad (2.11)$$

These are given in column 4 of Table 30 (see appendix). In sum for the calculation of these values 135,000 instantaneous latitudes were used.

TABLE 4

Pair	1903	1909	1915	1928	$(-x_1)$	$(-x_2)$
1	—	+0″,10	+0″.16	+0″,22	—0″.967	+0″.0029
2	+0″.10	+ ,09	+ .05	—	— .969	+ ,0024
3	+ .11	+ ,08	+ .07	—	— .953	+ .0130
5	+ .06	+ ,03	— .07	—	— ,917	+ ,0028
8	— .03	— ,06	— .12	—	— ,852	+ ,0030
9	+ .11	+ ,06	— .13	—	—1 ,027	+ ,0029
10	—	+ .33	+ .47	+ .64	—1 ,213	+ .0027
11	— .12	— .20	— .18	— ,09	— ,723	+ ,0022
13	+ .32	+ .26	+ ,39	+ .46	—1 ,163	+ ,0078
14	— .04	— .17	— .47	—	— ,925	+ ,0048
15	+ .06	— .03	— .13	—	—1 ,000	+ .0042
16	—	+ .07	0	+ .14	—1 .000	+ ,0002
17	+ .20	+ .15	+ .25	+ .30	—1 ,042	+ .0025
18	+ ,12	+ .10	+ .03	+ .20	— ,988	+ ,0024
19	—	+ .16	+ .22	+ .43	— ,978	— ,0003
20	+ ,02	+ ,07	— .01	—	— ,912	+ ·0035
21	+ ,09	+ .07	0	+ .15	— ,964	— ·0007
22	+ .01	— ,05	— .12	— .06	— ,919	+ .0054
23	+ .01	— ,01	— .09	+ .16	— ,898	— .0022
24	—	+ .04	+ ,07	+ ,08	— ,968	.0000
25	+ ,08	+ .04	+ .11	+ .22	— ,929	+ .0044
26	+ ,22	+ .22	+ .27	+ ,45	—1 ,060	+ .0053
27	—	— .08	— ,22	— ,07	— ,859	— .0004
28	— .05	— ,10	— .14	— .07	— ,850	+ .0065
29	—	+ ,05	+ ,10	+ .39	— ,799	— .0014
30	+ ,08	+ .05	0	+ .17	— ,979	+ .0012
32	+ .03	+ .05	— .01	+ .21	— ,964	+ .0057
34	—	+ .15	+ .05	+ .23	—1 .071	— .0019
35	— ,08	— .16	— .18	—	— .846	+ .0010
36	+ .01	+ ,02	+ .04	—	— .856	+ .0006
37	+ .11	+ .12	+ .13	—	— .972	— .0005
38	—	— ,15	— .19	— .17	— ,795	— .0020
39	+ ,14	+ ,11	+ .24	—	— ,974	— .0007
40	+ ,03	+ ,02	— .03	—	— .925	— .0010
41	— .07	— .11	— ,08	—	— .778	— ,0022
42	—	— ,45	— .59	— .62	— .517	— .0027
44	— .03	— ,10	— .12	+ .17	— ,841	+ ,0034
47	+ .16	+ .16	+ .16	—	—1 ,002	— .0036
48	—	+ ,80	+ .77	+1 .11	—1 .621	+ .0112
50	+ .01	— ,02	— .02	—	— .880	— .0048
51	+ ,13	+ ,11	+ .15	—	— .988	— .0048
52	—	— ,06	— .12	+ .23	— .696	— .0036
56	—	+ ,02	— ,05	— .01	— .930	— ,0036
57	— ,10	— ,16	— .08	—	— .743	— .0057
58	— ,08	— .12	— .22	— .15	— .797	— .0030
61	+ ,08	+ ,10	+ .08	—	— .857	— .0068
62	+ ,11	+ .10	— ,04	—	— .954	— .0075
64	— ,01	— ,04	+ ,07	—	— .803	— .0062
65	—	+ ,08	+ ,12	+ .08	— .915	— .0026
67	+ ,01	— ,04	+ .07	— .02	— .816	— .0056
68	—	— ,04	0	+ .02	— .829	+ .0049
69	—	— ,05	— ,06	— .04	— ,849	— ,0025
70	+ ,21	+ ,20	+ .13	+ .27	—1 .028	— .0066
71	— ,01	— ,02	— .07	— .01	— .798	— .0070
72	+ ,08	+ .11	+ .09	+ .27	— ,884	— ,0076

TABLE 4 (contd.)

Pair	1903	1909	1915	1938	$(-x_1)$	$(-x_2)$
73	+0″.12	+0″.06	−0″.01	+ ″.02	−1″.955	−0″.0071
74	− .09	− .15	− .26	− .17	− .743	− .0063
75	−	− .08	− .06	− .03	− .716	− .0004
76	− .01	− .07	− .02	+ .07	− .788	− .0071
77	− .01	− .04	− .01	+ .08	− .799	− .0074
78	+ .02	− .01	− .04	0	− .832	− .0076
80	+ .05	+ .01	− .26	−	− .878	− .0043
82	+ .05	− .02	− .06	+ .05	− .863	− .0074
83	0	− .10	− .21	−	− .866	− .0044
84	−	+ .19	+ .23	+ .46	− .924	+ .0004
85	− .05	− .10	− .31	− .31	− .807	− .0062
86	−	− .07	− .05	+ .14	− .751	+ .0021
87	+ .05	− .01	− .14	−	− .859	− .0033
88	+ .14	+ .04	+ .04	−	− .960	+ .0005
89	+ .08	+ .04	− .12	−	− .976	− .0020
90	−	− .13	− .12	+ .04	− .778	− .0024
91	−	− .29	− .32	− .15	− .611	+ .0024
92	− .09	− .20	− .19	−	− .787	+ .0002
96	+ .14	+ .12	+ .09	+ .32	− .969	− .0035

The expression (2.11) coincides in form with the usual expression for the z term, which is used in the derivation of the coordinates of the pole from observations at the three given stations. Hence the value F_1 does not depend on the motion of the pole. It is necessary, however, to notice that in (2.11) C, M and U do not denote instantaneous latitudes, but the means over a year taken for each pair separately. Hence, in the variation of F_1 the yearly component will not be present, since the mean time of observation comes each year at approximately the same part of the year. There remains only the slow variation of latitude, the non-periodic and long-period parts.

For the general analysis of all the material with the object of finding the long-period variation of latitude it was necessary to bring the results of different cycles to one system of declinations and proper motions. We took the system of B. Boss - GC. The declinations of 71 pairs, calculated from the data of the catalogue, were found for the four initial epochs mentioned above, and then the differences

$$\delta_{GC} - \delta_{LS}$$

TABLE 5

Pair	1903	1909	1915	1928	$(-y_1)$	$(-y_2)$
1	—	—0".006	+0".002	—0".008	—0".0025	—0".00014
2	+0".003	— .002	— .005	—	— .0034	— .00110
3	+ .001	— .004	— .001	—	— .0060	— .00152
5	— .001	— .006	— .008	—	— .0017	— .00081
8	.000	— .005	— .007	—	— .0036	— .00082
9	— .004	— .008	— .020	—	+ .0027	— .00083
10	—	+ .006	+ .010	+0 .001	— .0096	— .00020
11	— .009	— .013	— .002	— .002	— .0004	— .00008
13	— .005	— .009	+ .004	— .001	— .0045	— .00042
14	— .019	— .022	— .033	—	+ .0214	— .00068
15	— .013	— .016	— .017	—	— .0006	— .00083
16	—	— .006	— .010	— .014	+ .0012	— .00014
17	— .005	— .008	+ .006	— .004	— .0018	— .00022
18	— .002	— .004	— .007	— .010	— .0006	— .00017
19	—	— .001	+ .009	.000	— .0091	— .00019
20	+ .007	+ .005	— .005	—	— .0124	— .00109
21	— .003	— .004	— .005	— .007	— .0004	+ .00002
22	— .010	— .011	— .013	— .013	+ .0058	— .00029
23	— .003	— .004	— .010	— .004	— .0029	+ .00008
24	—	— .004	0	— .011	+ .0028	— .00020
25	— .007	— .007	+ .003	— .002	— .0029	— .00041
26	— .001	0	+ .004	— .002	— .0059	— .00038
27	—	— .014	— .023	— .007	+ .0036	— .00018
28	— .009	— .008	— .010	— .018	+ .0048	— .00042
29	—	+ .009	+ .008	+ .012	— .0138	— .00020
30	— .006	— .004	— .007	— .002	— .0003	— .00017
32	.000	+ .002	— .003	.000	— .0020	— .00039
34	—	+ .012	— .011	— .006	+ .0017	— .00015
35	— .016	— .012	— .006	—	.0000	— .00064
36	— .003	+ .001	+ .003	—	— .0025	— .00054
37	— .002	+ .002	+ .003	—	— .0032	— .00060
38	—	— .007	— .015	— .015	+ .0065	— .00011
39	— .009	— .005	+ .006	—	— .0036	— .00069
40	— .008	— .003	— .005	—	+ .0003	— .00043
41	— .011	— .006	— .001	—	+ .0007	— .00039
42	—	— .008	— .023	— .014	+ .0126	— .00001
44	— .015	— .010	— .003	+ .002	— .0046	— .00034
47	— .006	— .001	— .000	—	+ .0015	— .00041
48	—	+ .012	— .005	+ .008	— .0101	— .00085
50	— .009	— .004	— .004	—	+ .0037	— .00022
51	— .009	— .004	+ .002	—	+ .0011	— .00030
52	—	— .004	— .010	+ .017	— .0116	— .00001
56	—	— .004	— .012	— .006	+ .0059	+ .00006
57	— .014	— .010	— .001	—	+ .0055	+ .00035
58	— .010	— .006	— .011	— .009	+ .0061	+ .00002
61	+ .002	+ .005	+ .003	—	+ .0011	— .00020
62	— .003	0	— .007	—	+ .0102	— .00013
64	— .009	— .006	+ .005	—	+ .0014	— .00018
65	—	+ .022	+ .006	— .001	+ .0022	+ .00001
67	— .010	— .009	+ .001	+ .002	+ .0024	+ .00034
68	—	— .006	+ .004	.000	+ .0010	— .00029
69	—	— .001	— .006	— .005	+ .0039	+ .00009
70	— .001	— .001	— .005	+ .005	— .0009	+ .00029
71	— .002	— .002	— .006	+ .004	+ .0013	+ .00030

TABLE 5 (contd.)

Pair	1903	1909	1915	1928	$(-y_1)$	$(-y_2)$
72	+0".004	+0".004	−0".001	+0".009	−0".0065	+0".00031
73	− .010	− .010	− .010	− .004	+ .0057	+ .00034
74	− .009	− .010	− .012	+ .003	+ .0044	+ .00034
75	—	− .011	+ .001	0	− .0008	+ .00006
76	− .008	− .010	− .002	+ .006	− .0025	+ .00042
77	− .002	− .004	+ .001	+ .005	− .0024	+ .00042
78	− .003	− .005	− .005	+ .005	+ .0015	+ .00042
80	− .005	− .008	− .027	—	+ .0109	− .00051
82	− .008	− .011	− .008	0	+ .0002	+ .00040
83	− .014	− .017	− .016	—	+ .0028	− .00056
84	—	+ .004	+ .003	+ .012	− .0124	− .00003
85	− .005	− .009	− .021	− .011	+ .0113	+ .00038
86	—	− .003	+ .003	+ .005	− .0074	.00000
87	− .006	− .010	− .014	—	− .0013	− .00081
88	− .012	− .016	− .008	—	− .0116	− .00172
89	− .002	− .007	− .017	—	+ .0009	− .00086
90	—	0	.000	0	− .0035	+ .00007
91	—	− .003	− .003	− .004	− .0024	− .00011
92	− .013	− .018	− .008	—	− .0038	− .00098
96	+ .002	− .003	− .001	+ .003	− .0062	+ .00023

were formed, where δ_{GC} is the declination according to the GC and δ_{LS} is that taken immediately from the publications of the ILS. These differences are given in columns 2, 3, 4, 5 of Table 4. The reduction of pairs 42, 48 and 84 was carried out with initial declinations and proper motions taken from the catalogue published in "Results of the ILS" [43]. In Table 5, columns 2, 3, 4, 5 we give the differences of the proper motions in declination

$$\mu_{GC} - \mu_{LS} = \Delta\mu .$$

The latitudes published in Vol. 3 of the "Results of the ILS" were calculated with Struve's precession constant, and needed corrections in going over to Newcomb's value. These corrections were derived by means of the formula

$$\Delta p_\delta = -0.00026 p_\delta , \qquad (2.12)$$

where p_δ = yearly precession in declination. They are given in Table 6 in multiples of 0".001.

The corrections to declination (see appendix) with which

TABLE 6

Pair	Δp_δ	ζ	Pair	Δp_δ	ζ	Pair	Δp_δ	ζ
1	2	3	1	2	3	1	2	3
1	—	+10	30	+2	−8	68	—	0
2	−5	—	32	+3	−6	69	—	0
3	−5	—	34	—	−11	70	0	−1
5	−5	—	35	+3	—	71	0	−1
8	−5	—	36	+4	—	72	0	0
9	−4	+3	37	+4	—	73	0	+2
10	—	+5	38	—	−10	74	−1	+2
11	−4	+6	39	+4	—	75	—	+2
13	−4	+8	40	+5	—	76	−2	+1
14	−3	+8	41	+5	−9	77	−2	+1
15	−3	+10	42	—	−9	78	−2	+1
16	—	+11	44	+5	−9	80	−3	0
17	−3	−9	47	+5	−9	82	−3	+4
18	−2	−8	48	—	−9	83	−3	+4
19	—	−6	50	+5	—	84	—	+4
20	−2	−5	51	+5	—	85	−4	+3
21	−1	−4	52	—	−6	86	—	+3
22	−1	−3	56	—	−6	87	−4	+3
23	−1	−2	57	+4	−1	88	−4	+3
24	—	0	58	+4	−2	89	−5	+9
25	0	−13	61	+3	−2	90	—	+9
26	+1	−12	62	+3	−2	91	—	+9
27	—	−11	64	+2	−2	92	−5	+9
28	+1	−10	65	—	0	96	−5	+9
29	—	−10	67	+1	0			

we brought the values F_1, to a common system were calculated from the formula

$$D\delta = (\delta_{GC} - \delta_{LS} + \Delta\mu\tau) + \Delta\mu\,(k - k_0)\,, \qquad (2.13)$$

where k_0 is the difference between the epoch of the catalogue and the epoch 1900.0.

The terms enclosed in brackets maintain a constant value within each cycle; the last term is found simply by multiplying $\Delta\mu$ by successive whole numbers. For the first cycle of observations we used the sum

$$\Delta\mu + \Delta p_\delta\,.$$

As we pointed out earlier the annual component of the z-term does not affect the variation of the magnitude F_1 if the mean time of observation remains constant. At epoch 1922.7 these times changed and it was necessary to make at least an approximate estimate of the effect on F_1. We use the formula for the z-term given by Kimura from observations from 1922.7 to 1935.0,

$$z = +0''.019 \sin(2\odot - \alpha).$$

Here $\odot$ is the mean longitude of the Sun [45, p.170]. Hence we find the correction for the change of effect of the z-term, which must be introduced into all latitudes obtained after 1922.7,

$$\zeta = +0''.038 \sin(\odot_1 - \odot_2) \cos(\odot_1 + \odot_2 \quad \alpha), \qquad (2.14)$$

where $\odot_1$ and $\odot_2$ are the values of the Sun's longitude at times τ_1 and τ_2 after the beginning of the year. The corrections ζ, expressed in 0".001, are given in Table 6, column 3.

9. Corrections for Aberration due to Jupiter and Saturn

The aberration due to a planet is calculated from the following formula due to Batterman

$$\xi = c\,[\cos\lambda(\cos\Theta \sin\delta \sin\alpha - \sin\Theta \cos\delta) - \\ - \sin\lambda \sin\delta \cos\alpha]\ , \qquad (2.15)$$

where Θ is the inclination of the ecliptic to the equator, α, δ the right ascension and declination of the star, λ the longitude of the planet, c a constant coefficient. If we assume that the declination of the star is approximately equal to the latitude the formula may be put in the form

$$\xi = -c\,[\sin\varphi \sin(\lambda - \alpha) + \sin\Theta \cos\varphi \cos\lambda]\ . \qquad (2.16)$$

The coefficient c is +0".0086 for Jupiter, 0".0019 for Saturn. From formula (2.16) the corrections were calculated from 1900 to 1922. For later years the corrections were taken from the tables appearing in""Results of the ILS" Vol. 8, pp. 233-4. Table 7 gives a summary of the values of ξ in 0".001.

TABLE 7

Year	Correction for group											
	I	II	III	IV	V	VI	VII	VIII	IX	X	XI	XII
1900	+6	+5	0	−3	−5	−5	−4	−2	+1	+4	+6	+7
1	+5	+5	+2	−2	−5	−6	−7	−6	−4	−1	+2	+4
2	+3	+4	+3	−0	−3	−6	−8	−8	−7	−5	−2	+1
3	0	+2	+3	+2	−1	−4	−7	−9	−9	−8	−6	−3
4	−3	0	+3	+3	+1	−2	−5	−7	−9	−9	−8	−6
5	−5	−2	+2	+3	+3	+1	−1	−4	−6	−8	−8	−7
6	−5	−3	+1	+3	+4	+4	+2	−0	−3	−5	−6	−6
7	−4	−4	−1	+2	+4	+5	+5	+4	+2	−1	−3	−4
8	−2	−3	−2	0	+3	+5	+6	+6	+5	+3	+1	−1
9	−0	−1	−2	−1	+1	+3	+5	+6	+6	+6	+4	+2
10	+3	+1	−2	−2	−1	+1	+3	+5	+6	+6	+6	+4
11	+4	+2	−1	−2	−2	−2	0	+2	+4	+5	+6	+5
12	+4	+3	0	−2	−3	−4	−3	−2	0	+2	+3	+4
13	+3	+3	+1	−1	−3	−4	−5	−5	−4	−2	0	+1
14	0	+2	+2	+1	−1	−4	−6	−7	−7	−6	−4	−3
15	−2	0	+3	+2	0	−2	−4	−6	−8	−8	−6	−5
16	−5	−2	+2	+3	+2	+1	−1	−4	−6	−8	−8	−7
17	−6	−4	+1	+3	+4	+4	+2	0	−3	−6	−7	−7
18	−6	−5	−1	+2	+4	+6	+5	+4	+1	−2	−4	−6
19	−4	−4	−2	+1	+4	+6	+8	+7	+5	+3	0	−3
20	−2	−3	−3	−1	+2	+6	+8	+9	+9	+7	+4	+1
21	+2	−1	−4	−2	0	+3	+6	+9	+10	+9	+7	+5
22	+4	+1	−3	−3	−2	0	+4	+6	+9	+10	+9	+7
23	+6	+3	0	−3	−3	−2	0	+3	+6	+8	+8	+8
24	+6	+4	+1	−2	−4	−4	−3	−1	+2	+4	+6	+7
25	+5	+4	+2	−2	−4	−6	−6	−4	−2	0	+3	+5
26	+3	+3	+2	0	−3	−6	−7	−7	−6	−4	−1	+1
27	0	+2	+2	+2	−2	−4	−6	−7	−7	−6	−4	−2
28	−3	−1	+1	+2	+1	−1	−3	−5	−6	−7	−6	−5
29	−4	−2	0	+2	+2	+2	0	−2	−3	−5	−5	−5
30	−4	−3	−2	+2	+3	+4	+3	+2	0	−1	−3	−4
31	−2	−3	−2	0	+3	+4	+5	+5	+4	+2	0	−1
32	0	−1	−2	−2	+1	+3	+5	+6	+6	+5	+4	+2
33	+2	0	−1	−2	0	+2	+3	+5	+6	+6	+6	+4
34	+4	+2	0	−2	2	−1	+1	+3	+5	+6	+6	+6
35	+5	+3	+1	−2	−3	−3	−2	−1	+2	+4	+6	+6

10. Corrections for the Small Nutation Terms

In 1912 Ross pointed out that in the calculation of the quantities A and B published in the Berliner Jahrbuch not all the small nutation terms were taken into account, as they should be for such accurate observations [46]. He published a list of these terms and auxiliary tables for the calculation of the correction for their influence on the apparent right ascension and declination.

Up to 1922.7 Ross's corrections were introduced into the

ILS in the means for groups, after this time for the separate values of the latitude. However this introduced some errors, which later corrections have not completely cleared up. In effect the question of the introduction of Ross's corrections into the work of the ILS is somewhat confused. Here we attempt to elucidate it.

For the first six years the corrections for the influence of the Ross terms on the group means were calculated by B. Wanach [58]. He denoted the corrections by the symbols $\Delta\varphi_0$, $\Delta\varphi_1$, $\Delta\varphi_2$. . . , in which the suffix showed the year to which the correction related, 1900, 1901 and so on. The table of these corrections for the cycle of observations 1906.0 to 1911.0 appears in the "Results", Vol. 5, p.191. These tables, besides the Ross corrections, give the variation of the value taken for the constant of aberration and the aberration due to Jupiter and Saturn. These are denoted by $\Delta\varphi_a$. In the calculation of these corrections Wanach made an error, in consequence of which he got the same $\Delta\varphi_a$ for all years of observation, which in fact should not be so. Apparently Mühlig paid attention to this, though there is no direct reference to this in the publications of the ILS. "Results of the ILS" Vol. 6, p.56 mention only that there are errors in Wanach's tables and that it is necessary to replace them by those of Mühlig. The latter appear in the following pages of this volume. They are of exactly the same form as Wanach's tables. However, we are satisfied that the columns entitled $\Delta\varphi_0$, $\Delta\varphi_1$, $\Delta\varphi_2$. . . contain the Ross corrections added to the correction for aberration due to Jupiter and Saturn. Unfortunately this is nowhere pointed out.

Further, beginning in 1916, the formulae used for calculating A and B (Berliner Jahrbuch) were supplemented by some of the small nutation terms out of the number pointed out by Ross. Neither Mankoff nor Kimura paid attention to this, and in the reduction of observations appearing in Vols. 6 and 7 continued to take into account all the Ross terms. This error was discovered only in 1952 by S. Uemae [57]. As we have already mentioned, in Vol. 4 of the "Results of the ILS" the corrections for the influence of small terms was not made for individual latitudes. From the work of Uemae it follows that we cannot use the values for these corrections as given in this volume for 1916 and later years; they must be calculated afresh.

The position is somewhat worse for the data published in

Vol. 8 of the "Results". Here the Ross corrections were made to all individual latitudes, but the calculations are wrong. Their exclusion and the introduction of new corrections would involve cumbersome calculations. Fortunately we can avoid this, since for the cycle 1922-34 Uemae gives a table for the difference of the corrections

$$\Delta\eta = U - R,$$

where R is the value of the correction taking into account all the Ross terms and U only those that have not been considered since 1916.0. The values $\Delta\eta$ are given for the group means, taken separately for the morning and evening observations.

TABLE 8

Year	Correction for group											
	I	II	III	IV	V	VI	VII	VIII	IX	X	XI	XII
1900	+7	0	−7	−6	−4	−4	−6	−5	−2	+1	+4	+7
1	−1	−6	−4	−4	−2	0	−2	−4	−3	+1	+3	+2
2	−6	−12	−8	−6	−1	+4	+4	+4	+4	+6	+6	+2
3	−1	−8	−12	−9	−5	0	+4	+6	+6	+6	+6	+5
4	−3	−6	−8	−4	−2	+1	+2	+2	+2	+1	0	−2
5	−8	−9	−5	+1	+6	+10	+8	+5	+3	0	−4	−7
6	−6	−6	−6	0	+6	+11	+11	+8	+6	+3	0	−4
7	−2	−3	−4	0	+4	+6	+6	+5	+2	−1	−2	−1
8	−2	−2	+2	+7	+10	+8	+4	+2	−2	−7	−7	−2
9	0	0	+2	+9	+11	+8	+6	+2	−1	−4	−4	−1
10	+3	+3	+1	+4	+6	+6	+4	+1	0	−2	+1	+3
11	+2	+4	+6	+5	+4	+3	+2	−1	−6	−6	0	+2
12	+2	0	+6	+7	+5	+2	+2	−2	−6	−6	−2	+3
13	+4	+1	0	+2	+5	+2	+1	0	−2	−4	+2	+4
14	+5	+4	−1	0	+4	+1	0	−2	−4	−2	+2	+4
15	+2	0	+2	+1	0	+2	0	−5	−8	−4	0	+2
16	−2	−3	+4	+2	−1	+	+2	+2	+2	0	0	−1
17	+3	0	−2	−2	−2	−2	0	+2	+4	+2	+1	+2
18	+4	+4	−2	0	−2	−3	−4	−3	−2	−2	−1	+2
19	−2	−2	+2	+2	+2	+1	0	−2	−2	−2	−4	−2
20	−4	−5	−2	0	0	+2	+3	+4	0	+1	+1	0
21	+2	0	−4	−3	−2	−4	−2	+1	+2	0	+2	+4
22	−2	+2	+8	0	−1	−4	−4	−4	−4	−4	−2	−1
23	0	+4	+8	+8	+4	−2	−5	−6	−5	−4	−2	−1
24	+2	+4	+7	+6	0	−4	−7	−7	−5	−2	0	+2
25	+2	+4	+6	+5	−2	−6	−8	−7	−4	0	+2	+2
26	+2	+3	+4	+3	−2	−6	−8	−6	−2	+2	+4	+3
27	+2	+2	+1	0	−2	−6	−6	−4	−0	+4	+4	+2
28	0	0	0	−1	−4	−6	−6	−3	+2	+6	+4	0
29	0	0	−2	−2	−4	−6	−5	−2	+3	+6	+4	+2
30	−2	−2	−2	−2	−3	−4	−4	0	+4	+6	+4	0
31	−4	−3	−3	−2	−4	−4	−3	0	+6	+6	+2	−2
32	−3	−4	−2	−3	−2	−3	−2	+2	+6	+6	+2	−2
33	−4	−4	−3	−2	−2	−2	−2	+2	+6	+5	0	−3
34	−6	−5	−2	−1	0	−2	−1	+3	+6	+3	0	−3

We calculated afresh the corrections for the influence of the small terms from 1900 to 1922. For this we used for 1900-15 the tables of values of $\sin\varepsilon\delta\lambda$ and $\delta\varepsilon$ published by Ross, and for 1916-22 those of Uemae.

The following served as a check on the calculations.

1. Wanach's tables for 1900-1905.
2. The table for 1906-11 in "Results" Vol. 5, p.191.
3. The values $\Delta\varphi$ in "Results", Vol. 6, p.57, from which we excluded the correction for the aberration due to Jupiter and Saturn for 1912-15.

The corrections for 1922-34 are taken directly from the work of Uemae. In this for each group the mean value of the corrections was formed for morning and evening observations, which Uemae gives separately.

The results are summarized in Table 8, where η is expressed in 0".001.

In Table 30 (see appendix) we give the corrected values of F_1, that is

$$F_2 = F_1 + D\delta + \xi + \eta + \zeta. \tag{2.17}$$

11. Calculation of the Zenith Distances of the Centres of Pairs

One of the most exacting stages of our calculations was the determination of the correction for the ocular micrometer screw value. For this determination it is necessary to have the zenith distance of a pair. The zenith distance, expressed in micrometer turns, may be written as

$$m = \frac{\varphi - \delta}{R} = \frac{1}{R}[\varphi - \delta_{1900.0} - AV(k+\tau) - \Delta_\tau\delta], \tag{2.18}$$

where φ = latitude, $\delta_{1900.0}$ = the mean declination of the centre of the pair at the beginning of 1900, AV is the yearly variation of the mean declination, and $\Delta_\tau\delta$ the reduction to apparent position.

Since the value of R for all the three stations may in the cases considered be taken to be the same and equal to 39".74, we took

$$\frac{1}{R} = 0.02516.$$

Further, the instantaneous value of the latitude was given the constant value 39° 8'8". In calculating $\Delta_\tau\delta$ we took into account only the effect of aberration; then

$$\Delta_\tau\delta = -20''.47\,[\cos\odot\sin\Theta\sin\varphi + (\sin\odot\cos\alpha - \cos\odot\cos\Theta\sin\alpha)\sin\varphi]. \tag{2.19}$$

TABLE 9

Pair	m				$\frac{dm}{dt}$
	1900	1906	1922	1934	
1	—	+ 8.8	—	— 5.3	—0.504
2	+ 4.7	. . .	— 5.8	—	—0.501
3	+ 5.3	. . .	— 5.1	—	—0.497
5	+ 2.2	. . .	— 7.9	—	—0.479
8	+ 1.2	. . .	— 8.0	—	—0.440
9	— 3.1	. . .	—12.0	—	—0.420
10	—	+ 7 4	. . .	— 3.9	—0.403
11	+ 9.9	. . .	. . .	— 2.5	—0.378
13	+11.5	. . .	. . .	+ 0.3	—0.340
14	— 2.5	. .	— 9.1	—	—0.317
15	— 6.2	. . .	—12.3	—	—0.292
16	—	+ 1.3	. . .	— 6.2	—0.268
17	+11.8	. . .	. . .	+ 3.9	—0.233
18	+ 1.5	. . .	. . .	— 5.7	—0.212
19	—	+ 4.7	. . .	— 0.2	—0.177
20	— 7.0	. . .	—10.2	—	—0.149
21	— 0.1	. . .	. . .	— 4.0	—1.115
22	— 0.6	. . .	. . .	— 3.8	—0.095
23	— 5.0	. . .	. . .	— 7.1	—0.062
24	—	+ 3.5	. . .	+ 2.8	—0.024
25	+ 6.0	. . .	. . .	+ 6.9	+0.021
26	+ 4.8	. . .	. . .	+ 6.9	+0.061
27	—	— 8.0	. . .	+ 5.2	+0.095
28	— 1.2	. . .	. . .	+ 3.1	+0.126
29	—	+ 2.4	. . .	+ 6.9	+0.160
32	— 7.8	. . .	. . .	+ 0.7	+0.251
34	—	+ 5.2	. . .	+ 3.3	+0.304
35	—10.1	. .	— 2.5	—	+0.346
36	+ 0.4	. . .	+ 8.4	—	+0.368
37	— 1.2	. . .	+ 7.2	—	+0.379
38	—	— 2.8	. . .	+ 8.2	+0.394
39	+ 2.4	. . .	+11.6	—	+0.417
40	— 4.6	. . .	+ 5.1	—	+0.444
41	— 0.5	. . .	+10.2	—	+0.458
42	—	— 2.4	. . .	+11.6	+0.469
44	—11.5	. . .	. . .	+ 5.0	+0.487
47	+ 1.5	. . .	+12.6	—	+0.503
48	—	— 9.8	. . .	+ 4.4	+0.505
50	—5.7	. . .	+ 5.2	—	+0.495
51	—4.2	. . .	+ 6.6	—	+0.494
52	—	—11.6	. . .	+ 2.1	+0.488
56	—	— 5.1	. . .	+ 7.5	+0.440
57	— 0.7	. . .	+ 8.5	—	+0.417
58	—11.9	. . .	. . .	+ 1.7	+0.402
61	+ 2.4	. . .	+ 9.3	—	+0.314
62	3.0	. . .	+ 3.4	—	+0.290
64	+ 4.3	. . .	+ 9.6	—	+0.240
65	—	+ 2.3	. . .	+ 8.3	+0.214
67	+ 2.3	. . .	. . .	+ 6.9	+0.134
68	—	— 0.5	. . .	+ 2.5	+0.107
69	—	— 3.3	. . .	— 1.2	+0.075
70	— 6.1	. . .	. . .	— 4.7	+0.041
71	— 2.4	. . .	. . .	— 1.9	+0.017
72	— 5.0	. . .	. . .	— 5.5	—0.014
73	+ 0.7	. . .	. . .	— 0.5	—0.034

TABLE 9 (contd.)

Pair	m 1900	m 1906	m 1922	m 1934	$\frac{dm}{dt}$
74	−3.2	. . .	. . .	− 5.7	−0.073
75	—	+5.5	. . .	+ 2.7	−0.101
76	+2.2	. . .	. . .	− 3.1	−0.156
77	+3.6	. . .	. . .	− 2.5	−0.179
78	+4.1	. . .	. . .	− 3.0	−0.209
80	−3.5	. . .	− 9.5	—	−0.271
82	+5.5	. . .	. . .	− 5.0	−0.309
83	−0.3	. . .	− 7.7	—	−0.339
84	—	+5.8	. . .	− 4.1	−0.355
85	+4.9	. . .	. . .	− 7.8	−0.375
86	—	+5.5	. . .	− 5.5	−0.397
87	+2.1	. . .	− 7.0	—	−0.414
88	−2.1	. . .	−11.5	—	−0.427
89	−0.9	. . .	−10.6	—	−0.442
90	—	+4.7	. . .	− 8.1	−0.458
91	—	+5.6	. . .	− 7.6	−0.471
92	+3.8	. . .	− 5.8	—	−0.434
96	+7.1	. . .	. . .	−10.1	−0.504

We introduce the following notation

$$m_0 = \frac{1}{R}(\varphi - \delta_{1900.0}), \quad \frac{dm}{dt} = \frac{AV}{R}, \quad a = \frac{\Delta_\tau \delta}{R}; \quad m_0' = m_0 - \frac{dm}{dt}\tau - a.$$

Then formula (2.18) becomes

$$m = m_0' - \frac{dm}{dt}k. \qquad (2.20)$$

The values $\Delta_\tau \delta$ are given in groups in column 8 of Table 3. In Table 9 we give the values m for each pair at the beginning and end of the cycle of its observation. The last column of this table gives $\frac{dm}{dt}$.

12. Determination of the Correction for the Mean Micrometer Screw Value or Mean Scale Value

It was necessary to determine the errors in the following magnitude, which we call the mean micrometer screw value or mean scale value:

$$R = 0.402R_C + 0.302R_M + 0.296R_U, \qquad (2.21)$$

where R_C, R_M, R_U are the scale values at the three stations.

We found earlier that the values R used in the work of the

ILS were in some cases evidently erroneous. It is not possible to find their exact values, but we can obtain some data on their general behaviour. This is necessary, because errors in the values taken for R completely alter the curve of the non-polar variation of latitude, obtained from the observations of separate pairs, and because, besides, the effect of these errors on the final result of our calculations may be very significant.

After trying various methods we decided on the following well-known one based on the comparison of the mean latitudes obtained from the observations of the pairs with zenith distances of opposite sign.

We select some pairs with large positive zenith distances z. The mean of the values of z for these pairs, expressed in revolutions of the micrometer screw, we denote by m_{+}, and the mean of the values F_2 by S_{+}. By m_{-} and S_{-} we denote the corresponding quantities with negative zenith distances. Then the correction to R may be determined from the formula

$$\Delta R = \frac{S_{-} - S_{+}}{m_{+} - m} \, . \qquad (2.22)$$

This, however, would give the correct mean scale value only if the declinations were absolutely accurate. This was certainly not so. Moreover, on account of errors in the proper motions ΔR so calculated may have a fictitious linear behaviour. In the first stage of the calculation these inexactitudes can be tolerated inasmuch as we are interested only in the periodic part of the variation of F_2.

It was of more importance to take care that the corrections were all completely independent of the variations of latitude of a nutational character. Otherwise it could happen that after introduction of the corrections the said variations were smoothed out or quite disappeared. In order that this might not occur, in the selection of pairs for the determination of ΔR we observed the following rule: in each of the two groups of pairs (that is, with positive and negative zenith distances) the mean values of $\sin \alpha$ and $\cos \alpha$ must be near to zero.

We first estimated ΔR separately for the cycles 1900-22 and 1906-1934. Table 10 contains some data about the groups of pairs used.

TABLE 10

Beginning of cycle of observations End of cycle of observations	1900 1922		1906 1934	
Number of pairs in the group . .	12	15	15	9
Mean of zenith distances of pairs in the group at the beginning of the cycle in rotations of the micrometer screw	+4.92	−5.22	+3.78	−4.74
The same for the end of the cycle	+5.43	−5.29	+3.30	−4.12
Mean value of $\cos \alpha$	−0.04	+0.01	+0.01	−0.04
" " " $\sin \alpha$	−0.03	+0.03	−0.03	−0.04
" " " τ	0.28	0.24	0.27	0.25

The list of pairs composing the groups is given in Table 11. The initial data for the calculation of the corrections ΔR and these corrections expressed in 0".0001 are given in Table 12. Since the determination was made separately for the two series of observations we obtain two series of values, ΔR_1 (cycle 1900-22) and ΔR_2 (cycle 1906-34). It is clear that ΔR_1 and ΔR_2 differ systematically.

In order to combine the two series we found the mean difference

$$\Delta R_1 - \Delta R_2 = -0''.0032.$$

The trend in the variation $\Delta R_1 - \Delta R_2$ was not revealed; so we simply added to all values ΔR_1 a constant 0".0032 and took as final correction for the scale value

1901-1905 $\Delta R_1 + 0''.0032,$

1907-1921 $\frac{1}{2}(\Delta R_1 + \Delta R_2) + 0''.0016,$

1922-1934 $\Delta R_2.$

These values (ΔR) are given in Table 12. From them the graph (Fig. 3) is constructed; in this we clearly see the jump in ΔR in 1922. The general run of the values in 1905-15 indicates that in 1922 possibly a discontinuous change in ΔR took place. In order to see whether this was so, we followed the curve in more detail for 1909-11, guided by the following considerations. The values ΔR calculated from (2.22) represent corrections to R taken on an average for the successive annual

TABLE 11

1900—1922				1906—1934			
Pair	m_0	Pair	m_0	Pair	m_0	Pair	m_0
13	+11.5	9	− 3.1	11	+ 9.9	18	+ 1.5
17	+11.3	20	− 7.0	13	+11.5	22	− 0,6
25	+ 6.0	23	− 5.0	17	+11.8	23	− 5,0
26	+ 4.8	30	− 5.1	25	+ 6.0	27	− 8,6
36	+ 0.4	32	− 7.8	26	+ 4.8	52	−14,5
39	+ 2.4	35	−10.1	29	+ 1.4	70	− 6,1
61	+ 2.4	44	−11.5	38	− 5.8	71	− 2,4
64	+ 4.3	57	− 0.7	42	− 5.2	72	− 5,0
67	+ 2.3	58	−11.9	65	+ 1.0	74	− 3,2
77	+ 3.5	70	− 6.1	67	+ 2.3		
78	+ 4.1	74	− 3.2	68	− 1.2		
82	+ 5.5	80	− 3.5	75	+ 6.1		
		83	− 0.3	77	+ 3.6		
		88	− 2.1	78	+ 4.1		
		89	− 0.9	84	+ 8.0		

TABLE 12

Year	1900—1922			1906—1934			$\Delta R_1 - \Delta R_2$	ΔR
	S_-	S_+	ΔR_1	S_-	S_+	ΔR_2		
1900								
1	929	1001	− 71	—	—	—	—	− 39
2	870	970	− 98	—	—	—	—	− 66
3	899	954	− 54	—	—	—	—	− 22
4	922	975	− 52	—	—	—	—	− 20
5	917	953	− 35	—	—	—	—	− 3
6	897	934	− 36	—	—	—	—	− 4
7	891	913	− 21	888	869	+ 22	−43	+ 16
8	868	915	− 45	851	867	− 19	−26	− 16
9	846	928	− 79	838	884	− 55	−24	− 51
10	862	979	−112	853	906	− 63	−49	− 72
11	883	944	− 58	868	882	− 22	−36	− 24
12	848	963	−110	827	884	− 69	−41	− 74
13	799	992	−184	782	904	−148	− 36	−150
14	817	1009	−183	800	929	−157	−26	−154
15	795	1033	−226	765	943	−218	− 8	−206
16	801	1042	−228	783	927	−177	−51	−186
17	782	1076	−278	784	983	−246	−32	−246
18	797	1040	−229	776	955	−222	− 7	−210
19	773	1034	−246	759	932	−216	−30	−215
20	751	1026	−258	744	911	−210	−48	−218
21	739	995	−239	731	901	−214	−25	−210
22	—	—	—	732	895	−207	—	−207
23	—	—	—	839	848	− 11	—	− 11
24	—	—	—	852	851	+ 1	—	+ 1
25	—	—	—	827	862	− 45	—	− 45
26	—	—	—	839	861	− 23	—	− 28
27	—	—	—	—	—	—	—	—
28	—	—	—	867	846	+ 28	—	+ 28
29	—	—	—	864	878	− 18	—	− 18
30	—	—	—	850	868	− 24	—	− 24
31	—	—	—	863	860	+ 4	—	+ 4
32	—	—	—	848	860	− 16	—	− 16
33	—	—	—	851	864	− 17	—	− 17
34	—	—	—	869	860	+ 12	—	+ 12

series of observations. In such a case, when the succession of values of ΔR affords the possibility of constructing a smooth curve, the interpolation for the moment of observation of each pair gives no difficulty. However, those points where, to judge from the behaviour of the curve, we may expect breaks of the first or second order, make interpolation impossible.

In order to go into more detail for 1909-11 we found the values S_+ and S_- in this interval for the epochs following one another not by a year but by considerably less than a year. The results are given in Table 13.

Using the data of this table we constructed smooth curves of the variation of S_+ and S_- and from these took for each tenth part of the year the differences $S_- - S_+$. Then we again used (2.22), but the results of the calculation from this formula are now denoted by I instead of ΔR. The reason for this change of notation is as follows.

If we express the time t in years, the mean value over a year of the correction to R obtained from (2.22) may be given approximately as I equal to

$$\int_t^{t+1} \Delta R_t \, dt. \tag{2.23}$$

In the case of linear variation

$$I = \Delta R_{t+0,5}.$$

However, in the intervals of time considered a linear function is not even a rough approximation to ΔR. Then for the calculation of ΔR_t we may use the approximate formula

$$\Delta R_t = \Delta R_{t+1} - \frac{dI}{dt}, \tag{2.24}$$

but for this, clearly, it is necessary to know ΔR_{t+1}. The latter condition is easily fulfilled if we approach step by step the part of the curve to be investigated from a neighbouring part where the variation of R can be well represented by a linear function of the time. The part of the curve for 1911-12 has this form and we start our calculations there, successively working backwards along the axis of abscissae. The results of the calculation are given in Table 14. In the last column of this table the values of ΔR, beginning from

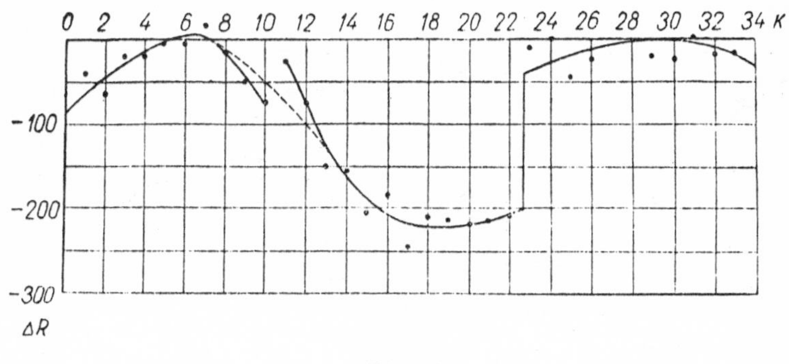

Fig. 3

TABLE 13

1900—1922				1906—1934			
t_m	S	t_m	S_+	t_m	S_-	t_m	S_+
1910.24	862	1910.28	979	1910.25	853	1910.27	906
.31	859	.36	981	.36	849	.33	904
.38	858	.44	977	.47	844	.40	907
.44	859	.53	973	.58	844	.47	905
.51	859	.61	967	.69	850	.53	901
.58	863	.69	967	.81	856	.60	897
.64	869	.78	963	.92	866	.67	898
.71	875	.86	961	1911.03	868	.73	903
.78	873	.94	955	.14	873	.80	905
.84	879	1911.03	956	.25	868	.87	903
.91	885	.11	952	.36	873	.93	903
.98	885	.19	944	.47	875	1911.00	903
1911.04	882	.28	914	.58	875	.07	898
.11	883	.36	951	.69	863	.13	895
.18	883	.44	952	.81	851	.20	888
.31	884	.53	953	.92	841	.27	882
.38	884	.61	948	1912.03	836	.33	886
.44	887	.69	950	.14	831	.40	887
.51	887	.78	956	.25	827	.47	888
.58	884	.86	952	—	—	.53	884
.64	884	.94	951	—	—	.60	879
.71	880	1912.03	955	—	—	.67	874
.78	880	.11	961	—	—	.73	870
.84	880	.19	960	—	—	.80	870
.91	868	.28	963	—	—	.93	872
.98	863	—	—	—	—	1912.00	875
1912.04	861	—	—	—	—	.07	880
.11	852	—	—	—	—	.13	880
.18	850	—	—	—	—	.20	883
.24	848	—	—	—	—		

TABLE 14

Epoch	I	$\frac{dI}{dt}$	ΔR	Epoch	I	$\frac{dI}{dt}$	ΔR
1909.8	−75			1911.4	−38	−110	+24
.9	−78	+10	−65	.5	−50	−110	+19
1910.0	−75	+40	−100	.6	−60	−100	+4
.1	−69	+80	−150	.7	−70	—	−44
.2	−60	+80	−116	.8	—	—	−50
.3	−52	+80	−81	.9	—	—	−55
.4	−44	+70	−46	1912.0	—	—	−60
.5	−38	+60	−41	.1	—	—	−70
.6	−31	+60	−56	.2	—	—	−76
.7	−26	+40	−84	.3	—	—	−81
.8	−22	+20	−70	.4	—	—	−86
.9	−22	0	−55	.5	—	—	−91
1911.0	−22	0	−60	.6	—	—	−96
.1	−21	0	−70	.7	—	—	−102
.2	−23	−40	−36	.8	—	—	−107
.3	−28	−80	−1	.9	—	—	−112

1911.7, are taken from the graph constructed earlier, but the remainder are extrapolated according to (2.24).

We give an example. To get the value of ΔR for 1911.3 we first take from Table 14 the value for 1912.3, that is, -0".0081, then opposite the date 1911.3 we find

$$\frac{dI}{dt} = -0''.0080,$$

from which we obtain the required quantity

$$\Delta R_{1911.3} = -0''.0081 + 0''.0080 = -0''.0001.$$

From the data of Tables 12 and 14 we formed a large scale graph of ΔR, and from it we took the final corrections given in Table 15 (in 0".001).

The fact that the method described does not, strictly speaking, give the corrections themselves but only their variation does not greatly affect our final results; but this cannot be asserted beforehand as regards the fictitious linear variations of ΔR which may be a consequence of errors in the proper motions of the pairs of stars used in finding the corrections. Their effect will be considered in detail in section 16.

TABLE 15

k	Corrections for group											
	I	II	III	IV	V	VI	VII	VIII	IX	X	XI	XII
0	−6	−6	−7	−7	−7	−7	−7	−7	−6	−6	−6	−6
1	−5	−5	−6	−6	−6	−6	−6	−6	−5	−5	−5	−5
2	−4	−4	−5	−5	−4	−4	−4	−4	−4	−4	−4	−4
3	−2	−2	−3	−3	−3	−3	−3	−3	−3	−3	−2	−2
4	−1	−1	−2	−2	−2	−2	−2	−2	−2	−1	−1	−1
5	0	0	−1	−1	−1	−1	−1	−1	0	0	0	0
6	+1	+1	0	0	0	0	0	0	0	0	0	+1
7	0	−1	+1	+1	0	0	0	0	0	0	0	0
8	−4	−4	−1	−1	−1	−2	−2	−2	−2	−3	−3	−3
9	−9	−10	−4	−4	−5	−5	−5	−6	−6	−6	−7	−8
10	−6	−6	−10	−14	−14	−11	−8	−6	−5	−4	−5	−6
11	−5	−6	−6	−6	−5	−3	0	+2	+2	+1	−1	−3
12	−10	−11	−6	−6	−7	−7	−8	−8	−9	−9	−9	−10
13	−15	−16	−11	−12	−12	−12	−13	−13	−14	−14	−14	−15
14	−18	−19	−16	−16	−16	−17	−17	−17	−17	−18	−18	−18
15	−20	−20	−19	−19	−19	−19	−19	−19	−20	−20	−20	−20
16	−21	−21	−20	−20	−20	−20	−20	−21	−21	−21	−21	−21
17	−22	−22	−21	−21	−21	−21	−21	−21	−21	−21	−21	−22
18	−22	−22	−22	−22	−22	−22	−22	−22	−22	−22	−22	−22
19	−22	−22	−22	−22	−22	−22	−22	−22	−22	−22	−22	−22
20	−21	−21	−22	−22	−22	−22	−21	−21	−21	−21	−21	−21
21	−21	−21	−21	−21	−21	−21	−21	−21	−21	−21	−21	−21
22	−3	−3	−21	−21	−21	−21	−21	−21	−21	−21	−21	−12
23	−3	−3	−3	−3	−3	−3	−3	−3	−3	−3	−3	−3
24	−2	−2	−3	−3	−3	−3	−3	−3	−3	−3	−2	−2
25	−2	−2	−2	−2	−2	−2	−2	−2	−2	−2	−2	−2
26	−2	−2	−2	−2	−2	−2	−2	−2	−2	−2	−2	−2
27	−1	−1	−2	−2	−2	−2	−2	−2	−2	−1	−1	−1
28	−1	−1	−1	−1	−1	−1	−1	−1	−1	−1	−1	−1
29	−1	−1	−1	−1	−1	−1	−1	−1	−1	−1	−1	−1
30	−1	−1	−1	−1	−1	−1	−1	−1	−1	−1	−1	−1
31	−1	−1	−1	−1	−1	−1	−1	−1	−1	−1	−1	−1
32	0	0	−1	−1	−1	−1	−1	−1	−1	−1	0	0
33	0	0	0	0	0	0	0	0	0	0	0	0
34	0	0	0	0	0	0	0	0	0	0	0	0

The method described does not permit of following the variation of ΔR in close detail. For this it would probably be necessary to consider afresh all the material of the ILS and vast calculations would be needed; in general we consider that it would be very important to do this since errors discovered by us indicate that the methods used by the ILS do not allow the determination of the scale value with sufficient accuracy.

However for our immediate purpose such a detailed analysis was not essential. We could limit it to the examination of the general run of ΔR.

The numbers giving the values of F_2 corrected for errors in the mean scale value, obtained from the formula

$$F_3 = F_2 + m\Delta R,$$

are given in Table 30 (see appendix).

13. Non-Periodic Variation of Latitude

In order to diminish accidental errors in the subsequent

TABLE 16

k	S_A	S_B	S_C	S'_B	S'_C	ΔS
0	+28	+43	—	+39	—	+34
1	+50	+53	—	+50	—	+50
2	+ 7	+10	—	+ 8	—	+ 8
3	+16	+21	—	+20	—	+18
4	+41	+29	—	+29	—	+35
5	+20	+27	—	+28	—	+24
6	+16	− 1	+14	+ 1	+13	+10
7	0	− 7	− 3	− 4	− 5	− 3
8	− 9	−26	− 4	−22	− 7	−13
9	−24	− 1	− 6	+ 4	−10	−10
10	+ 5	+ 6	+16	+13	+12	+10
11	− 5	− 7	+ 2	+ 1	− 3	− 2
12	− 3	−29	+ 1	−20	− 5	− 9
13	−18	−21	−14	−11	−21	−17
14	+ 4	− 6	+14	+ 5	+ 6	+ 5
15	− 6	− 4	+ 8	+ 8	− 1	0
16	+ 9	−20	+12	− 7	+ 2	+ 1
17	+17	+14	+29	+28	+18	+21
18	− 8	−18	+ 7	− 3	− 5	− 5
19	−10	−42	− 4	−26	−17	−18
20	−45	−47	−40	−30	−54	−43
21	−57	−78	−43	−60	−58	−58
22	−57	—	−45	—	−61	−59
23	−39	—	−20	—	−37	−38
24	−35	—	−17	—	−35	−35
25	−42	—	−19	—	−37	−40
26	−40	—	− 9	—	−28	−34
27	−34	—	−16	—	−36	−35
28	−24	—	− 4	—	−25	−24
29	−28	—	− 4	—	−26	−27
30	−37	—	−11	—	−34	−36
31	−35	—	−15	—	−39	−37
32	−47	—	−19	—	−34	−40
33	−44	—	−16	—	−42	−43
34	−37	—	−18	—	−45	−41

TABLE 17

k	Corrections for group											
	I	II	III	IV	V	VI	VII	VIII	IX	X	XI	XII
0	−30	−30	−30	−30	−30	−30	−30	−30	−30	−30	−30	−30
1	−30	−30	−30	−30	−30	−30	−30	−30	−30	−30	−30	−30
2	−30	−30	−30	−30	−30	−30	−30	−30	−30	−30	−30	−30
3	−30	−30	−30	−30	−30	−30	−30	−30	−30	−30	−30	−30
4	−28	−27	−30	−30	−30	−29	−29	−29	−29	−28	−28	−28
5	−19	−18	−27	−26	−25	−25	−24	−23	−22	−22	−21	−20
6	− 5	− 4	−17	−16	−15	−14	−12	−11	−10	− 9	− 8	− 6
7	+ 4	+ 4	− 3	− 2	− 2	− 1	0	0	+ 1	+ 2	+ 2	+ 3
8	+ 8	+ 8	+ 5	+ 5	+ 6	+ 6	+ 6	+ 6	+ 7	+ 7	+ 7	+ 7
9	+ 8	+ 8	+ 8	+ 8	+ 8	+ 8	+ 8	+ 8	+ 8	+ 8	+ 8	+ 8
10	+ 8	+ 8	+ 8	+ 8	+ 8	+ 8	+ 8	+ 8	+ 8	+ 8	+ 8	+ 8
11	+ 8	+ 8	+ 8	+ 8	+ 8	+ 8	+ 8	+ 8	+ 8	+ 8	+ 8	+ 8
12	+ 7	+ 7	+ 8	+ 8	+ 8	+ 8	+ 8	+ 8	+ 8	+ 7	+ 7	+ 7
13	+ 5	+ 4	+ 7	+ 7	+ 7	+ 6	+ 6	+ 6	+ 6	+ 5	+ 5	+ 5
14	+ 1	0	+ 4	+ 4	+ 3	+ 3	+ 3	+ 2	+ 2	+ 2	+ 1	+ 1
15	− 4	− 5	0	0	− 1	− 1	− 2	− 2	− 3	− 3	− 3	− 4
16	− 7	− 8	− 5	− 5	− 5	− 6	− 6	− 6	− 6	− 7	− 7	− 7
17	− 5	− 4	− 8	− 8	− 7	− 7	− 7	− 6	− 6	− 6	− 5	− 5
18	+10	+11	− 4	− 3	− 1	0	+ 2	+ 3	+ 4	+ 6	+ 7	+ 9
19	+27	+28	+13	+14	+16	+17	+19	+20	+21	+23	+25	+26
20	+46	+48	+30	+32	+33	+35	+37	+38	+40	+41	+43	+43
21	+57	+58	+50	+51	+52	+52	+53	+54	+54	+55	+56	+57
22	+50	+49	+59	+58	+57	+56	+55	+54	+54	+53	+52	+51
23	+40	+39	+48	+47	+46	+45	+44	+43	+43	+42	+42	+41
24	+36	+36	+38	+38	+38	+38	+37	+37	+37	+37	+36	+36
25	+36	+36	+36	+36	+36	+36	+36	+36	+36	+36	+36	+36
26	+35	+35	+36	+36	+36	+36	+36	+36	+35	+35	+35	+35
27	+32	+32	+35	+35	+34	+34	+34	+33	+33	+33	+33	+32
28	+30	+30	+32	+32	+32	+32	+32	+31	+31	+31	+31	+30
29	+32	+32	+30	+30	+31	+31	+31	+31	+31	+32	+32	+32
30	+34	+34	+32	+32	+32	+33	+33	+33	+34	+34	+34	+34
31	+38	+39	+35	+35	+35	+36	+36	+36	+37	+37	+37	+38
32	+42	+42	+39	+39	+40	+40	+40	+40	+41	+41	+41	+41
33	+43	+43	+42	+42	+42	+42	+42	+42	+43	+43	+43	+43
34	+43	+43	+43	+43	+43	+43	+43	+43	+43	+43	+43	+43

harmonic analysis of F_3, it is expedient to determine and exclude the non-periodic variation of this magnitude. With this in view we combined the mean annual values of F_3 separately for the pairs in the groups A, B and C (see section 7). Their differences from 0".900 are denoted by S_A, S_B, S_C and given in columns 2-4 of Table 16 (in 0".001). The systematic differences of these quantities may be given as

$$S_A - S_B = \Delta_{AB} = +0''.0048 - 0''.0009k,$$

$$S_A - S_C = \Delta_{AC} = -0''.0051 + 0''.0011k .$$

Then we reduced the results obtained for the two other groups to that obtained for the group A, that is, we found the quantities

$$S'_B = S_B + \Delta_{AB}, \qquad S'_C = S_C + \Delta_{AC},$$

given in columns 5 and 6 of Table 16 (in 0".001).

As final values of the correction for the slow variation of F_3 common to all pairs we took the following means:

$$\Delta S = -\frac{S_A + S'_B}{2} \qquad 1900\text{-}1905$$

$$\Delta S = -\frac{S_A + S'_B + S'_C}{3} \qquad 1905\text{-}1921$$

$$\Delta S = -\frac{S_A + S'_C}{2} \qquad 1922\text{-}1934$$

They were plotted on a graph. The values ΔS taken from a smooth curve are given in Table 17.

The values

$$F_4 = F_3 + \Delta S$$

are given in Table 30 (see appendix).

14. Determination of Corrections for Declinations and Proper Motions (first approximation)

We may now consider that the initial data are ready for the determination of the coefficients in the nutation terms. If we put

$$F_1 = x + ky + v, \qquad (2.25)$$

where v denotes the right side of (2.6) or (2.8), then the problem is reduced to the determination of six unknowns. Of these the constant x may be taken as the error in the declination for the epoch 1900.0, and the coefficient y as the error in the proper motion of the pair in declination. These errors will of course be different for different pairs.

We may attempt the solution in two ways. First, we might determine from observations of each pair separately the whole six unknowns, and then from the combination of the values of the coefficients of the periodic terms in (2.6) or (2.8) find the most probable values. For this it is necessary to solve in general 74 systems of equations with six unknowns. This method of solution was used by Przybyllok [41], but his case was different from ours since he had to find not six but three unknowns, his object being only to determine N, n and the phase lags being taken as given.

Secondly, the problem may be solved in the following way, by successive approximation. First, for each pair separately we find x and y, neglecting the periodic part v in (2.25). When this is done we determine the coefficients of the periodic terms in (2.6) or (2.8), using the remaining deviations v, not for separate pairs but directly for all the observational material. Further, if it appears necessary, we can exclude from F_4 the periodic terms and repeat the whole process for a second approximation. We chose this method principally for its comparative simplicity.

Thus for the determination of the constant correction x and the correction to the proper motion for each pair, we have the system of equations of condition

$$x_1 + ky_1 = F_4$$

where $k = l,\ l+1,\ l+2, \ldots m$. The normal equations may be written in the form

$$(m - l + 1)x_1 + \sum_l^m ky_1 = \sum_l^m F_4, \qquad \sum_l^m kx_1 + \sum_l^m k^2 y_1 = \sum_l^m kF_4\,,$$

and their solution as

$$\left.\begin{aligned} x_1 &= p\sum_l^m F_4 + q\sum_l^m kF_4 \\ y_1 &= p_1\sum_l^m kF_4 + q\sum_l^m F_4 \end{aligned}\right\}. \tag{2.26}$$

The coefficients p, p_1, q are given in Table 18.

The values of the corrections $-x_1$ are given in Table 4, column 6, and those of $-y_1$ in Table 5, column 6. The difference

$$F_4 - (x_1 + ky_1)$$

we denote by F_5 and give in Table 30 (appendix).

TABLE 18

k	$p \times 10^2$	$q \times 10^2$	$p_1 \times 10^4$
0—21	+16.996	—1.185	+11.293
0—22	+16.304	—1.086	+ 9.881
0—34	+10.952	—0.476	+ 2.801
6—34	+23.152	—0.985	+ 4.926

15. Determination of the Coefficients a_1, a_2, b_1, b_2

The values found for F_5 were used for the determinations of the nutation terms. We write them in the form (2.8):

$$F_5 = a_1 \cos(\text{☊} - \alpha) + b_1 \sin(\text{☊} - \alpha) + a_2 \cos(\text{☊} + \alpha) + b_2 \sin(\text{☊} + \alpha) \quad . \qquad (2.27)$$

First we distribute all values F_5 by phase of ☊ $- \alpha$ and then by phase of ☊ $+ \alpha$. These phases expressed in hours are given in Table 30 (see appendix). However to simplify the calculation we proceeded somewhat differently. All pairs were broken up into eight groups in such a way that the mean right ascensions of the centres of the groups were 0, 3, 6, 9, 12, 15, 18 and 21 hours. Then we took the mean of F_5 for the pairs in each group; these we call M_1 (for the cycle 1900-31) and M_2 (for the cycle 1906-34). These are given in Table 19 in 0".001. These values were distributed according to phases of ☊ $- \alpha$ and ☊ $+ \alpha$, as indicated in the table, and for each phase the mean is formed afresh. The results are given in Table 20.

By harmonic analysis of the results of Table 20 we obtained the following values of the coefficients in (2.8).

1900—1921

$a_1 = -0''.0027 \pm 0''.0017$, $b_1 = -0''.0108 \pm 0''.0017$,
$a_2 = -0\ .0048 \pm 0\ .0021$, $b_2 = +0\ .0031 \pm 0\ .0021$.

1906—1934

$a_1 = -0''.0034 \pm 0''.0013$, $b_1 = -0''.0124 \pm 0''.0013$.
$a_2 = -0\ .0051 \pm 0\ .0016$, $b_2 = -0\ .0015 \pm 0\ .0016$.

TABLE 19

k	Phase		M_1	M_2	Phase		M_1	M_2
	☊ − α	☊ + α			☊ − α	☊ + α		
1	2	3	4	5	6	7	8	9
		0^h				3^h		
0	16^h	17^h	−39	—	13^h	19^h	+26	—
1	15	15	+6	—	12	18	+22	—
2	13	14	+3	—	10	17	−16	—
3	12	13	+16	—	9	15	−19	—
4	11	11	+9	—	8	14	−14	—
5	9	10	+19	—	6	13	−11	—
6	8	9	+6	+6	5	11	+13	+18
7	7	8	−5	−23	4	10	+2	−20
8	6	6	+5	−11	3	9	−22	−23
9	4	5	+16	−6	1	8	+12	−20
10	3	4	+20	+18	0	6	+1	−4
11	2	2	−20	−36	23	5	−7	−16
12	0	1	−11	+1	21	4	−22	+1
13	23	0	−8	−21	20	2	−7	−5
14	22	23	+14	+23	19	1	+18	+23
15	20	21	−3	−2	18	0	−4	+12
16	19	20	−26	+7	16	23	0	+9
17	18	19	+28	+24	15	21	+7	−6
18	17	17	−22	−11	14	20	−8	−10
19	15	16	+31	+20	12	19	−1	+19
20	14	15	−18	+6	11	17	+4	−15
21	13	14	−18	−12	10	16	−34	−15
22	12	12	—	+42	9	15	—	+1
23	10	10	—	+28	7	14	—	+7
24	9	9	—	+3	6	12	—	−3
25	8	8	—	+6	5	11	—	−33
26	7	6	—	−4	4	10	—	−9
27	5	5	—	−19	2	8	—	−11
28	4	4	—	−26	1	7	—	+12
29	3	3	—	+4	0	6	—	+6
30	1	1	—	−9	22	5	—	+1
31	0	0	—	+2	21	3	—	+19
32	23	23	—	−16	20	2	—	+1
33	21	21	—	+6	18	1	—	−11
34	20	20	—	−39	17	23	—	+5
		6^h				9^h		
0	11	23	−22	—	8	2	+14	—
1	10	22	+35	—	7	1	+36	—
2	8	21	−16	—	5	0	−40	—
3	7	19	−22	—	4	22	−25	—
4	6	18	−3	—	3	21	−29	—
5	5	17	−10	—	1	20	−5	—
6	3	16	+3	+6	0	19	−14	−70
7	2	14	−16	−16	23	17	−26	37
8	1	13	−24	−18	22	16	−31	+12
9	23	12	+2	−3	20	15	+4	+20
10	22	10	+32	+28	19	13	+12	+13
11	21	9	+16	+20	18	12	+25	+78
12	20	8	+25	+6	16	11	+26	+54

TABLE 19 (contd.)

k	Phase		M_1	M_2	Phase		M_1	M_2
	☊ − α	☊ + α			☊ − α	☊ + α		
1	2	3	4	5	6	7	8	9
		6^h					9^h	
13	18	7	−7	−6	15	10	+9	−7
14	17	5	+7	0	14	8	+17	+35
15	16^h	4^h	−3	+1	13^h	7^h	−7	+6
16	14	3	−5	−3	11	6	−30	−15
17	13	1	−10	−7	10	4	−9	+11
18	12	0	−14	−12	9	3	−20	+20
19	11	23	+2	−4	7	2	−5	0
20	9	21	−22	−19	6	0	−36	−70
21	8	20	+4	+5	5	23	−27	−62
22	7	19	—	−11	4	21	—	−17
23	5	18	—	−3	3	20	—	−6
24	4	16	—	+12	2	19	—	−8
25	3	15	—	+3	0	17	—	−29
26	2	14	—	−22	23	16	—	+23
27	0	13	—	+4	22	15	—	+8
28	23	11	—	+11	21	13	—	+28
29	22	10	—	+6	19	12	—	+14
30	20	9	—	+1	18	11	—	−24
31	19	7	—	−2	17	10	—	−31
32	18	6	—	−10	15	8	—	−4
33	17	5	—	−10	14	7	—	+21
34	15	4	—	+3	13	6	—	−21
		12^h					15^h	
0	5	5	+28	—	1	8	−9	—
1	4	3	−8	—	0	7	+11	—
2	3	2	−37	—	23	6	−42	—
3	1	1	−29	—	22	4	+4	—
4	0	23	−7	—	20	3	+21	—
5	23	22	−6	—	19	2	+19	—
6	22	21	−30	−1	18	0	−29	−20
7	20	20	−20	−14	16	23	−3	+14
8	19	19	+14	+24	15	22	−16	+28
9	18	17	+16	+42	14	21	−9	+32
10	16	16	+10	+26	13	19	+49	+37
11	15	15	+8	+7	11	18	+32	+45
12	14	13	−23	+10	10	17	−40	−16
13	13	12	+8	−6	9	15	−35	−27
14	11	11	−4	+34	7	14	−35	−23
15	10	10	+13	0	6	13	−5	−32
16	9	8	−8	−2	5	12	−4	−15
17	7	7	+30	+6	3	10	+5	0
18	6	6	−40	−38	2	9	−33	+5
19	5	4	−41	−24	1	8	−53	−21
20	4	3	−12	−59	0	6	−6	−77
21	2	2	−38	−47	23	5	−11	−9
22	1	0	—	−8	22	3	—	+37
23	0	23	—	−6	21	2	—	+18
24	23	22	—	−6	19	0	—	−20

TABLE 19 (contd.)

k	Phase		M_1	M_2	Phase		M_1	M_2
	☊ − α	☊ + α			☊ − α	☊ + α		
1	2	3	4	5	6	7	8	9
		12^h				15^h		
25	22	20	—	—19	18	23	—	+14
26	20	19	—	+47	17	22	—	+41
27	19	17	—	+ 4	16	20	—	— 9
28	17^h	16^h	—	+26	14^h	19^h	—	+11
29	16	15	—	+12	13	18	—	—17
30	15	14	—	+ 8	12	17	—	+14
31	14	13	—	—34	10	15	—	+ 6
32	12	11	—	— 6	9	14	—	—13
33	11	10	—	+30	8	13	—	+13
34	10	9	—	—15	7	11	—	—37
		18^h				21^h		
0	23	11	0	—	20	14	+ 5	—
1	21	10	+ 7	—	18	12	+24	—
2	20	8	—34	—	17	11	— 4	—
3	19	7	+ 1	—	16	10	—11	—
4	17	6	+33	—	14	8	+21	—
5	16	4	+12	—	13	7	+ 5	—
6	15	3	+ 8	+ 4	12	6	—14	+ 7
7	14	2	+25	+18	10	5	— 6	— 6
8	12	0	+14	+ 6	9	3	—23	—19
9	11	23	—13	— 9	8	2	—40	—26
10	10	22	— 8	+ 2	6	0	0	+32
11	8	21	—19	—13	5	23	—33	—46
12	7	19	— 5	— 8	4	22	—41	—26
13	6	18	—36	—40	3	21	—22	+19
14	5	17	—24	—14	2	20	+ 2	+ 6
15	3	16	—21	—27	0	18	— 4	+ 7
16	2	14	—16	—14	23	17	— 9	—16
17	1	13	+31	+32	22	15	+ 5	+24
18	23	12	+14	+14	20	14	+17	—11
19	22	10	— 7	— 9	19	13	+12	+27
20	21	9	+ 8	+ 4	18	12	+21	+25
21	20	8	+ 7	+ 8	16	10	— 3	+12
22	18	6	—	— 6	15	9	—	+19
23	17	5	—	+ 4	14	8	—	+16
24	16	4	—	+ 2	12	7	—	— 2
25	14	2	—	+ 4	11	5	—	— 2
26	13	1	—	+18	10	4	—	— 3
27	12	0	—	— 4	9	3	—	—28
28	11	22	—	—11	7	1	—	— 4
29	10	21	—	+ 5	6	0	—	—12
30	8	20	—	— 8	5	23	—	—12
31	7	19	—	0	4	22	—	—21
32	5	17	—	— 8	2	20	—	+ 4
33	4	16	—	— 6	1	19	—	— 7
34	3	15	—	+ 2	0	18	—	— 2

The results of the two series of observations agree satisfactorily. It is true that these results are not wholly independent of each other, but the observational data common to both series form only a quarter of all the initial material.

Taking the mean of the results obtained from the two cycles we obtain

$$F_5 = -0''.0031 \cos(\Omega - \alpha) - 0''.0116 \sin(\Omega - \alpha) - \\ - 0''.0050 \cos(\Omega + \alpha) + 0''.0008 \sin(\Omega + \alpha)\,. \qquad (2.28)$$

Hence from (2.10) we have

$$\begin{aligned} \Delta N &= -0''.00124 \pm 0''.00018. \\ \Delta n &= -0\,.0002 \pm 0\,.0002. \\ \beta_1 &= +0\,.0012 \pm 0\,.0003. \\ \beta_2 &= +0\,.0002 \pm 0\,.0002\,. \end{aligned}$$

TABLE 20

Phase	Means of the values of F_5, distributed according to the phases of the argument (in 0''.001)				Phase	Means of the values of F_5, distributed according to the phases of the argument (in 0''.001)			
	$\Omega-\alpha$		$\Omega+\alpha$			$\Omega-\alpha$		$\Omega+\alpha$	
	$k=0-21$	$k=6-34$	$k=0-21$	$k=6-34$		$k=0-21$	$k=6-34$	$k=0-21$	$k=6-34$
0^h	−4	−5	−15	−13	12	+4	+8	+13	+5
1	−7	−13	+4	0	13	+7	+6	+1	+4
2	−20	−13	−10	−7	14	0	+2	−9	−2
3	−13	−9	−6	+4	15	+4	+11	−7	+2
4	−11	−13	+1	−5	16	−1	+8	−4	+5
5	−15	−15	+4	−17	17	+4	+13	−17	+3
6	−16	−19	−11	−4	18	+8	+2	+2	−4
7	−5	−18	+6	−1	19	+7	+15	+5	+4
8	−9	−8	−3	+4	20	−1	+2	−9	−5
9	−15	−4	−8	0	21	+20	+9	−16	−1
10	−8	−5	+7	+11	22	−5	+8	−10	+2
11	−3	+1	+7	+1	23	−9	+2	−10	−14

16. On a Possible Cause of the Appearance of a Semi-Annual Term in the Values of the Correction to the Constant of Nutation

According to our original plan we ought to take out the periodic part of the variation of F_5 and then redetermine the corrections to the declinations and proper motions. However we return first to the question of the influence of the error in the scale-value R on the final results of our calculations. The need for this comes from the following considerations.

Firstly, from the method of determining R that we used, the variations of this quantity may have a fictitious linear behaviour (see section 12). Secondly, we obtained earlier some indication that the value found for n ought to be somewhat increased. Now however the correction Δn appears to be practically zero. The last result certainly merits greater confidence. We concluded that the assumed value of n needed correction because of the dependence of the separate values of the correction to the constant of nutation on the right ascension of the pair from the observation of which this correction was obtained. This kind of dependence, appearing as a semi-annual term in the values of ΔN was discovered in the results of Przybyllok [41], Kulikov [4] and Jackson [29].

Inasmuch as the previous explanation of this term now fails, we come to the conclusion that it is caused by some systematic error in the observations. In particular, it may arise just as a consequence of the apparent linear variation in R.

We put the difference between the true mean scale value R and that assumed, R', in the form of a series, from which we take out the first two terms.

$$R - R' = C_0 + C_1 t. \tag{2.29}$$

The difference in micrometer readings for the pair with right ascension α may also be put approximately as a linear function of the time

$$m = m_0 - \frac{p}{R} t \cos\alpha,$$

where p is the precession in declination. We obtain

$$\left.\begin{aligned} m(R - R') &= C_0 m_0 + \left(C_1 m_0 - C_0 \frac{p}{R}\cos\alpha\right) t + ct^2 \\ c &= -C_1 \frac{p}{R}\cos\alpha \end{aligned}\right\} \tag{2.30}$$

For the determination of the constant of nutation the equation of condition takes the form

$$x + ty + \nu\Delta N = v, \tag{2.31}$$

where x and y have the same meanings as in (2.25) and ν is the coefficient of N_0 in (2.2).

The free term v includes both accidental and systematic error. Since we are now interested only in the influence of the quadratic term, we use (2.31) together with the following equation,

$$ty + \nu\Delta N' = ct^2, \tag{2.32}$$

in which $\Delta N'$ is just that part of the correction that owes its origin to the influence of the fictitious linear behaviour in the assumed values R'.

Then the normal equations take the form

$$\left.\begin{aligned} [t^2]y + [t\nu]\,\Delta N' &= c\,[t^3] \\ [t\nu]y + [\nu^2]\,\Delta N' &= c\,[t^2\nu] \end{aligned}\right\}. \tag{2.33}$$

In the calculation of the free terms of these equations and of the coefficients of the unknowns we may replace summation by integration. We do not dwell on the elementary but rather heavy transformations that have to be performed and we do not give the solutions of (2.33) in a general form. We limit ourselves to giving the formula in the particular case of the determination of the constant of nutation from the ILS observational data for 1900–15, namely

$$\Delta N' = \frac{1.8 \cos^2 \alpha C_1}{1 + 0.2 \cos 2\alpha - 0.3 \sin 2\alpha - 0.3 \sin^2 \alpha}. \qquad (2.34)$$

If we take

$$C_1 = -0''.003$$

a curve is obtained that represents sufficiently well the half-yearly term that we found in the corrections to the constant of nutation found by Przybyllok [41]. Figure 4 shows graphically the dependence of the constant of nutation on the right ascension of the observed pairs for a linear behaviour of R ($C = 0''.001$). For abscissa we take the right ascension expressed in hours, for ordinate the correction to the constant of nutation in 0".001. In constructing the curve the scale on the left gives the ordinate (ΔN_C). That on the right is related to the points representing the values of ΔN_0 found by Przybyllok.

Przybyllok found the correction to the constant of nutation from observations of each pair from each station separately. We first took the mean for all stations and then divided the pairs into 12 groups and calculated the mean of ΔN for each group. These means are given by dots in Fig. 4.

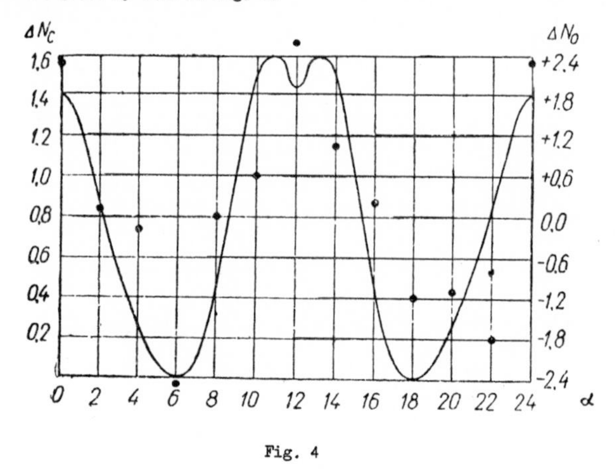

Fig. 4

These considerations are not enough to prove that the actual cause of the appearance of the "semiannual" term in the values of the nutation constant is an error in the adopted value of R. They show only that such a cause is possible.

We thought it necessary to examine whether it was possible for the fictitious linear behaviour in the variations of R to affect the results of our calculations. The method used to determine ΔR does not exclude the possibility of such behaviour.

This check was done as follows. First with the help of (2.28) we removed the nutational variation of latitude from F_5, getting the values F_6. These are given in Table 30. Further, taking

$$F_6 = x_2 + ky_2 + k^2 z_2 \qquad (2.35)$$

and using the method of least squares we obtained the following formula for z_2:

$$z_2 = 10^5 (p_0 \Sigma F_6 + p_1 \Sigma k F_6 + p_2 \Sigma k^2 F_6). \qquad (2.36)$$

The coefficients in this formula are given in Table 21.

TABLE 21

k	p_0	p_1	p_2
0—21	+375.93	—98.07	+4.45
0—22	+324.67	—81.16	+3.52
0—34	+ 2.12	— 0.35	+0.01
6—34	+ 3.33	— 0.40	+0.01

We do not give all values of z_2. It is sufficient to record that no dependence of these values on α was discovered. Apparently the values of R adopted are almost free from the systematic errors that can be represented by a linear function of the time.

In relation to this, in the determination of the correction to the declinations and proper motions, in a second approximation we omitted the last term on the right side of (2.35); that is, we again used (2.26) with F_4 replaced by F_6. This time we took the calculation to a larger number of figures. The results are given in column 7 of Table 4 and column 7 of Table 5. Then we calculated the values of

$$F_7 = F_4 - (x_2 + ky_2),$$

which are given in Table 30 (see appendix). In Figure 5 we show the successive stages in the improvement of the initial data in their preparation for harmonic analysis, taking as example the pair 96. F_1 is the immediate result of calculation from (2.11); F_2 the results reduced using the same values of the initial declination and proper motion of the centre of the pair through the whole period; F_3 the same after introduction of the correction for error in R. F_7 gives the data finally ready for harmonic analysis. The ordinates are in 0".001.

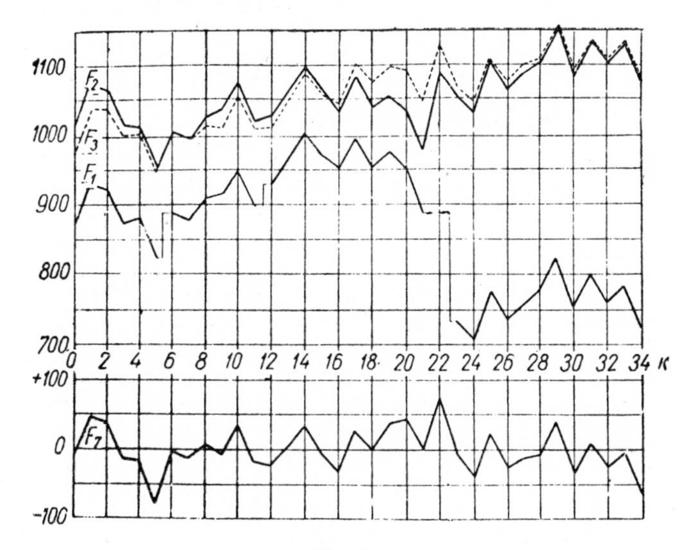

Fig. 5

17. Periodogram Analysis of the Non-Polar Variation of Latitude

From studies of the non-polar variation of latitude from observations at the international stations during 1922-34, Kimura discovered an 11-yearly term [45, p.173].

$$0''.018 \sin[\alpha - 32^\circ.43(t-t_0) + 86^\circ], \qquad t_0 = 1924.058 .$$

Although later Panchenko pointed out that this result is not genuine, we judged it necessary to consider the question of its existence afresh, on the basis of more ample observational material than Kimura had. Further, it was important to answer the more general question: is there some long-period variation of latitude other than the 19-yearly period of nutational motion? If such oscillations exist, they may be the cause of systematic errors in the constant of nutation, the ratio of the axes of the nutation ellipse, and the retardation in phase, and also the cause of the appearance of a semi-annual term in ΔN.

In order to reveal this kind of concealed periodicity several methods are possible. However, our problem has some peculiarities that forbade the use of any of these methods directly without some preliminary calculations. After a series of experiments we settled on the following scheme of solution.

Putting F_7 for the expression, analogous to (2.6),

$$F_7 = A_1 \cos\mu t \cos\alpha + B_1 \cos\mu t \sin\alpha + + A_2 \sin\mu t \cos\alpha + B_2 \sin\mu t \sin\alpha , \qquad (2.37)$$

where μ is the frequency, related to the required period by

$$\mu = \frac{2\pi}{T} ,$$

and setting

$$\left.\begin{aligned} A_1 \cos\mu t + A_2 \sin\mu t = A \\ B_1 \cos\mu t + B_2 \sin\mu t = B \end{aligned}\right\} , \qquad (2.38)$$

then

$$F_7 = A\cos\alpha + B\sin\alpha . \qquad (2.39)$$

Since we consider only the long-period variation of latitude, we may assume as an approximation that the coefficients A and B are constant over a year, and for their determination

TABLE 22

k	Values for the groups											
	I	II	III	IV	V	VI	VII	VIII	IX	X	XI	XII
	Cycle 1900-1921											
0	−38	+52	−10	+21	−6	+9	+44	−13	+18	+12	+15	−3
1	−3	+36	+32	+35	+22	−28	+20	+10	+31	+2	+47	+33
2	+1	−24	−17	−22	−33	−49	−34	−39	−28	−24	+17	+1
3	−14	−17	−34	−22	−24	−33	−22	+10	+12	+1	−6	−17
4	+12	−31	−6	−8	−18	−14	+7	+30	+44	+39	+21	−19
5	−3	−32	−18	−5	+12	+18	−12	+31	+23	+10	0	−33
6	+7	+12	+10	−17	−25	−9	−29	−23	+3	+14	−12	−3
7	+1	−12	+3	−29	−22	−11	−12	+2	+28	+18	−1	+9
8	−6	−12	−40	−13	−29	+3	+16	−9	+24	+8	−7	−6
9	+20	+30	−5	−5	+12	+12	+26	−2	−21	−4	−52	+23
10	+31	−6	+30	+25	+23	+8	+14	+55	−13	+6	+10	+13
11	−4	−3	+4	+31	+25	+17	−2	+39	+10	−39	−28	−4
12	−17	−26	+30	+27	+27	−8	−26	−34	+1	−28	−21	−4
13	−9	−7	−2	−8	+22	+28	−4	−29	−48	−20	−10	−2
14	+17	+16	+14	+19	+36	+42	−38	−28	−33	−14	+22	+35
15	−17	−8	+5	−4	+1	+14	+16	+1	−38	+9	+1	−6
16	−28	0	−2	+9	−34	+14	−36	+2	−32	+13	0	−28
17	+41	+10	+3	−15	−4	+23	+55	+11	+11	+46	+4	+42
18	−27	+5	−8	−12	−12	−39	−24	−26	+16	+15	+26	+40
19	+31	+2	+50	+22	+1	−30	−38	−47	−22	+9	+23	+46
20	−26	+32	−14	−34	−34	−2	+16	+12	+5	+20	+43	+5
21	−9	−37	+18	−21	+10	−40	−12	−5	+10	+6	+9	+10
	Cycle 1906-1934											
6	+6	+16	+8	−9	−68	−25	+20	−26	−5	+23	+16	−7
7	−24	−48	−9	−23	−27	−24	+5	+26	+19	+21	+4	−29
8	−10	−12	−32	−8	+26	+21	+34	+16	+13	+15	−3	−20
9	−17	−17	−11	+1	+34	+36	+55	+20	−11	+8	−38	+2
10	−1	−6	+26	+33	−4	+8	+60	+51	+5	+18	+31	+24
11	−31	−12	+4	+39	+71	−5	−49	+77	+12	−36	−50	−39
12	+39	−1	+22	+9	+34	+19	−12	−14	−3	−17	−23	−15
13	+6	−10	−4	−11	+2	+5	−20	−9	−41	−30	+20	−14
14	0	+21	−1	+19	+27	+48	−27	+28	−21	−9	+20	+20
15	−24	+13	+15	−11	+16	+29	−32	−40	−41	−6	0	+10
16	+40	+10	+1	+6	−40	+59	0	+2	−25	+1	−40	+7
17	+15	−10	+20	−24	+23	+31	−36	−22	+23	+44	−20	+35
18	−24	−3	−8	−10	+26	−28	−10	−7	−13	+8	−14	−5
19	−13	+17	0	+10	−28	−13	48	+22	−22	+7	+26	+37
20	−43	−6	−7	−31	−74	−42	−104	−42	−11	+14	+27	+22
21	−51	−16	+27	−17	−70	−30	−47	+11	+6	+4	+10	+15
22	+33	+13	−4	−10	+4	+8	−6	+47	+4	−1	+9	+39
23	+38	+12	+11	−5	+9	−7	+11	+32	+12	−4	+23	+11
24	+25	−7	+9	+18	+8	−3	−2	+7	−6	−2	−2	−4
25	+8	−35	+6	+2	+48	−6	−8	+32	+2	−1	−2	+6
26	+51	−3	−20	−8	+31	+55	+42	+61	+18	+8	−4	−13
27	−24	−13	−8	+17	+10	+10	−12	−2	+7	−22	−29	−17
28	−42	−7	+26	+11	+47	+36	+32	−14	−5	−24	+4	−14
29	−9	−1	−1	+16	+35	+17	+5	23	+2	+2	−23	+6
30	+12	+4	−12	+15	−16	+5	+46	+6	−5	−14	−20	−15
31	+1	+34	−1	+4	−26	−35	0	−5	+2	−6	−5	−32
32	−13	+16	+5	−11	+6	−10	+16	−38	−15	−3	+16	−24
33	+16	−1	−12	+3	+28	+26	+54	−22	+5	−15	−22	+4
34	−35	+4	+4	+25	−38	−8	−17	−35	−3	+2	−19	−25

TABLE 23

k	A'	$y'(A')$	$y''(A')$	$\mu_a k$	v_a	B'	$y'(B')$	$y''(B')$	$\mu_b k$	v_b
1	2	3	4	5	6	7	8	9	10	11
0	−3	—	—	0°	−15	−8	—	—	0°	−10
1	+13	+46	+77	21	−2	+2	+60	+82	21	+7
2	+26	+30	+51	41	+10	−3	+34	+55	43	+2
3	+3	+21	+33	62	−11	−18	+36	+29	64	−8
4	−1	+10	+7	82	−12	−28	+18	+8	86	−15
5	−16	−2	−19	103	−27	−13	−4	−20	107	−1
6	+18	−22	−42	124	+13	−5	−33	−50	128	+7
7	+1	−36	−61	144	+3	−21	−54	−72	150	−13
8	−11	−51	−79	165	−9	−15	−56	−82	171	−13
9	−14	−67	−85	185	−6	+7	−48	−75	193	+9
10	−5	−49	−76	206	+6	−2	−23	−66	214	−7
11	−31	−31	−46	227	−21	+13	−32	−48	235	+3
12	−1	−22	−21	247	+9	+20	−11	−10	257	+7
13	+1	−12	+2	268	+8	+14	+29	+24	278	+1
14	+7	−9	+32	288	+8	+17	+31	+45	300	+5
15	+1	−13	+63	309	+2	+11	+39	+54	321	+3
16	+2	+25	+77	330	−4	+6	+50	+67	342	−2
17	+8	+67	+84	350	−4	−8	+68	+72	4	−10
18	+8	+58	+80	11	−4	−7	+57	+61	25	−2
19	+30	+35	+53	31	+15	+7	+35	+34	47	+17
20	+25	+9	+41	52	+11	−18	+12	+8	68	−8
21	+13	+20	+20	73	−1	−12	+8	+5	89	+1
22	+10	+13	−4	93	−1	−7	+30	−27	111	+5
23	+9	−6	—	114	+4	−4	+19	—	132	+8
24	+4	−31	—	134	−1	+7	−21	—	154	+15
25	−8	−4	—	155	−6	0	−38	—	175	+2
26	−21	−40	—	176	−13	−8	+1	—	196	−13
27	−13	−58	—	196	−2	+8	+16	—	218	+3
28	−23	+1	—	217	−12	+16	+10	—	239	+6
29	−7	—	—	237	+3	+11	—	—	261	−2
30	−10	—	—	258	−3	+3	—	—	282	−10
31	+9	—	—	279	+16	+3	—	—	303	−9
32	+4	—	—	299	+5	+7	—	—	325	−1
33	−13	—	—	320	−19	+9	—	—	346	+7
34	+3	—	—	340	−3	+7	—	—	8	+5

we use the usual methods of harmonic analysis.

For each of the 12 groups of pairs and for each year we found the mean of the quantities F_7. They are denoted by F and given in Table 22.

Thus for each year of observation we obtain the 12 values F, from which again we found for each year separately the coefficients A and B. The calculation followed the usual method of harmonic analysis for 12 ordinates, in which for simplification it was assumed that α takes the values 0, 2,

4 ... hours, but not 1, 3, 5 ... hours, as this takes place in fact. We thus obtain directly not the coefficients A and B, but two other magnitudes A' and B' related to them by the relations:

$$\left.\begin{aligned} A &= A'\cos 15^\circ - B'\sin 15^\circ = 0.996A' - 0.259B' \\ B &= A'\sin 15^\circ + B'\cos 15^\circ = 0.259A' + 0.996B' \end{aligned}\right\}. \qquad (2.40)$$

The results originally obtained for the cycles 1900-21 and 1906-24 separately were later combined. The values for A' and B', expressed, as in F_7, in 0".001, are given in columns 2 and 7 of Table 23. We used these as initial data for the determination of hidden periodicities in the non-polar variation of latitude.

We used the method of Fuhrich [25] as more appropriate to the conditions of our problem than the usual Schuster method. Pollak used this method in the periodogram analysis of the motion of the pole, and we took the formulae and the scheme of calculation directly from his paper [40], in particular the calculation of auto-correlation coefficients in formula (3). Even the second coefficients, which we have denoted by $y''(A)$ and $y''(B)$, may so well be seen to be of cosine form (Fig. 6) that the frequency of the largest oscillation is reliably determined. For A' it was found equal to 20°.6 per year, for B' 21°.4 per year. These correspond to periods 17.5 years and 16.8 years.

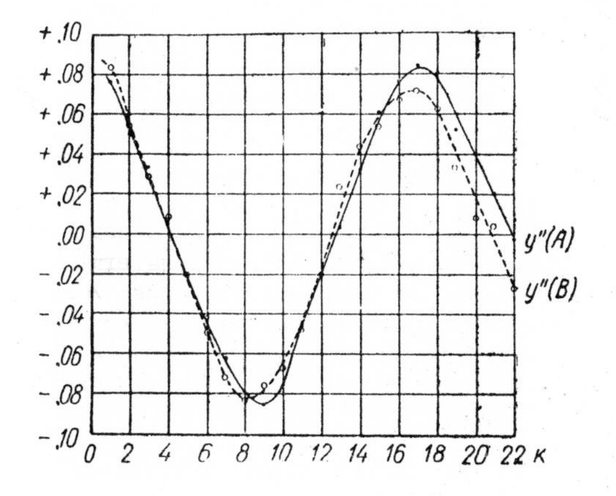

Fig. 6

In order to detect other periods we removed from the data the greatest periodic terms. For this we put A' and B' in the form

$$A' = m_1 \cos \mu_a k + m_2 \sin \mu_a k + v_a ,$$
$$B' = n_1 \cos \mu_b k + n_2 \sin \mu_b k + v_b ,$$

where $\mu_a = 20^\circ.6$, $\mu_b = 21^\circ.4$. The values of the arguments $\mu_a k$ and $\mu_b k$ are given in Table 23, columns 5 and 10. After this we found by harmonic analysis the following values of the coefficients of the periodic terms:

$$m_1 = +0''.0021, \qquad m_2 = -0''.0130,$$
$$n_1 = +0''.0096, \qquad n_2 = +0''.0086,$$

and finally the remainders v_a and v_b, which are given in Tables 23, columns 6 and 11 (in 0."001). These are apparently random so that the continuation of the periodogram analysis would have no meaning.

Thus we have succeeded in discovering only one oscillation of period approximately 17 years. Although the method of Fuhrich does not allow us to estimate strictly the accuracy of the value obtained, an error of one or two years is fully possible; hence we can identify the oscillation discovered with the nutation term, with a period of 18.6 years. Thus we have justification for thinking that no other long-period term of the form (2.37), including the 11-yearly term, appears in the non-polar variation of latitude.

18. Determination of ΔN, Δn, β_1 and β_2 (second approximation)

So far we have used A' and B', which was quite permissible for investigating the periods. For the determination of the coefficients in (2.6) it is necessary to use A and B, which were calculated from (2.40). The results are given in Table 24, in columns 3 and 4 for 1900-21 and columns 7 and 8 for 1906-34. The remaining columns give the residuals, v_a and v_b (in 0."001)

On the basis of the results of the preceding paragraph we put

$$A = A_1 \cos \Omega + A_2 \sin \Omega + v_a, \quad B = B_1 \cos \Omega + B_2 \sin \Omega + v_b \qquad (2.41)$$

TABLE 24

k	☊	1900—1921				1906—1934			
		A	B	v_a	v_b	A	B	v_a	v_b
1	2	3	4	5	6	7	8	9	10
0	250°	−5	−8	−14	−3	—	—	—	—
1	232	+11	+2	+2	+11	—	—	—	—
2	212	+23	−3	+15	+10	—	—	—	—
3	193	+1	−18	−6	−3	—	—	—	—
4	173	−3	−28	−7	−13	—	—	—	—
5	154	−18	−13	−20	+1	—	—	—	—
6	135	+15	0	+17	+11	+18	−10	+22	−2
7	115	+7	−16	+11	−10	−10	−26	0	−21
8	96	−5	−18	+2	−16	−22	−11	−8	−9
9	77	−2	+14	+6	+10	−30	+1	−13	−1
10	57	−4	+5	+5	−3	−10	−8	+8	−13
11	38	−18	+13	−9	+1	−48	+13	−31	+5
12	19	−4	+21	+4	+7	−2	+20	+12	+10
13	359	−5	+18	0	+3	+4	+9	+13	−1
14	340	+12	+23	+14	+9	−2	+10	+2	0
15	321	−7	+4	−7	−8	+5	+18	+3	+8
16	301	0	+2	−4	−6	0	+10	−8	+4
17	282	+4	−13	−2	−16	+8	−3	−5	−6
18	263	+14	−15	+6	−13	−2	+1	−18	+2
19	243	+36	+16	+27	+23	+21	−3	+3	+1
20	224	+7	−22	−2	−11	+39	−15	+21	−8
21	205	+7	−9	−1	+5	+15	−15	0	−6
22	186	—	—	—	—	+8	−7	−3	+3
23	167	—	—	—	—	+7	−4	+1	+6
24	147	—	—	—	—	+2	+7	+2	+16
25	128	—	—	—	—	−10	0	−4	+7
26	109	—	—	—	—	−23	−8	−12	−4
27	89	—	—	—	—	−15	+8	+1	+8
28	76	—	—	—	—	−25	+16	−7	+13
29	51	—	—	—	—	−9	+11	+9	+5
30	31	—	—	—	—	−12	+3	+4	−6
31	12	—	—	—	—	+7	+3	+20	−7
32	353	—	—	—	—	+2	+7	+10	−3
33	333	—	—	—	—	+15	+9	−13	−1
34	314	—	—	—	—	+1	+7	−3	−1

and by means of harmonic analysis we found the coefficients A_1, A_2, B_1, B_2 and then the remainder terms v_a, v_b. Thus we obtained for 1900-21

$$A_1 = -0''.0053 \pm 0''.0034, \quad A_2 = -0''.0073 \pm 0''.0034,$$
$$B_1 = +0''.0151 \pm 0''.0033, \quad B_2 = +0''.0001 \pm 0''.0033;$$

and for 1906-34

$$A_1 = -0''.0097 \pm 0''.0031, \quad A_2 = -0''.0155 \pm 0''.0031,$$
$$B_1 = +0''.0105 \pm 0''.0021, \quad B_2 = -0''.0007 \pm 0''.0021.$$

Hence, using (2.10) we found for 1900-21

$$\Delta N = \ 0''.0151 \pm 0''.0033, \quad \Delta n = +0.0004 \pm 0.0005\,,$$
$$\beta_1 = +2'.6 \pm 1'.7, \quad \beta_2 = 0'.0 \pm 1'.7\,;$$

and for 1906-34

$$\Delta N = \ 0''.0105 \pm 0''.0021, \quad \Delta n = -0.0008 \pm 0.0004\,,$$
$$\beta_1 = +4'.9 \pm 1'.7, \quad \beta_2 = -0'.3 \pm 0'.8.$$

Taking a weighted mean of the two cycles we obtain

$$\Delta N = -0''.0120 \pm 0''.0018, \quad \Delta n = -0''.0003 \pm 0''.0003,$$
$$\beta_1 = +3'.8 \pm 1'.2, \quad \beta_2 = -0'.2 \pm 0'.7.$$

These values agree well with those in section 15.

From these results we may draw the conclusion that the retardation in phase is peculiar to the nutation in longitude. At the same time they give some indication of the general turning of the ellipse of nutation.

Ordinarily in constructing this ellipse we use a system of rectangular axes in a plane touching the celestial sphere at the mean pole of the Earth, which is also the origin of coordinates. The axis OY is directed along the mean solstitial colure from the pole of the ecliptic, and OX along the equinoctial colure to the vernal equinox. Then the equations of the ellipse of nutation can be put in the parametric form

$$x = nN\cos\varphi, \qquad y = N\sin\varphi,$$

where

$$\varphi = 90^\circ + \text{☊}.$$

Since we have modified the ordinary expression (2.2) to (2.3) it is necessary to replace the preceding expression by

$$x = nN\cos(\varphi - \beta_1), \quad y = N\sin(\varphi - \beta_2)\,. \tag{2.42}$$

Hence from formulae of analytic geometry we find the value for the angle between the axis OY and the major axis of the ellipse of nutation

$$\gamma = -\frac{n}{1-n^2}(\beta_1 - \beta_2), \tag{2.43}$$

and with the values found for the constants

$$\gamma = -6'.8 \pm 2'.4 .$$

Hence the positive end of the major axis of the ellipse of nutation diverges from the solstitial colure by 6'.8 towards the vernal equinox.

The theory of the rotation of the Earth has not yet given any indication of such a turning of the axes of the ellipse of nutation. This casts some doubt on the reality of the results obtained above. Nevertheless we think that in further development of the theory based on new data on the inner structure of the Earth it may be useful to keep this result in mind.

Putting in the numerical values we have found in (2.8) we obtain

$$\Delta\delta = -6''.850 \cos\alpha \sin(\Omega - 3'.8) + 9''.198 \sin\alpha \cos\Omega . \qquad (2.44)$$

19. Comparison with Results of Other Authors

The new value of the constant of nutation obtained here is one of the results in the solution of more general problems of the joint determination of the coefficients of the principal terms in nutation and the retardation in phase. Hitherto the theoretical value of the ratio of the axes of the ellipse of nutation has always been used and the initial phases β_1 and β_2 have been taken equal to zero.

Thus there is no immediate profit in a detailed discussion of results found on the basis of the assumptions mentioned, and we give here for comparison only a summary of the values for the constant of nutation.

S.Newcomb, from meridian observations at Greenwich, Pulkovo and Washington [37]	9".210 ± 0.008
E.Przybyllok from ILS, 1900-15 [41]	9".2069 ± 0.0030
J.Jackson from Greenwich latitude observations [29]	9".2066 ± 0.0082
H.Spencer Jones from Greenwich latitude observations [54]	9".2173 ± 0.0060
also [55]	9".2134 ± 0.0063

H.Morgan from observations of circumpolar stars at Washington 1903-25 [32] . .	9".206	± 0.010
K.A.Kulikov, from latitude observations at Pulkovo 1904-1941 [4] . . .	9".2108	± 0.0019
T.Hattori from ILS observations [26]		
26 pairs 1900-1934	9".1985	± 0.0051
53 pairs 1900-1922	9".2073	± 0.0041
44 pairs 1906-1935	9".1967	± 0.0043
57 pairs 1912-1935	9".1955	± 0.0034
Our result for N	9".1980	± 0.0018

In connexion with these results we find it necessary to make the following remark. Newcomb's value for the constant of nutation is the mean of 27 values found by other authors. Of these, ten, and not one as erroneously stated by Idelson [2], are less than Przybyllok's value and five are less than ours.

The accuracy that Kulikov attributes to his values for N must be considered exaggerated, since in deriving his value he considered results by different methods from the same initial data as independent of each other.

T.Hattori used the same initial data for the determination of the constant of nutation as we used for the solution of the more general problem. We became acquainted with his work only after our calculations were concluded and were able to remark with satisfaction agreement in the choice of method of solution of some particular problems, arising in the separate stages of reduction of the initial data. For example Hattori brought all latitudes to the GC system, and in the same formula as our (1.11) he found the non-polar variation of latitude in common for the three stations; that is, just the magnitude that we have denoted by F_1.

However, Hattori did not exclude the slow variation of latitude common to all pairs, and, what is particularly important, did not try to determine the errors of the scale value and correct for them; we have seen that their effect was sometimes appreciable. We noticed also that in four cases the corrections to the proper motions obtained by us did not agree with those given by Hattori. For these we give his values for $\Delta\mu$; ours are given in brackets.

Number of pair	Epoch	$\Delta\mu$
24	1928.0	-0".003 (-0".001)
35	1903.0	-0".022 (-0".016)
72	1903.0	-0".004 (+0".004)
86	1915.0	+0".008 (+0".003)

For the determination of the constant of nutation Hattori used various methods. The first of these, including the analysis of the mean monthly groups of latitudes, is open to objections, the gravity of which the author, apparently, fully understood. In the second method he used the results of observations of those pairs that remained in the ILS programme for more than 19 years, that is, the same material as we have used. The pairs that consist of stars not in Boss's catalogue were omitted by Hattori, while we retained them. On the other hand Hattori included 13 pairs observed from 1912 to 1935. We did not do this, inasmuch as these pairs are distributed so unevenly in right ascension that it did not seem possible to determine the coefficients of the principal nutation terms from them separately.

Since Hattori did not exclude the slow variation of latitude the yearly term appears clearly in his results for N, as in those of Przybyllok. This however does not affect the mean value N from all pairs. A more important effect is that of the errors of the scale values, to which we paid particular attention.

The paper [17] was, as far as we know, the first attempt at a separate determination of the coefficients of the principal nutation terms. Later A.Yă.Orlov carried out the determination of these coefficients from material of the Pulkovo observations with a zenith telescope from 1915 to 1928 [10] and found that none of them needed correction. Orlov's investigation at first excited some doubt in us in one respect. As initial data he used the instantaneous values of latitude obtained by Korol. In determining the correction for the scale value Korol, like us, applied the method of comparing the latitudes obtained separately for pairs with positive and negative zenith distances; but in selecting pairs, he did not take care to obtain results known to be free from the effect of possible errors in the coefficients of the nutation terms. This could lead to the exclusion or weakening of the 19-yearly terms; however in fact it appears that this did not happen. Although in some cases the variation of the mean values of both cos α and sin α for groups of zenith distances of opposite sign amount to appreciable values (up to ± 0.8) they vary from year to year unsystematically, even with changes of sign.

The only attempt to examine the question of the existence of lag of the nutation in phase was made by Morgan [33]. Analysing the observations of circumpolar stars in Washington from 1903 to 1925 he used the equations of condition

$$\Delta\delta = -(0.037a' \sin \Omega + b' \cos \Omega)\,\Delta N + \\ + (b' \sin \Omega - 0.037a' \cos \Omega)\,N\Delta\Theta \quad ,$$

where a' and b' are reduction constants. Our (2.6) takes such a form if we substitute in it from (2.7) and take

$$\Delta n = 0, \quad \beta_1 = \beta_2 = -\Delta\Theta .$$

From observations of declination Morgan found

$$\Delta\Theta = 0'.0 \pm 4'.8 \ ,$$

and from observations of right ascension

$$\Delta\Theta = +13'.2 \pm 3'.6 \ .$$

The difference between these values, together with the mean error of each, raises doubt as to the reality of the results found by Morgan. It may be that Morgan shared these doubts and that this was the reason why he did not publish the details of his calculations, but confined himself to a short communication.

The constant of precession, the ratio of the masses of the Earth and Moon, and the constant of nutation are connected, as is known, by a certain relation, which is determined by the theory of the rotating Earth. With the use of this relation we may find the theoretical value of N if we take the other two constants as known. The value found thus is, as a rule, greater than that found directly from the observations, namely from 9".215 [27] to 9".226 [23]. We may thus notice that our new value differs from the theoretical value by an amount twice as great as that of the value 9".210 taken at the Paris conference in 1896, which hitherto has been applied in calculation of the reduction to apparent place.

CHAPTER III

FORCED MOTION OF THE POLE OF THE EARTH

20. Introduction

From the kinematics of a rigid body it is known that the motion of the axis of rotation of the body in space is always accompanied by a shift of the axis relative to the body. Thus in the Earth the nutational motion of the instantaneous axis of rotation is accompanied by a circular motion of the pole. The latter, in its turn, appears to cause weak variations of latitude of period approximately a day, which are known as the Oppolzer terms. In Chapter I we obtained the following theoretical expression for these terms, starting from the assumption that the Earth is an ideally elastic body.

$$\Delta\varphi = -0''.0066 \sin S - 0''.0051 \sin (S - 2☾) -$$
$$- 0''.0022 \sin (S - 2L) - 0''.0010 \sin (S - 2☾ - ☊)$$
$$- 0''.0010 \sin (S - 3☾ + \Gamma') + 0''.0009 \sin (S - ☊), \quad (3.1)$$

where S = sidereal time at the place, L, ☾, ☊, Γ' are the mean longitudes of the Sun and Moon, the rising node of the Moon's orbit, and the Moon's perigee respectively.

We now attempt to examine whether the observations fully corroborate the validity of this theoretical formula. The problem obviously consists in the investigation in the variation of latitude of all or at least some of the periodic terms appearing in (3.1). We have already pointed out some difficulties arising in the interpretation of the results of the analysis of the observations. We now consider them in detail.

The effect of the fortnightly nutation on the declination

may be expressed by the formula*

$$\Delta\delta = -0'',085 \sin(2☾ - \alpha) + 0'',003 \sin(2☾ + \alpha). \qquad (3.2)$$

If the actual fortnightly variation of declination does not correspond exactly with this formula, then in the variation of latitude there appear terms with arguments $2☾-\alpha$ and $2☾+\alpha$; and since in the definition of latitude according to Talcott the stars are observed at culmination, the sidereal time at the place at the moment of observation is always equal to the right ascension of the star. Consequently the arguments $2☾-\alpha$ and $2☾-S$ coincide; hence, if in the variation of latitude a term with argument $2☾-\alpha$ is discovered and its amplitude has a different value from the theoretical one, this may be explained as an inexactitude in the coefficient of the first term of formula (3.2) and also as an inexactitude in the theoretical expression of the lunar diurnal term, that is, the second term on the right in (3.1). Generally speaking, we may take either of these explanations, but it stands to reason that we should choose the one that is both in theoretical investigations and in the reduction of observations the most suitable.

Theory and observation should make it possible to find at any moment the position of the system of principal axes of inertia of the Earth relative to any fixed system of axes. For this it would be enough to take, for instance, three equations, giving the dependence on time of Euler's angles, by means of which the relative configuration of two systems with the same origin is determined. However in considering the rotation of the Earth these equations are unsuitable; they are complicated and inconvenient for calculation. The solution is more simple and descriptive if we use a chosen auxiliary coordinate system and define its motion, on the one hand relative to the fixed system, and on the other relative to the principal axes of inertia of the Earth.

In the choice of such an auxiliary system we are free to act at discretion, and to this there is related a seeming arbitrariness in the interpretation of the results of analysis of observations in considering the lunar terms in the variation of latitude. The axis OZ of this system may be taken, for instance, as the instaneous axis of rotation, or of angular momentum, but if we assume that the Earth consists of a solid shell and a liquid core we may take it as the axis of

*See Orlov [8].

rotation or of angular momentum of the shell. In each case, evidently, we shall get somewhat different equations of motion of the auxiliary system, both relative to the fixed system and to the system of principal axes of inertia of the Earth.

In Fig. 7 OZ is the axis of the auxiliary system of coordinates, OZ' the vertical defined by the plumb line, OS the direction to any given star. We neglect the tidal variation of the vertical and the proper motion of the star S; that is, we assume that OZ' does not change its direction relative to the principal axes of inertia of the Earth, nor OS its direction relative to the system of fixed axes, for instance the system of the ecliptic at some initial epoch.

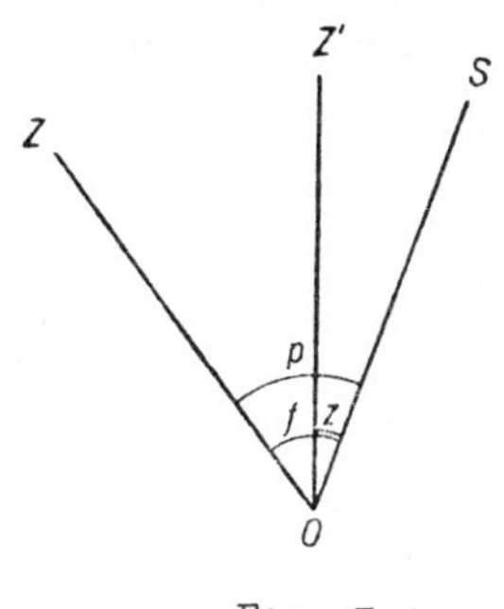

Fig. 7

We have pointed out that there are several possible directions of the axis OZ. However they are all so close together that in any case we can take the plane of the diagram as the meridian plane. We put

$$Z'OS = z, \quad Z'OZ = f, \quad ZOS = p.$$

Then

$$z = p + f. \qquad (3.3)$$

We suppose that the dependence of p and f on the time is obtained on the basis of some or other assumptions about the mechanical properties of the Earth. From the observations we can take the empirical expression for the variation of z. Thus it is possible to test the theory by comparison with observation. However the results of such a comparison will not show how far any discrepancies that may be discovered are to be attributed to $p(t)$ or to $f(t)$.

We turn now to the question of the lunar terms in the variation of latitude. Up to now they have usually been explained as an inexactitude in the fortnightly nutation term, which enters into the equation of motion of the axis OZ in space.* However, as we pointed out in section 5, the formula of nutation describing the motion of the angular momentum **G** remains the same for any reasonable assumptions about the mechanical properties of the Earth; hence if we take the auxiliary axis OZ along the vector **G**, its motion in any case satisfies the equations obtained on the assumption that the Earth is absolutely rigid. Then the difference between the theoretical and observed variations of z can be attributed entirely to inaccuracy of the expression for the angle $f(t)$, that is, in the equations determining the motion of the auxiliary system relative to the principal axes of inertia.

However

$$f = 90^\circ - \varphi ,$$

hence comparison with observation may give us the answer to the question whether the expression for the forced variation of latitude, which we obtained taking the Earth as an ideally elastic body, corresponds to reality. For this comparison we limit ourselves to the second term of (3.1), that is, to the lunar diurnal term. The first term enters as some constant magnitude in the value of the latitude taken from observation of an individual pair; the coefficients of the other terms are so small that they can hardly be accurately determined from observation.

21. The Lunar Diurnal Term in the Variation of Latitude according to the Data of the ILS. Initial Data and Scheme of Calculation

The harmonic analysis of the ILS observations in order to determine the amplitude and phases of the lunar diurnal terms in the variation of latitude requires a great deal of calculation. In order to shorten it, it was necessary to put the initial data in as compact a form as possible. For this reason we divided the 96 pairs of the ILS programme into 24 groups with 4 pairs in each. These hourly groups, in contrast to the two-hourly ones ordinarily used in work on the ILS observations, we shall call "links" - a term used by us in the description of the concurrent observations with the two zenith telescopes at Poltava. The mean right ascensions of the stars

*That is, the periodic variation of argument $2☾ - \alpha$, and not the tidal variation of latitude.

forming the links are 0.5, 1.5 ... 23.5 hours.

TABLE 25

2☾	Date	Sidereal time	2☾	Date	Sidereal time
1	2	3	1	2	3
0^h	1913, Jan. 12.47	0.28	12^h	1913, Jan. 19.30	0.13
1	13.04	.85	13	19.86	.70
2	13.61	.42	14	20.43	.27
3	14.18	.99	15	21.00	.84
4	14.74	.56	16	21.57	.41
5	15.31	.13	17	22.14	.98
6	15.88	.70	18	22.71	.56
7	16.45	.27	19	23.28	.13
8	17.02	.84	20	23.85	.70
9	17.59	.42	21	24.42	.27
10	18.16	.99	22	24.99	.84
11	18.73	.56	23	25.56	.41
	19.30	.13		26.13	.98

Further we chose the complete observations of the link, that is, those for which no pair of the link was omitted. For each full link we found the mean value of the latitude, that is, the simple mean of four instantaneous latitudes, obtained from observations of the pairs belonging to the link. All incompletely observed links were rejected. In consequence the initial quantity of material at Carloforte was reduced by 18 per cent, at Ukiah by 7 per cent and at Mizusawa by 31 per cent. At the cost of this abridgement we were able to obtain greater compactness of the data and simplicity of calculation.

After this preparation we took the residuals of latitude obtained for separate links from the smoothed curve of oscillation of latitude. The residuals denoted by $\Delta\varphi$ had to be subjected to harmonic analysis for the lunar diurnal term. The first step was to arrange the values $\Delta\varphi$ according to the phase of the argument 2☾ $- \alpha$ and then of the argument 2☾ $+ \alpha$, where α is the mean right ascension of the pair forming the link. For this it was necessary first to find the mean value of double the moon's longitude, for all mean times of observation of the complete link. For this we constructed the auxiliary table 25. In column 1 we give 2☾ for the mid-points of the intervals of time bounded by the moments given in column 2 in universal time. In column 3 we give the corresponding Greenwich mean times. We do not give the complete table here; it has 96 pages and covers the time from 1899 to 1934.

We explain the method of use by means of an example. Suppose that we want the approximate value of twice the longitude of the Moon at the mean moment of observation of the fifth link at Mizusawa on the night of 1913 January 18-19. The local sidereal time of observation of this link is its right ascension, that is, $4^h.5$. Since the longitude of Mizusawa is $-9^h.4$, the mean moment of observation of the link is always $19^h.1$ Greenwich sidereal time. This is 0.80 of a day. In Table 25 we find that the time of observation lies in the interval between January 18.73 and January 19.30, since the first time corresponds in the column of sidereal time to 0.56 and the second to 0.13. From this we find that twice the longitude of the Moon at the time of observation was approximately 11.

In this way we divided all the values $\Delta\varphi$ into 24 groups according to argument $2☾$, expressed in hours. Further, for each group we calculated the mean of $\Delta\varphi$ and put it in a square table, the scheme of which is given in Table 26. In the cells of this table we write the values of the arguments $2☾ - \alpha$ and $2☾ + \alpha$. In order to obtain the means of all values $\Delta\varphi$ corresponding to equal values of the argument it is necessary to divide the sum of the numbers in a descending diagonal by 24. Thus, for example, the argument $2☾ - \alpha$ will be equal to one hour for all values $\Delta\varphi$ which we write in the cells outlined. Similarly we get the mean for argument $2☾ + \alpha$ by dividing by 24 the sum on a rising diagonal.

We used the values of the instantaneous latitude at Carloforte, Mizusawa and Ukiah from 1899 to 1934. During this period the programme of observation changed three times, at 1906.0, 1912.0, and 1922.7.

For the calculation of reduction to apparent place the central bureau of the ILS used the reducing quantities published in the <u>Berliner Jahrbuch</u>. The formula for the calculation of these quantities was somewhat changed in 1916. Some small nutation terms were introduced that had not previously been taken into account. Consequently we decided to divide the whole series of observations from 1899 to 1934 into five cycles; I, from the beginning to 1906-0; II, from 1906.0 to 1912.0; III, from 1912.0 to 1916.0; IV, from 1916.0 to 1922.7; and V, from 1922.7 to 1935.0.

TABLE 26

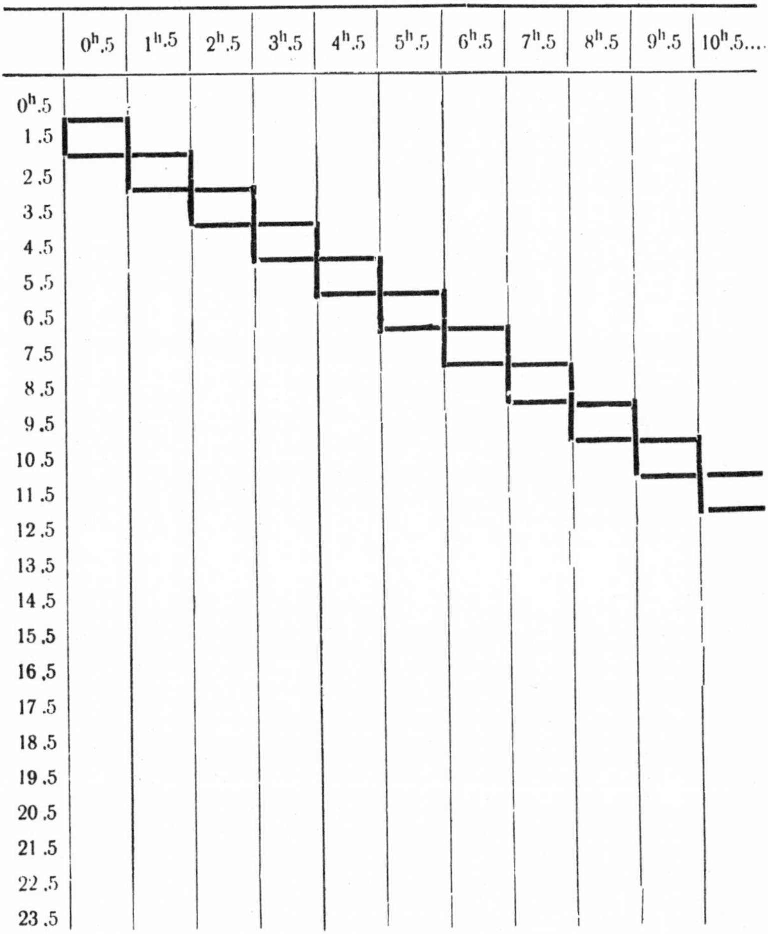

	$0^h.5$	$1^h.5$	$2^h.5$	$3^h.5$	$4^h.5$	$5^h.5$	$6^h.5$	$7^h.5$	$8^h.5$	$9^h.5$	$10^h.5$...
$0^h.5$											
1.5											
2.5											
3.5											
4.5											
5.5											
6.5											
7.5											
8.5											
9.5											
10.5											
11.5											
12.5											
13.5											
14.5											
15.5											
16.5											
17.5											
18.5											
19.5											
20.5											
21.5											
22.5											
23.5											

The work on the observations was first done on each cycle separately. The values of $\Delta\varphi$ obtained from the observations of each link are broken up, as explained already, into 24 groups according to argument 2☾. In order to exclude completely the effect of error in the declinations of the pairs

T A B L E 27

2☾ \ α	$0^h.5$	$1^h.5$	$2^h.5$	$3^h.5$	$4^h.5$	$5^h.5$	$6^h.5$	$7^h.5$	$8^h.5$	$9^h.5$	$10^h.5$	$11^h.5$	$12^h.5$
$0^h.5$	−10	−20	−42	+32	−52	+23	+46	+25	+24	−34	−12	+ 5	− 5
1.5	+ 2	+49	− 4	−56	−10	−16	−56	−37	− 7	+47	− 8	+23	−44
2.5	+40	+35	+18	− 4	−86	−20	− 7	+ 3	−19	+ 5	+14	−16	+30
3.5	+ 6	+11	+23	− 6	−43	−42	− 8	− 5	−36	−40	0	+26	− 4
4.5	+17	+ 1	+ 8	−43	− 1	−16	−63	− 5	−25	−16	−63	−31	−20
5.5	− 8	−30	+45	+39	+43	−34	+28	−15	+14	−11	−35	−73	−11
6.5	+ 5	+30	+ 4	+18	+42	−10	−46	−36	−22	−41	−38	−14	−14
7.5	+15	+17	+32	− 4	+13	−25	− 3	−18	−48	− 9	−27	−49	+ 2
8.5	+17	+24	+70	+16	−13	− 9	−37	−12	−30	−65	−31	+11	+ 8
9.5	+ 7	+ 5	+24	+54	+24	−14	−14	− 6	+19	+ 4	+39	+29	−26
10.5	−12	− 8	+17	+22	−14	+14	+14	− 8	+ 6	+36	+ 9	+ 2	− 3
11.5	+ 3	− 4	−10	−15	− 1	+27	+ 9	−30	−26	− 6	+14	−31	−12
12.5	+ 1	− 8	−44	− 0	+35	+ 8	+12	0	+37	− 1	+14	+ 1	−13
13.5	−19	−34	+26	−19	+18	+13	+49	+18	+33	+ 3	−19	+ 8	− 6
14.5	+21	+ 8	+ 9	+28	− 6	+ 4	+52	− 1	− 5	−26	+ 5	−47	−28
15.5	− 1	+ 7	+42	− 2	−17	+26	−49	− 2	−18	+10	+ 1	+10	+14
16.5	−10	+64	−40	−55	+13	+ 8	− 6	+44	+32	+13	+14	+22	+21
17.5	−59	+ 1	−20	+ 7	+29	−11	−10	−36	+15	+16	+40	−18	+41
18.5	− 8	−33	−44	−16	−42	−27	+37	0	+45	+12	+42	−53	+22
19.5	−14	−11	0	+ 6	+ 3	+36	+63	+27	− 5	+120	+31	+62	+23
20.5	+21	+ 8	−36	− 5	+ 5	−28	+16	+53	− 3	+31	+43	+61	+ 6
21.5	−60	−21	−46	+ 8	+ 4	−18	+22	+22	+17	− 4	−10	+26	+ 3
22.5	− 8	− 3	+20	− 5	+ 9	+21	+ 4	+ 3	− 7	+36	+33	+28	+22
23.5	+36	−19	−49	− 9	+22	+77	−31	+ 2	− 4	− 2	−25	+38	+23

that may occur in the combination of results of separate cycles, if the observations are not distributed evenly with respect to phase, we proceeded as follows. We took the mean for each column of Table 26. This mean we deducted from the values $\Delta\varphi$ in the separate cells of the column. After this we combined the results of observations of the first three cycles, and of the two later cycles, that is, we found the weighted mean of the three values $\Delta\varphi$, obtained for cycles I, II, III, and separately for the cycles IV and V. To allow for differences in the numbers of observations we gave weight 1 to the results of all cycles except cycle V at Carloforte and Ukiah, to which we gave weight 2. Thus we obtained two tables for each station, that is, six tables in all. We give here as an example one of these, the cycle 1900-1915 for Carloforte (Table 27). Under the heading "Diagonal Sum" is given in the first column ("Descending") the sum of the numbers

T A B L E 27 (continued)

$13^h.5$	$14^h.5$	$15^h.5$	$16^h.5$	$17^h.5$	$18^h.5$	$19^h.5$	$20^h.5$	$21^h.5$	$22^h.5$	$23^h.5$	Diagonal Sum		Phase
											Descending	Ascending	
+43	+40	+ 7	+33	− 7	+ 5	+15	+15	+27	+21	+29	− 65	− 20	0^h
+30	+ 9	+27	+ 7	− 1	+ 4	− 7	+ 4	+ 1	+ 4	+ 4	− 9	+125	1
−32	−43	−12	+27	+16	+ 7	+22	−15	+12	+ 2	+24	+ 79	− 61	2
+ 7	− 3	+ 7	−12	+31	+27	− 1	− 1	+29	+22	+19	+ 69	+118	3
+ 1	− 8	+16	− 6	−34	−16	+ 3	+ 5	+29	+18	+29	− 2	+227	4
−62	+40	− 2	+ 4	+16	− 9	+ 4	−18	− 5	+12	−23	+291	+ 65	5
−10	+32	+ 7	+16	+13	−12	0	−29	−13	− 7	−20	+290	+ 52	6
−43	−10	+13	+ 3	+ 7	+ 2	− 3	−15	−10	+23	+31	+175	+ 40	7
−21	+ 1	−38	−23	−24	− 7	−12	− 7	− 7	− 2	+ 6	+413	+ 74	8
+15	+ 3	+31	+24	−14	+25	+ 6	− 8	−15	+12	+11	+226	− 67	9
+43	−12	− 9	−10	+15	+ 1	+ 1	−15	−12	−27	− 1	+270	+ 61	10
+ 7	−15	+15	+ 6	− 7	−42	− 1	+12	−12	−21	−34	+ 71	+ 56	11
−39	− 6	+21	+ 8	+39	+17	+18	− 8	+20	−35	− 7	+ 13	− 77	12
+ 1	− 7	−38	+ 4	−32	+ 6	−15	− 1	+20	−64	− 8	+ 23	−154	13
−34	−19	−43	+10	+12	−10	+ 6	−11	+13	+10	− 5	− 36	−128	14
− 4	+17	− 5	−18	−17	−12	+17	+ 5	−39	−46	−23	− 23	−133	15
+24	− 4	+ 8	−14	−18	+ 3	−25	−16	− 5	− 7	+ 1	− 18	−126	16
+ 9	−13	−37	−25	+ 3	−20	−12	− 5	−23	+19	−21	−198	− 70	17
−16	− 1	+18	− 2	−18	+ 5	− 7	− 8	−17	− 8	−32	−292	+ 11	18
−11	+ 2	−25	−37	−14	−22	− 9	− 2	+ 3	+19	−12	−147	−184	19
+25	+ 8	+ 1	+25	− 1	+ 3	+ 6	−11	+11	−10	− 9	−242	+ 3	20
+37	−12	+12	+ 8	−12	+14	+21	+32	+24	− 3	−15	−176	+196	21
+37	+ 3	+10	+50	+40	+15	+ 5	+37	+11	+37	+24	−450	+ 21	22
− 6	+ 3	+21	−32	+20	−14	−20	+31	−12	+30	+32	−265	− 27	23

in the diagonal, going from the upper left corner of the table to the lower right corner, and in the column "Ascending" the sum of the numbers in the diagonal from the lower left corner to the upper right. Under the heading "Phase" we give the values of the phases of the arguments $2☾ - \alpha$ and $2☾ + \alpha$ corresponding to these sums. The values $\Delta\varphi$ in Table 27 are given in 0".01. The means, that is, these sums divided by 24, are given in Table 28 in the column headed $\Delta\varphi_m'$ for the cycle 1900-15 and $\Delta\varphi_m$ for the cycle 1916-34, expressed in 0".001.

22. Correction for the Nutation Term of Argument $2☾ - ☊$

The preliminary analysis of the values of $\Delta\varphi_m$ showed that the expressions for the lunar diurnal term obtained from the

TABLE 28

Phase	Carloforte			Mizusawa			Ukiah			Carlo-forte		Mizusawa	
	$\Delta\varphi'_m$	$\Delta\varphi_m$	O-C	$\Delta\varphi'_m$	$\Delta\varphi_m$	O-C	$\Delta\varphi'_m$	$\Delta\varphi_m$	O-C	$\Delta\varphi_m$	O-C	$\Delta\varphi_m$	O-C
	$2☾-\alpha$ (1900-1915)									$2☾-\alpha$ (1916--			
0^h	-3	-1	+2	-4	-2	+3	-2	0	+3	+7	+9	-6	-6
1	0	+2	+3	+3	+5	+3	+10	+12	+12	+2	+1	-20	-21
2	+3	+5	+3	-7	-5	-4	-4	-2	-5	+2	-1	+5	+3
3	-3	-1	-6	-4	-3	-4	-3	-1	-7	+10	+4	+14	+11
4	0	+1	-6	+10	+11	+9	+4	+6	-2	+5	-3	+6	+2
5	+12	+13	+4	+2	+2	-2	+5	+6	-3	+1	-8	+14	+10
6	+12	+13	+3	+2	+2	-4	+10	+10	0	+9	-1	+7	+3
7	+7	+7	-4	+3	+2	-5	+4	+5	-6	+10	0	+4	0
8	+17	+17	+6	+1	0	-7	+9	+9	-1	+8	-2	-3	-6
9	+9	+8	-2	+2	0	-7	+32	+32	+23	+16	+7	-9	-12
10	+11	+10	+2	+22	+21	+15	+5	+4	-4	+8	0	-6	-8
11	+3	+1	-5	+9	+7	+1	+4	+2	-3	-2	-7	+1	0
12	0	-2	-5	+20	+18	+13	+13	+11	+6	+2	0	+13	+13
13	+1	-1	-2	-2	-4	-7	-8	-11	-11	-2	-1	0	0
14	-2	-4	-2	+2	0	-1	+3	+1	+4	-1	+2	+5	+6
15	-1	-3	+2	+1	0	+1	-11	-13	-7	-2	+4	-20	-18
16	-1	-2	+5	-9	-10	-8	-2	-4	+4	-14	-6	-4	-1
17	-8	-9	0	-8	-8	-4	-7	-8	+1	+3	+12	+4	+8
18	-12	-13	-3	-16	-16	-10	-7	-7	+3	-10	0	-14	-10
19	-6	-6	+5	+6	+7	-14	-14	-14	-3	-21	-11	-6	-2
20	-10	-10	+1	-3	-2	+5	-3	-3	+7	-9	+1	+10	+13
21	-7	-6	+4	-10	-9	-2	-6	-5	+4	-17	-8	+10	+13
22	-19	-17	-9	-8	-6	+1	-21	-20	-12	-1	+7	-8	-6
23	-11	-9	-3	-16	-14	-8	+1	+3	+8	-7	-2	-5	-4

observations for 1899-1915 and 1916-1934 differed systematically. In trying to explain this discrepancy we paid attention to the fact that from 1916 some new nutation terms were brought into the formula giving the quantities A' and B' in the Berliner Jahrbuch. Among these are the following:

$$\Delta\delta = -0''.014 \sin(2☾ - ☊)\cos\alpha + 0''.018\cos(2☾ - ☊)\sin\alpha. \quad (3.4)$$

Since up to 1916 this term was not taken into account, in analysis of the variation of latitude there had to appear a fictitious term of argument $2☾ - ☊$. The introduction of the correction for this omitted nutation term in the initial data would require long additional calculations. However, we can dispense with them if we use the following method of approxi-

TABLE 28 (continued)

Ukiah		Carlo-forte		Mizusawa		Ukiah		Carlo-forte		Mizusawa		Ukiah	
$\Delta\varphi_m$	O-C	$\Delta\varphi_m$	O-C	$\Delta\varphi_m$	O-C	$\Delta\varphi_m$	O-C	$\Delta\varphi_m$	O-C	$\Delta\varphi_m$	O-C	$\Delta\varphi_m$	O-C
--1934)		2☾+α (1900–1915)						2☾+α (1916–1934)					
−9	−8	−1	−4	−6	−5	+1	+2	0	0	−8	−4	+1	−2
+2	0	−1	−3	+8	+9	−5	−3	+8	+9	−11	−6	+5	+3
+4	−1	+1	0	−13	−13	+5	+8	+5	+7	−26	−21	−2	−3
+11	+4	+8	+8	0	−1	0	+3	−4	−2	0	+5	−4	−4
+11	+2	0	+2	0	−1	−11	−7	−12	−9	0	+4	−2	−1
+2	−8	−7	−5	−3	−5	+2	+6	−12	−9	+2	+5	+3	+5
+13	+3	0	+3	+22	+20	−8	−4	0	+3	+5	+7	−1	+2
+6	−4	−3	+1	+2	−1	−1	+2	+3	+6	+1	+2	+7	+11
+13	+4	−5	−1	+3	0	+4	+6	−5	−2	+4	+4	−6	−2
+1	−7	−6	−2	−4	−6	−10	−8	−1	+1	−2	−3	−6	−2
+12	+6	−5	−1	+7	+5	0	+1	+1	+3	+4	+1	−7	−3
+9	+6	−6	−3	+5	+3	+6	+6	−2	−1	+1	−3	−5	−1
+1	−2	−3	0	−10	−11	+7	+6	−1	−1	−8	−12	−6	−3
+1	−3	+2	+4	−8	−9	−4	6	+5	+4	−3	−8	−9	−7
−12	−7	+2	+4	−2	−2	−2	−5	+2	0	+4	−1	+9	+10
−3	+4	−3	3	+9	+10	+10	+7	−2	−4	+12	+7	−5	−5
−7	+2	+2	+1	5	4	2	6	−1	−4	+19	+15	+1	5
−9	+1	+2	0	+6	+7	+11	+7	+7	+4	+9	+6	+4	+0
−25	−15	+2	−1	−3	−1	+8	+4	+6	+3	−8	−10	+12	+2
−4	+6	+2	−1	+2	+6	+4	−7	+1	−2	−12	−13	−1	−9
−10	−1	+9	+5	−3	0	−2	−4	+5	+2	−6	−6	+9	+5
+2	+10	+5	+1	−7	−5	+6	+4	+1	−1	+9	+10	−1	−5
0	+6	−3	−7	−4	−2	+8	+7	−8	−10	+11	+14	+9	+4
−2	+1	+5	+2	0	+2	−6	−6	+4	+3	0	+4	0	−4

mation, allowing for the introduction of the correction directly into the mean values $\Delta\varphi_m$. These corrections we denote by $\Delta\delta_m$.

We transform the expression (3.4) into the following form:

$$\Delta\delta = U\cos\text{☊} + V\sin\text{☊}, \tag{3.5}$$

where

$$\left.\begin{aligned} U &= -0''.016\sin(2☾-\alpha) - 0''.002\sin(2☾+\alpha) \\ V &= +0''.016\cos(2☾-\alpha) + 0''.002\cos(2☾+\alpha) \end{aligned}\right\}. \tag{3.6}$$

Starting from (3.5) we obtain the expression

$$\Delta\delta_m = U\frac{1}{n}\sum\cos\Omega + V\frac{1}{n}\sum\sin\Omega,$$

where n is the number of values of $\Delta\varphi$ from which the mean $\Delta\varphi_m$ is formed for the given group. Since the values are distributed over the phases Ω almost uniformly, we may replace summation by integration in the preceding formula, that is

$$\frac{1}{n}\sum\cos\Omega = \frac{1}{\Omega_1 - \Omega_0}\int_{\Omega_0}^{\Omega_1}\cos\Omega\, d\Omega$$

$$\frac{1}{n}\sum\sin\Omega = \frac{1}{\Omega_1 - \Omega_0}\int_{\Omega_0}^{\Omega_1}\sin\Omega\, d\Omega,$$

where Ω_1 and Ω_2 are the values of the longitude of the Moon's ascending node at the beginning and end of the cycle of observations. For the calculation of these values we took 1899.8 for the beginning of the cycle of observations at Carloforte and Ukiah, 1900.0 at Mizusawa; the end of the cycle for all these stations was 1916.0. After substitution of the numerical values we obtain finally for the correction for the nutation term of argument $2☾ - \Omega$: for Carloforte and Ukiah

$$\Delta\delta_m = +0''.0006\sin(2☾ - \alpha) + 0''.0020\cos(2☾ - \alpha), \qquad (3.7)$$

and for Mizusawa

$$\Delta\delta_m = +0''.0021\cos(2☾ - \alpha). \qquad (3.8)$$

The corrected values $\Delta\varphi'_m$ are in Table 28 under the heading $\Delta\varphi_m$.

23. Results

The values $\Delta\varphi_m$ of Table 28 may be put in the form

Cycle 1900-1915

Carloforte

$$\underset{\pm 11}{0''.0108}\sin(2☾ - \alpha \underset{\pm 6}{-18°}) + \underset{\pm 10}{0''.0040}\sin(2☾ + \alpha \underset{\pm 14}{+39°}),$$

Mizusawa

$$0''.0074 \sin(2☾ - \alpha - 39^\circ) + 0''.0024 \sin(2☾ + \alpha - 158^\circ),$$
$$\pm 22 \qquad\qquad \pm 17 \qquad\qquad \pm 21 \qquad\qquad \pm 46$$

Ukiah

$$0''.0104 \sin(2☾ - \alpha - 15^\circ) + 0''.0035 \sin(2☾ + \alpha - 16^\circ).$$
$$\pm 23 \qquad\qquad \pm 12 \qquad\qquad \pm 17 \qquad\qquad \pm 27$$

Cycle 1916-1934

Carloforte

$$0''.0105 \sin(2☾ - \alpha - 11^\circ) + 0''.0032 \sin(2☾ + \alpha - 2^\circ),$$
$$\pm 16 \qquad\qquad \pm 9 \qquad\qquad \pm 14 \qquad\qquad \pm 24$$

Mizusawa

$$0''.0041 \sin(2☾ - \alpha + 5^\circ) + 0''.0046 \sin(2☾ + \alpha - 63^\circ),$$
$$\pm 28 \qquad\qquad \pm 39 \qquad\qquad \pm 26 \qquad\qquad \pm 30$$

Ukiah

$$0''.0104 \sin(2☾ - \alpha - 3^\circ) + 0''.0043 \sin(2☾ + \alpha + 46^\circ).$$
$$\pm 17 \qquad\qquad \pm 9 \qquad\qquad \pm 15 \qquad\qquad \pm 18$$

The differences between the observed values and those calculated from these formulae, expressed in multiples of 0".001, are given in Table 28 in the column headed O - C. The numbers in these columns serve for the determination of the mean errors of the values found for the amplitude and initial phase of the lunar terms.

The expression for the lunar diurnal term may be written in the following form:

$$\Delta\varphi = M_1 \sin(2☾ - \alpha) + N_1 \cos(2☾ - \alpha) + M_2 \sin(2☾ + \alpha) + N_2 \cos(2☾ + \alpha), \qquad (3.9)$$

which is more convenient for the combination of the results of several series of observations. A summary of the values of the coefficients M_1, N_1, M_2, N_2 is given below in Table 29.

An important part of the calculations for the lunar diurnal term was carried out by Miss Ye. I. Yevtushenko, and the preliminary results of the calculations were published jointly by us.

24. Results of Investigations by Other Authors

The study of the lunar terms in the variation of latitude was until recently limited to derivation of the principal lunar semi-diurnal tidal term with argument $2☾ - 2S$, where S is local sidereal time. The first attempts to discover the lunar diurnal term were made, almost simultaneously and apparently independently, by Sekiguchi, Morgan and Popov. They, as well as I, have previously explained this term as an inexactitude in the fortnightly term. The fact that we now give it another explanation does not prevent us from using the results of these authors in the general discussion, which will be given in section 26.

In determining the coefficients of the lunar terms Sekiguchi had the following aim. He made a general revision of the deduction of the formulae of precession and nutation [49] and obtained calculated values of the coefficients, which, for some terms, differed from those found by Oppolzer [38]. Thus, for the fortnightly term we get according to Oppolzer

$$\Delta\delta = 0''.088 \sin\alpha \cos 2☾ - 0''.0081 \cos\alpha \sin 2☾$$

while Sekiguchi's result is

$$\Delta\delta = 0''.095 \sin\alpha \cos 2☾ - 0''.088 \cos\alpha \sin 2☾$$

or, in the form of (3.2),

$$\Delta\delta = -0''091 \sin(2☾ - \alpha) + 0'',003 \sin(2☾ + \alpha).$$

If the last expression is right and in the reduction to apparent place we take formula (3.2) there should appear a term

$$+0''.006 \sin(2☾ - \alpha).$$

To this we must add the lunar diurnal term of Oppolzer, accidentally coinciding for the absolutely rigid Earth with the last expression, so that we get for the sum

$$\Delta\varphi = 0''.012 \sin(2☾ - \alpha).$$

If such a term is discovered in the variation of latitude, then according to Sekiguchi it may be taken as showing that his theory of nutation is better than Oppolzer's. However we consider such a conclusion not valid, since the difference between the formulae is simply explained by a mistake made by Sekiguchi. This error (see introduction) was pointed out by Woolard [59].

As initial material for determining the amplitude of the lunar diurnal term, Sekiguchi used the data from Carloforte, Ukiah and Mizusawa from 1922 to 1934. The above remarks concern only the interpretation of the results. These on the whole agree sufficiently well with ours. We limit ourselves here to this remark and shall not put the result of Sekiguchi in the general summary, firstly since the observations of the ILS for 1922-34 are part of the more general material we used, and secondly because his method of reduction is open to some objections.

Morgan first announced the results of his study of the fortnightly term at the conference on astronomical constants at Paris, 1950 March 27-April 1. His results were based on the working out of the four-yearly series of observations with the P.Z.T. at Washington [34]. After this, fuller material was worked up; 13 yearly series of observations were used, but they were not taken consecutively but with some interruptions, so that the whole range embraces an interval of 19 years.

Morgan presents the lunar diurnal term in the form

$$\varphi_0 - \varphi = (\cos 2☾ \sin \alpha - 0.92 \sin 2☾ \cos \alpha)\,\Delta k$$

and determines from the observations the coefficient Δk. If we arrange this in the form

$$\varphi - \varphi_0 = 0.96\Delta k \sin(2☾ - \alpha) + 0.04\Delta k \sin(2☾ + \alpha),$$

we notice at once that this coefficient practically coincides with the coefficient M_1 in (3.9).

Morgan found

$$\Delta k = +0''.0067 \pm 0''.0020 \tag{3.10}$$

which coincides with the theoretical value of the coefficient of the corresponding term in Oppolzer's formula. On these grounds Morgan concluded that the lunar diurnal term in the variation of latitude of Washington is wholly caused by the forced motion of the pole, and therefore the coefficient of the fortnightly term does not require correction.

From Morgan's work we may take only the value of M_1; the results are given in such a form that it is not possible to calculate from them the coefficients of other terms in the expression (3.9).

From the analysis of observations of two bright zenith stars in Poltava, Popov deduced a result in contradiction with that of Morgan; he found in these observations clear evidence of fortnightly terms and explained them by an inaccuracy in the value taken for the amplitude of the fortnightly nutation term [13]. From 780 observations of α Persei and 925 of η Ursae Majoris he found respectively

$$\Delta\varphi_\alpha = 0''.028 \cos(2☾ + 232^\circ),$$
$$\Delta\varphi_\eta = 0''.034 \cos(2☾ + 29^\circ) .$$

If we give these expressions the form in which we put the lunar diurnal term, we have

$$\Delta\varphi_\alpha = 0''.028 \sin(2☾ - \alpha + 12^\circ),$$
$$\Delta\varphi_\eta = 0.034 \sin(2☾ - \alpha - 35^\circ) .$$

As we see, the amplitudes of these terms obtained by Popov are approximately twice as large as those which we obtained earlier. It is necessary, of course, to take into account the fact that his results contain also the principal lunar semi-diurnal tidal term, but it does not appear possible to attribute the striking difference to it. Nor, apparently, is it possible to explain it as due to the unreliability of Popov's results, since the separate reduction of three series of observations gave expressions for the lunar diurnal term agreeing well among themselves; hence the question of the causes of the anomalously large values of the amplitudes of these terms, obtained from the observations of bright zenith stars at Poltava, remains open until more general material has been collected and reduced.* For the time being in view of the relatively small number of observations we do not include Popov's results in the general résumé (see section 26).

Attempts have also been made to find a lunar diurnal term in the observations with two zenith telescopes in the common programme, which was initiated in Poltava in 1949 and which

---

*Such a reduction has now been completed by Popov and his new result is in good agreement with (3.13). - Note added by author.

is continued up to the present. A description of this programme is given in the reference [16]. Matveyev used as initial material the differences between the values obtained for the latitude from morning and evening observations for the first three years. As the mean from the two instruments he found [6],

$$\Delta\varphi = 0''.018 \sin(2☾ - \alpha - 29^{\circ}).$$
$$\pm 4 \qquad\qquad \pm 13$$

With the same observations, but over a somewhat longer period, Filippov, using a method similar to that which we used in analysing the ILS observations [20], found the following value for the term considered:

$$\Delta\varphi = 0''.0126 \sin(2☾ - \alpha + 8^{\circ}).$$
$$\pm 26 \qquad\qquad \pm 12$$

Finally we once more investigated the lunar diurnal term for the difference "evening minus morning", taking observations for six years. The result was:

$$\Delta\varphi = 0''.0090 \sin(2☾ - \alpha + 21^{\circ}).$$
$$\pm 30 \qquad\qquad \pm 19$$

To sum up, all the results indicate that, in the Poltava observations of the 1949 programme, there is actually found a lunar diurnal term with amplitude exceeding the corresponding term in Oppolzer's formula. However the number of observations from which these results were obtained is still insufficient for it to be right to include them in the general summary.

We give the expression for the lunar diurnal term deduced by Orlov from the observations with the zenith telescope at Pulkovo from 1915 to 1928 [9]:

$$\Delta\varphi = 0''.0127 \sin(2☾ - \alpha - 3^{\circ}) + 0''.0027 \sin(2☾ + \alpha - 56^{\circ}). \quad (3.11)$$
$$\pm 16 \qquad\qquad \pm 7 \qquad\qquad \pm 22 \qquad\qquad \pm 47$$

25. Correction for the Tidal Variation of the Vertical

Besides the forced motion of the pole the tidal variations of the vertical may be a cause of short-period variations of latitude. Their effect must be excluded, which may be done only by a calculation based on Tidal Theory. For an absolutely rigid Earth we have the following expression for the tidal variation of latitude:

$$\Delta\varphi = -\frac{1}{ag} \cdot \frac{\partial V}{\partial \varphi},$$

where a is the radius of the Earth, g is the acceleration due to gravity and V the potential of the tide-producing force. The latter is the sum of periodic terms of which we use only the one having the same period as the lunar diurnal term in which we are interested, that is O_1. We put in the preceding equation the following expression for this term

$$-9.86 \sin 2\varphi \sin (2☾ - \alpha);$$

then

$$\Delta\varphi = +0''.0065 \cos 2\varphi \sin (2☾ - \alpha). \qquad (3.12)$$

In order to obtain the value of $\Delta\varphi$ for an elastically deformed Earth it is sufficient to multiply the expression by some coefficient d depending on the mechanical properties of the Earth, which can only be calculated roughly. Apparently d is somewhat greater than 1, and we shall take it as 1.1; then from (3.12) we find the following expression for the tidal variation of latitude (the O_1 term in tidal notation).

	φ	$\Delta\varphi$
Carloforte, Mizusawa, Ukiah	39°8'	$+0''.0015 \sin (2☾-\alpha)$
Washington	38°55'	$+0''.0016 \sin (2☾-\alpha)$
Pulkovo	59°46'	$-0''.0035 \sin (2☾-\alpha)$

These values of $\Delta\varphi$ must be subtracted from the expressions of the lunar diurnal variation of the latitude that we found earlier from analysis of the observations.

26. Final Expression for the Lunar Diurnal Term in the Variation of Latitude

For the most probable values of the coefficients M_1, N_1, M_2, N_2 in (3.9) we take the results that we have obtained from the ILS observations and also those of Morgan and Orlov.

These results are given in Table 29. Column 4 has the value of M_1 found directly from observation, but column 5 its value corrected for the influence of the tidal variation of the vertical. The calculation was carried out in two ways. In the first the weights of the individual values were taken proportional to the numbers of observations of the corresponding series and denoted by P. In the second the weights were taken inversely proportional to the standard errors. Since the errors of the values of M_1 and N_1 are always taken equal, for these we give a single weight p_1. Similarly for M_2 and N_2 we take weight p_2.

The first method gives

$$M_1 = +0''.0086 \pm 0''.0014, \quad N_1 = -0''.0019 \pm 0''.0006,$$
$$M_2 = +0''.0021 \pm 0''.0007, \quad N_2 = +0''.0001 \pm 0''.0010.$$

The errors were determined from the deviations of the separate values of the coefficients from the weighted means given above.

The second gives

$$M_1 = +0''.0091 \pm 0''.0006, \quad N_1 = -0''.0023 \pm 0''.0006,$$
$$M_2 = +0''.0026 \pm 0''.0006, \quad N_2 = +0''.0007 \pm 0''.0006.$$

Here the mean errors were calculated from the separate errors of measurements unequal in accuracy [see for example, A.S. Chebotarev, Method of Least Squares (Sposob naimen'shikh kvadratov), Scientific and Technical Printing Office, U.S.S.R. 1936, section 29].

Corresponding to the two methods of calculation we find the following expressions for the lunar daily term

$$\Delta\varphi = \underset{\pm 13}{0''.0088} \sin(2☾ - \alpha - \underset{\pm 8}{12^\circ}) + \underset{\pm 7}{0''.0021} \sin(2☾ + \alpha + \underset{\pm 19}{3^\circ}),$$
$$\Delta\varphi = \underset{\pm 6}{0''.0094} \sin(2☾ - \alpha - \underset{\pm 4}{15^\circ}) + \underset{\pm 6}{0''.0027} \sin(2☾ + \alpha + \underset{\pm 13}{15}).$$

After replacing the right ascension α of the observed pair by the local sidereal time S we get finally

$$\Delta\varphi = -0''.009 \sin(S - 2☾ + 14^\circ) + 0''.002 \sin(S + 2☾). \quad (3.13)$$

TABLE 29

Observatory	Cycle of observations	Number of observations, in thousands	M_1	M_1'
Carloforte	1900—1915	36	+0",0103	+0",0088
"	1916—1934	31	+ ,0103	+ ,0088
Mizisawa	1900—1915	21	+ ,0057	+ ,0042
"	1916—1934	23	+ ,0040	+ ,0025
Ukiah	1900—1915	28	+ ,0104	+ ,0089
"	1916—1934	37	+ ,0104	+ ,0089
Washington	1931—1951	28	+ ,0067	+ ,0051
Pulkovo	1915—1928	28	+ ,0127	+ ,0162

Then the equation for the lunar diurnal forced motion of the pole may be written

$$\left.\begin{array}{l} x = -0''.009 \sin(S_0 - 2☾ + 14^\circ) + 0''.002 \sin(S_0 + 2☾) \\ y = -0''.009 \cos(S_0 - 2☾ + 14^\circ) + 0''.002 \cos(S_0 + 2☾) \end{array}\right\}, \quad (3.14)$$

where S_0 is Greenwich sidereal time.

In section 6 we gave the equations of this motion found theoretically on the assumption that the Earth is a perfectly elastic body. They also contained terms with arguments $S_0 - 2☾$ and $S_0 + 2☾$, representing circular motions with periods of 1.079 and 0.932 days. However the radius of the path of the pole in the second motion does not reach 0".0006, so that the lunar terms in (1.38) give, essentially, simply a motion of the pole in a circle of radius 0".005 with period 1.079 days.

Equations (3.14), obtained by analysis of a vast amount of observational material, show that in reality the forced oscillation of the pole that we have considered takes place somewhat differently. First, the motion with period 1.079 sidereal days takes place in a circle, but the radius is almost twice the theoretical one, nearly 0".009. Secondly, all the series of observations that we have considered, with the exception of Mizusawa 1916-34, give negative values of N_1. This suggests that in fact the initial phase of the motion considered is not zero, as assumed in the theory.

TABLE 29 (continued)

N_1	ε_1	M_2	N_2	ε_2	P	p_1	p_2
−0″.0034	+0″.0011	+0″.0031	+0″.0025	±″0.0010	4	8	10
− .0021	.0016	+ .0032	− .0001	.0015	3	4	5
− .0047	.0022	− .0022	− .0009	.0021	2	2	2
+ .0003	.0028	+ .0021	− 0041	.0026	2	1	2
− .0027	.0023	+ .0034	− .0010	.0017	3	2	3
− .0005	.0017	+ .0030	+ .0031	.0015	4	3	4
−	.0020	−	−	−	3	2	−
− .0007	.0016	+ .0015	+ .0022	.0022	3	4	2

Finally, the observations show a second circular motion of the pole of period 0.932 sidereal days, which would be impossible if the path of the pole in this motion had the theoretical value of 0".0006.

CHAPTER IV

SOME CONCLUSIONS ABOUT THE INTERACTION BETWEEN THE CORE AND SHELL OF THE EARTH

27. Short Historical Introduction

The results of the preceding chapters indicate that there really are some discrepancies between the results of the theory of the rotation of an ideally elastic Earth and the data of astronomical observations. The cause of these discrepancies must be sought in the assumptions embodied in the theory, and the Earth in fact cannot be perfectly elastic.

The next step must naturally be to examine some assumptions about the mechanical properties of the Earth. To decide what assumptions to test we must first consider all the combinations of data about the inner layers of the Earth that can at present be considered reliable.

The fact that transverse seismic waves either do not penetrate the Earth's core, or, if they do penetrate it, are quickly damped, has been interpreted by many geophysicists as evidence that the core is liquid. This naturally raises the question of the effect of fluidity of the core on the Earth's rotation. This question actually arose long before research began on the propagation of seismic waves in the interior of the Earth. The first to undertake it seriously was Hopkins in the 1830s, but his memoirs, published in 1839, 1840 and 1842 have now only historical interest. Somewhat later, W.Thomson considered the problem, and in particular pointed out that the effect would noticeably increase the semiannual and especially the fortnightly nutation. His result, published without proof, was confirmed by later workers.

The problem of a rotating Earth, consisting of an absolutely rigid shell and liquid core, was first considered with the necessary rigour and completeness by Sloudsky [53], who used the earlier work of Joukowsky [1]. At the same time as Sloudsky, Hough [28] considered the problem but examined only the free oscillation. He was followed by Steklov [47].

In 1910 Poincaré published his investigation of the precession of a deformable Earth [39]. Considering the case of a rigid shell and liquid core, he reached equations that differed only in form from those found by Sloudsky.

From 1910 to 1948, as far as we know, nothing was published on the effect of a liquid core on the Earth's rotatory motion. Meanwhile the development of seismology gave fundamental information about the inner structure of the Earth. In an essential way our understanding of the nature of the core changed. The hypothesis of a liquid interior was advanced originally to explain volcanic eruptions and the geothermal gradient. In the last century supporters of this hypothesis imagined the Earth as a liquid mass, with a thin crust whose thickness was of the order of 10 km.

Now we believe in a solid shell going to a depth of about 2900 km, with a liquid core inside it. We have sufficiently reliable data on the size, mass, density and compressibility of the core. This enabled Jeffreys in two recent papers to give not only a qualitative but also a quantitative estimate of the dynamical effect of the core. He had in mind the explanation of the known discrepancy between the theoretical and observed values of the nutation constant. In the first paper [30] he used Lamb's equations and Bullen's values of the moments of inertia of the core and shell and neglected the elastic deformation of the shell. He found that on these assumptions the constant of nutation is less than the value for an absolutely rigid Earth. While the latter, from the work of Spencer Jones, is equal to 9".227, that for the Earth with a liquid core was found to be 9".172.

In the second paper [31] Jeffreys took into account the effect of elasticity of the shell and obtained the theoretical value 9".181. Moreover, he found that the coefficients of the principal nutation in obliquity and longitude are affected in different ratios by the core, so that the ratio of the axes of the nutation ellipse needs a correction Δn = -0".003.

Our results do not confirm the latter conclusion, although the correction Δn found by Jeffreys is large enough for it to be disclosed in analysis of the observations.

This last work of Jeffreys is apparently the only attempt to take account of the influence both of the motion of the core and of the elastic deformation of the shell. However this model, having a homogeneous incompressible liquid core in an envelope homogeneous in its mechanical properties, is so simplified that the comparison of his results with observation has no great weight.*

In the works of Joukowsky and Sloudsky an attempt had been made to take into account the viscosity of the core. This problem has been considered recently by Sekiguchi [52] and by Bondi and Lyttleton [21]. The authors of the latter work used the methods of the modern theory of the motion of a viscous fluid, but they, like Sekiguchi, consider only the case of a spherical core boundary.

From our short summary it is clear that investigation of the effect of the Earth's core on its rotary motion has up to the present time borne the character of solution of certain particular problems. We have not yet a general theory developed to a point where a strict test can be made by comparison with observation. However for the future development of such a theory it is useful to know what sort of observed peculiarities it has to explain.

28. Determination of the Moments of the Forces, exerted on the Shell by the Core

Our results allow us to draw some conclusions about the forces exerted by the core on the shell. Without knowing the nature of these forces, we attempt to determine their moment.

The equation for the rotary motion of the shell may be written in the form

$$\dot{\mathbf{G}}_s = \mathbf{L}_s + \mathbf{M}, \tag{4.1}$$

where $\mathbf{G}_s$ is the angular momentum, $\mathbf{L}_s$ the moment of the forces due to the Sun and Moon, $\mathbf{M}$ the moment of the forces due to the core. As before we denote the whole angular momentum of the Earth by $\mathbf{G}$. The derivative of $\mathbf{G}$ with respect to the time is, as we have seen, a vector in the plane of the equator.

*In two papers, published later by H.Jeffreys and R.O.Vicente, inhomogeneity of the Earth's core and shell is taken into account. - Translator.

Then we can represent it by the complex magnitude

$$\dot{\mathbf{G}} = G(\sin\Theta\dot{\psi} + i\dot{\Theta}). \tag{4.2}$$

We have already met this formula in section 1, but there $\dot{\mathbf{G}}$ was put in the form of a vector product $\Omega \wedge \mathbf{G}$ and before the first term on the right there was a - sign. This is explained by the fact that in Chapter I we consistently used a right-handed set of axes. We now use the more usual astronomical method of taking a counter-clockwise motion positive, thus changing the sign of $\dot{\psi}$.

We write the following theoretical expressions for the sum of the principal and fortnightly terms in longitude and obliquity:

$$\left.\begin{aligned} \sin\Theta\psi &= -6''.869 \sin ☊ - 0''.0812 \sin 2☾ \\ \Theta - \Theta_0 &= +9''.220 \cos ☊ + 0''.0884 \cos 2☾ \end{aligned}\right\} . \tag{4.3}$$

For obvious reasons we use the value of the constant of nutation based on the known relation between this constant, the dynamical ellipticity H and the ratio of the mass of the Moon to that of the Earth,

$$N = 231981''.8H\frac{\mu}{1+\mu} .$$

We took $N = 9''.220$ and with this value calculated the other coefficients, and in the second term on the right of (4.3) we took them to a greater number of figures than in the first, since the observations give the expression for the fortnightly term somewhat more accurately.

If there were no interaction between the core and the shell, that is, if the moment $\mathbf{M}$ in (4.1) could be taken as zero, then we should have

$$\dot{\mathbf{G}}_s = hG_s(\sin\Theta\dot{\psi} + i\dot{\Theta}), \tag{4.4}$$

in which h is the ratio of the dynamical ellipticity of the shell to that for the whole Earth. Then (4.4) can be substituted for $\mathbf{L}_s$ in (4.1).

Since the observer is always connected with the shell, the equation of nutation derived from astronomical observations will describe just the vector $\mathbf{G}_s$. We take here only the 19-yearly and fortnightly parts of this motion.

The expression for the principal nutation term may be obtained from the coefficients and the corrections found in section 18, or we may take directly (2.44), from which it follows that

$$\left.\begin{aligned} \sin\Theta\psi_r &= -6''.850 \sin \Omega + 0''.008 \cos \Omega + F_\psi \\ \Theta_r &= +9''.198 \cos \Omega - 0''.001 \sin \Omega + F_\Theta \end{aligned}\right\}. \tag{4.5}$$

Here F_ψ and F_Θ are the sums of all remaining terms entering the formulae.

In order to find the fortnightly term, we use the results of section 26, that is, the following equation for the lunar diurnal term (first method of solution):

$$\Delta\varphi = +0''.0086 \sin(2☾ - \alpha) - \\ -0''.0019 \cos(2☾ - \alpha) + 0''.0021 \sin(2☾ + \alpha). \tag{4.5a}$$

We deduct from this the theoretical expression for the lunar diurnal term that we found in Chapter I for a perfectly elastic Earth,

$$0''.0051 \sin(2☾ - \alpha).$$

The remainder, namely

$$0''.0035 \sin(2☾ - \alpha) - 0''.0019 \cos(2☾ - \alpha) + 0''.0021 \sin(2☾ + \alpha), \tag{4.6}$$

we may now regard as the difference between two expressions for the fortnightly nutation of the shell: that adopted for reduction to apparent place, and the result obtained directly from astronomical observations. This is founded on the following considerations.

The equation of motion of the angular momentum of the Earth in space remains the same for any assumption about the mechanical properties of the Earth, but this need not be true for the angular momentum of the shell alone. Conversely, since the shell is an elastic body, we may take it that the vector $\mathbf{G}_s$ behaves relative to the shell according to the theory of the rotation of a perfectly elastic body, that is, according to (1.35). Now, when we consider the motion of the shell, we need not change the theoretical equation for the forced variation of latitude, and the difference between the results of theory and the observational data may be ascribed to inexactitude of the theoretical expression for the fortnightly nutation of the shell, which, taking the values of the coefficients given by Woolard [59], we write as

$$\Delta\delta = -0''.0811 \sin 2☾ \cos\alpha + 0''.0884 \cos 2☾ \sin\alpha. \qquad (4.7)$$

Taking (4.6) from (4.7) we have

$$(-0''.0866 \sin 2☾ + 0''.0019 \cos 2☾) \cos\alpha + \\ + (0\ .0894 \cos 2☾ + 0\ .0019 \sin 2☾) \sin\alpha\ .$$

Combining this result with (4.5) and discarding all the remaining nutation terms (since these are also excluded in the subsequent transformations) we find*

$$\left.\begin{aligned} \sin\Theta\psi_r &= -6''.850 \sin ☊ + 0''.008 \cos ☊ - \\ &\quad - 0''.0866 \sin 2☾ + 0''.0019 \cos 2☾ \\ \Theta_r &= +9''.198 \cos ☊ - 0''.001 \sin ☊ + \\ &\quad + 0''.0894 \cos 2☾ + 0''.0019 \sin 2☾ \end{aligned}\right\}. \qquad (4.8)$$

We may now determine $\dot{\mathbf{G}}_s$ from observation, putting (4.8) in (4.9),

$$\dot{\mathbf{G}}_s = G_s (\sin\Theta\dot{\psi}_r + i\dot{\Theta}_r)\ . \qquad (4.9)$$

Since the vector **M** lies in the equatorial plane it may be written as $X + iY$, and using (4.1) we may write

$$X + iY = G_s [\sin\Theta (\dot{\psi}_r - h\dot{\psi}) + i(\dot{\Theta}_r - h\dot{\Theta})]\ . \qquad (4.10)$$

It is of interest to compare with this expression what we should obtain for full coupling between core and shell, that is, for a rigid core. The moment of the forces exerted by the core in this case we denote by $X' + iY'$. In this case $\mathbf{G}_s$ and **G** are practically collinear. Then for substitution in (4.2) we must take the theoretical expression for the nutation (4.3). Then we obtain

$$X' + iY' = G_s (1 - h)(\sin\Theta\dot{\psi} + i\dot{\Theta}). \qquad (4.11)$$

---

*Fedorov informs us in a letter that the $2☾ - \alpha$ terms in these expressions are wrong. For the whole displacement of the shell the correction (4.5a) should be subtracted directly from the theoretical value (4.7), since (4.7) has been used as the trial value. Thus the term 0".0051 sin $(2☾ - \alpha)$ should be restored and the terms -0."0866 sin 2☾ and +0".0894 cos 2☾ in (4.8) should read -0".0918 sin 2☾ and +0".0949 cos 2☾. - Translator.

In order to calculate h we used the following data on the moments of inertia of the core A_n and C_n taken from Bullen [35]:

$$\varepsilon = \frac{C_n - A_n}{A_n} = 0.00260, \quad \eta = \frac{A_n}{A} = 0.112, \tag{4.12}$$

and we find h = 1.027. We now put (4.3) in (4.11) and write ☊ and 2☾ as

$$☊ = \alpha t, \quad 2☾ = \beta t$$

where $\alpha = -0.000146n$, $\beta = 0.073n$, and n is the angular velocity of rotation of the Earth. Then we find

$$X' + iY' = \alpha G_s (0''.217 e^{i\alpha t} - 0''.032 e^{-i\alpha t}) + \\ + \beta G_s (0''.0023 e^{i\beta t} - 0''.0001 e^{-i\beta t}).. \tag{4.13}$$

The moment of the force arising from the principal nutation may therefore be written as the sum of two vectors

$$\mathbf{U}_1 = 0''.217 \alpha G_s e^{i\alpha t}, \quad \mathbf{U}_2 = -0''.032 \alpha G_s e^{-i\alpha t}.$$

Since α is negative the first vector rotates in the plane clockwise and the other counterclockwise. Relative to the Earth, the two vectors rotate with angular velocities $-n + \alpha$ and $-n - \alpha$ respectively.

The moment arising from the fortnightly nutation can also be expressed as the sum of two vectors:

$$\mathbf{V}_1 = 0''.0023 \beta G_s e^{i\beta t}, \quad \mathbf{V}_2 = -0''.0001 \beta G_s e^{-i\beta t};$$

further, substituting (4.3) and (4.8) in (4.10) we find

$$X + iY = \alpha G_s (0''.236 e^{i\alpha t} - 0''.035 e^{-i\alpha t} + 0''.004 i e^{i\alpha t} - 0''.004 i e^{-i\alpha t}) + \\ + \beta G_s (-0''.0010 e^{i\beta t} - 0''.0024 e^{-i\beta t} + 0''.0019 i e^{i\beta t}) = \\ = (1.09 + 0.02i)\mathbf{U}_1 + (1.09 + 0.13i)\mathbf{U}_2 + \\ + (-0.43 + 0.83i)\mathbf{V}_1 + 24\mathbf{V}_2.. \tag{4.14}$$

We do not think it possible on the basis of these results to give a quantitative estimate of the effect of the fluidity of the core on the reaction between the core and the shell. However, some qualitative conclusions can be drawn. Among these the following appear to be the most reliable.

1. The modulus of the vector $\mathbf{U}_1$ is increased.

2. The vector $\mathbf{V}_1$ reverses its direction.
3. The vectors $\mathbf{U}_1$ and $\mathbf{U}_2$ are deflected in the sense opposite to the direction of rotation of these vectors relative to the Earth.

29. Comparison with the Theory of Sloudsky and Poincaré

The results 1 and 2 just given (section 28) seem at first sight to be contradictory. However, this contradiction is easily explained if we use even the simplest form of the theory of the rotation of the Earth with a liquid core as developed by Sloudsky and Poincaré. There is an account in Lamb's Hydrodynamics. We use for the calculation of the moment the equations as given by Lamb *

$$\left.\begin{array}{l} A\dot{\omega}+F\dot{\omega}_n-i(C-A)n\omega+iFn\omega_n=ke^{i\sigma t} \\ F\dot{\omega}+A_n\dot{\omega}_n+iC_n n\omega_n=0 \end{array}\right\}. \tag{4.15}$$

Here

$$\omega=p+iq, \quad \omega_n=p_n+iq_n \tag{4.16}$$

where p, q are the components of the angular velocity of rotation of the Earth about perpendicular equatorial axes rigidly fixed to the shell; p_n, q_n are the components of the angular velocity of the core relative to the shell. (Here by rotation we mean "elliptical rotation" as Joukowsky [1] uses the term; and F is a quantity of the dimensions of a moment of inertia and in this case is equal to $A_n\sqrt{1-\varepsilon^2}$.

We put

$$\gamma=\frac{C_n-A_n}{C-A}\ . \tag{4.17}$$

(4.15) can be transformed to

$$A_s\dot{\omega}-i(C_s-A_s)n\omega=(1-\gamma)ke^{i\sigma t}+X+iY,.$$

where C_s, A_s are the principal moments of inertia of the shell. Hence we find

$$X+iY=\gamma ke^{i\sigma t}-A\dot{\omega}-F\dot{\omega}_n+i(C_n-A_n)n\omega-iFn\omega_n\ , \tag{4.18}$$

If there is no relative motion of the core $\omega_n=0$ and

* Lamb, Hydrodynamics, 6th edition, p.726, Cambridge University Press (1932).

$$X' + iY' = \gamma k e^{i\sigma t} - A_n\omega + i(C_n - A_n)n\omega. \tag{4.19}$$

The solution of (4.15) is

$$\omega = -\frac{A_n\sigma + C_n n}{\Delta(\sigma)} ike^{i\sigma t}, \quad \omega_n = \frac{F\sigma}{\Delta(\sigma)} ike^{i\sigma t}, \tag{4.20}$$

where

$$\Delta\sigma = \begin{vmatrix} A\sigma - (C - A)n & F(\sigma + n) \\ F\sigma & A_n\sigma + C_n n \end{vmatrix}. \tag{4.21}$$

Substitution of these values of ω and ω_n in (4.19) and (4.20) and some re-arrangement gives

$$\frac{X}{X'} = \frac{Y}{Y'} = 1 + s(\sigma + n), \tag{4.22}$$

$$s = \frac{F^2\sigma}{S}, \tag{4.23}$$

$$S = \gamma\Delta(\sigma) - (A_n\sigma + C_n n)[A_n\sigma - (C_n - A_n)n]. \tag{4.24}$$

With the help of (4.12) we can express the moments of inertia of the core in terms of the greatest moment of inertia of the Earth as follows

$$A_n = \eta(1 - H)C = 0.1116C,$$
$$C_n = \eta(1 - H)(1 + \varepsilon)C = 0.1119C,$$
$$F^2 = \eta^2(1 - H)^2(1 - \varepsilon^2)C^2 = 0.0124C^2,$$
$$\gamma = \frac{\eta(1 - H)}{H}\varepsilon = 0.0884$$

We substitute these numerical values in (4.22) to (4.25) and obtain for the principal and fortnightly nutation terms the following results:

Quantity	Principal nutation vector $\mathbf{U}_1$	Fortnightly nutation vector $\mathbf{V}_1$
σ	$(-1-0{,}000146)\,n$	$(-1+0{,}073)\,n$
$\Delta(\sigma)$	$-0{,}00028n^2C^2$	$-0{,}00695n^2C^2$
S	$+0.00001n^2C^2$	$+0.00026n^2C^2$
sn	-1400	-44
$1+s(\sigma+n)$	$+1.20$	-2.21

We see that the effect of the fluidity of the core must produce an increase of the vector $\mathbf{U}_1$ and a reversal of the direction of $\mathbf{V}_1$. It is natural to suppose that the deflexions of $\mathbf{U}_1$ and $\mathbf{U}_2$ in the sense of the diurnal rotation of the Earth are explained by friction at the boundary of the core.

We cannot expect quantitative agreement between these theoretical results and those derived from observation, because the model of the Earth used in the theory is a gross simplification; in it no account is taken of the elasticity of the shell and the viscosity of the core. At the same time, the effect of the core on the motion of the shell is probably not limited to that of mechanical forces over its boundary; an important role may be played by other forces, for example, those of a magnetic nature.

APPENDIX

Table 30 in this appendix shows the successive stages in the correction of the initial data with the object of putting them in a form suitable for harmonic analysis.

Principal Steps	Results given in column
Values of F_1 calculated according to (2.11)	4
Correction for declination and right ascension according to (2.13)	5
Reduction of observational data to a common system of declinations and right ascensions, introduction of the correction for aberration due to Jupiter and Saturn and for the small nutation terms and also the change of phase of the annual z-term at the mean time of observation of the group	6
Correction for inaccuracy in the value taken for R	7
Elimination of the slowly varying terms in F_3, common to all pairs	8
Elimination of the constant part and linear variations (first approximation)	9
Elimination of periodic terms (first approximation)	10
Elimination of constant part and linear variations (second approximation)	11

All quantities given in columns 4-11 of Table 30 are expressed in 0".001.

TABLE 30

k	☊ − α	☊ + α	F_1	$D\delta$	F_2	F_3	F_4	F_5	F_6	F_7
1	2	3	4	5	6	7	8	9	10	11
					Pair 1					
6	8^h	9^h	+882	+118	+ 989	+ 995	+ 990	+ 8	+12	+ 6
7	7	7	856	112	962	958	962	−22	−14	−24
8	6	6	897	106	999	971	979	− 8	+ 3	−10
9	4	5	931	100	1031	967	975	−15	− 3	−17
10	3	3	928	94	1028	984	992	0	+13	− 1
11	2	2	892	88	986	956	964	−30	−18	−31
12	1	1	929	154	1089	1030	1037	+40	+51	+39
13	23	0	920	156	1083	1002	1007	+ 7	+12	+ 6
14	22	22	927	158	1090	1002	1003	+ 1	+ 3	0
15	21	21	911	160	1071	985	981	−23	−25	−24
16	19	20	980	162	1135	1055	1048	+41	+34	+40
17	18	18	940	164	1101	1030	1025	+15	+ 4	+15
18	17	17	875	166	1039	978	988	−24	−36	−24
19	16	16	859	168	1021	974	1001	−13	−27	−13
20	14	15	800	170	964	928	974	−43	−54	−43
21	13	13	761	172	937	912	969	−51	−62	−51
22	12	12	737	268	1007	1005	1055	+33	+25	+33
23	11	11	757	260	1023	1022	1062	+38	+33	+38
24	9	9	754	252	1014	1015	1051	+24	+26	+25
25	8	8	748	244	999	1001	1037	+ 7	+12	+ 8
26	7	7	804	236	1045	1047	1082	+50	+58	+51
27	5	6	744	228	974	977	1009	−25	−14	−24
28	4	4	744	220	961	964	994	−43	−29	−42
29	3	3	787	212	995	998	1030	−10	+ 3	− 9
30	1	2	818	204	1016	1019	1053	+11	+21	+12
31	0	0	813	196	1003	1005	1043	− 1	+ 7	+ 1
32	23	23	803	188	988	990	1032	−15	−10	−13
33	22	22	841	180	1019	1021	1064	+14	+16	+16
34	20	21	+801	+172	+ 971	+ 972	+1015	−37	−41	−35
					Pair 2					
0	16	17	+867	+106	+ 971	+ 939	+ 909	−60	−57	−47
1	15	15	909	104	1007	984	954	−18	−21	− 9
2	13	14	910	102	1004	989	959	−17	−22	−12
3	12	13	878	100	977	969	939	−40	−48	−39
4	11	11	930	98	1027	1023	995	+12	+ 2	+ 9
5	9	10	890	96	983	982	963	−23	−32	−30
6	8	9	963	96	1048	1050	1045	+56	+60	+60
7	7	8	904	94	992	991	995	+ 2	+ 9	+ 7
8	6	6	936	92	1024	1020	1028	+32	+43	+38
9	4	5	933	90	1023	1017	1025	+25	+37	+33
10	3	4	939	88	1033	1032	1040	+37	+49	+46
11	2	2	891	86	983	984	992	−14	− 2	− 4
12	0	1	941	65	1012	1020	1027	+17	+25	+ 6
13	23	0	934	60	1001	1021	1026	+13	+18	+ 1
14	22	23	913	55	973	1006	1007	−10	− 8	+ 3
15	20	21	929	50	979	1025	1021	+ 1	− 3	+15
16	19	20	889	45	927	986	979	−44	−51	−29
17	18	19	957	40	994	1065	1060	+33	−23	+49
18	17	17	860	35	893	975	985	−45	−57	−28
19	15	16	886	30	910	1002	1029	− 5	−17	+14
20	14	15	827	25	846	948	994	−43	−54	−23
21	13	14	+809	+ 20	+ 833	+ 944	+1001	−39	−49	−18

TABLE 30 (Contd.)

k	☊ $-\alpha$	☊ $+\alpha$	F_1	D☊	F_2	F_3	F_4	F_5	F_6	F_7
1	2	3	4	5	6	7	8	9	10	11
					Pair 3					
0	16^h	17^h	+876	+122	+ 996	+ 960	+ 930	−23	−20	−21
1	14	16	911	118	1023	997	967	+ 8	+ 8	+ 7
2	13	14	940	114	1046	1029	999	+34	+29	+29
3	12	13	878	110	987	978	948	−23	−31	−31
4	10	12	919	106	1024	1019	991	+14	+ 7	+ 2
5	9	10	909	102	1008	1007	988	+ 5	− 4	−10
6	8	9	908	92	989	991	986	− 3	+ 1	− 7
7	7	8	896	88	978	977	981	−14	− 7	−16
8	5	6	901	84	981	974	982	−19	− 8	−20
9	4	5	947	80	1027	1015	1023	+16	+28	+17
10	3	4	940	76	1022	1016	1024	+11	+23	+13
11	1	3	869	72	947	945	953	−66	−57	−62
12	0	1	920	73	999	1000	1007	−18	−10	−13
13	23	0	937	72	1016	1025	1030	− 1	+ 4	+ 6
14	22	23	976	71	1052	1072	1073	+36	+38	+44
15	20	21	915	70	985	1017	1013	−30	−34	−20
16	19	20	929	69	991	1035	1028	−21	−28	−10
17	18	19	974	68	1039	1095	1090	+35	+25	+48
18	16	18	835	67	900	967	977	−84	−95	70
19	15	16	961	66	1021	1098	1125	+58	+46	+74
20	14	15	861	65	920	1007	1053	−20	−31	− 3
21	13	14	+857	+ 64	+ 925	+1021	+1078	− 1	−11	+18
					Pair 5					
0	15	17	+820	+ 78	+ 896	+ 879	+ 849	−68	−63	−56
1	14	16	885	72	951	940	910	− 9	− 9	− 1
2	12	15	895	66	953	947	917	− 3	− 4	+ 1
3	11	14	917	60	976	973	943	+21	+17	+21
4	10	12	953	54	1006	1005	977	+53	+45	+48
5	9	11	921	48	965	966	947	+17	+ 8	+ 8
6	7	10	876	38	903	903	898	−29	−24	−27
7	6	8	895	32	921	921	925	− 4	+ 5	− 1
8	5	7	864	26	886	890	898	−33	−23	−29
9	3	6	910	20	930	944	952	+20	+29	+24
10	2	4	918	14	938	952	960	+26	+36	+31
11	1	3	919	+ 8	933	945	953	+17	+26	+23
12	0	2	915	− 56	865	897	904	−33	−26	−26
13	22	1	899	64	842	895	900	−39	−37	−31
14	21	23	910	72	843	916	917	−24	−25	−15
15	20	22	977	80	897	987	983	+40	+37	+49
16	18	21	925	88	830	935	928	−16	−24	− 6
17	17	19	952	96	853	971	966	+20	+10	+31
18	16	18	895	104	789	917	927	−21	−32	− 9
19	15	17	942	112	824	962	989	+40	+30	+53
20	13	16	842	120	716	862	908	−43	−51	−30
21	12	14	+821	−128	+ 697	+ 852	+ 909	−41	−51	−30
					Pair 8					
0	14	18	+871	− 15	+ 854	+ 843	+ 813	−39	−31	−27
1	13	17	901	20	875	869	839	−17	−13	− 9
2	12	16	909	25	876	873	843	−16	−16	−12
3	10	14	919	30	888	887	857	− 6	− 7	− 7
4	9	13	926	35	890	890	862	− 4	− 8	− 9
5	8	12	961	40	918	918	899	+29	+22	+20
6	7	10	935	45	879	878	873	− 1	+ 4	+ 1

TABLE 30 (Contd.)

k	☊ $-\alpha$	☊ $+\alpha$	F_1	$D\delta$	E_2	F_3	F_4	F_5	F_6	F_7
1	2	3	4	5	6	7	8	9	10	11
					Pair 8					
7	5^h	9^h	+938	− 50	+ 882	+ 883	+ 887	+10	+18	+ 13
8	4	8	909	55	850	856	864	−17	− 8	− 13
9	3	7	919	60	859	878	886	+ 2	+10	+ 6
10	1	5	952	65	893	910	918	+30	+36	+ 35
11	0	4	953	70	889	904	912	+20	+25	+ 26
12	23	3	912	109	809	845	852	−43	−40	− 36
13	22	1	922	116	813	874	879	−20	−18	− 12
14	20	1	967	123	849	930	931	+29	+26	+ 37
15	19	23	958	130	828	924	920	+14	+ 9	+ 23
16	18	21	959	137	815	926	919	+ 9	+ 1	+ 19
17	16	20	967	147	820	943	938	+25	+16	+ 36
18	15	19	911	151	758	893	903	−14	−22	− 2
19	14	18	886	158	722	864	891	−29	−36	− 16
20	12	16	839	165	668	816	862	−62	−67	− 49
21	11	15	+862	−172	+ 694	+ 851	+ 908	−20	−23	− 6
					Pair 9					
0	14	18	+ 997	+124	+1114	+1130	+1100	+73	+78	+ 82
1	13	17	958	116	1065	1080	1050	+26	+28	+ 32
2	11	16	921	108	1017	1030	1000	−22	−20	− 19
3	10	14	896	100	990	998	968	−51	−52	− 51
4	9	13	932	92	1022	1027	1000	−16	−19	− 20
5	7	12	914	84	995	995	977	−37	−40	− 44
6	6	11	928	74	993	989	985	−26	−19	− 24
7	5	9	940	66	999	1003	1007	− 1	+ 7	+ 2
8	4	8	890	58	943	967	975	−30	−21	− 26
9	2	7	903	50	952	1016	1024	+21	+27	+ 26
10	1	5	888	42	934	979	987	−13	− 7	− 8
11	0	4	888	+ 34	928	971	979	−18	−13	− 12
12	22	3	972	− 90	885	968	975	−20	−20	− 13
13	21	2	984	110	878	1006	1010	+18	+16	+ 26
14	20	0	1016	130	892	1052	1052	+63	+60	+ 72
15	19	23	943	150	793	974	969	−17	−22	− 7
16	17	22	910	170	735	935	927	−57	−64	− 47
17	16	20	968	190	774	988	984	+ 3	− 6	+ 14
18	15	19	923	210	712	936	947	−31	−39	− 19
19	13	18	949	230	713	943	971	− 5	−10	+ 8
20	12	17	1014	250	756	991	1039	+66	+63	+ 80
21	11	15	+ 890	−270	+ 619	+ 860	+ 918	−52	−55	− 37
					Pair 10					
6	6	11	+ 955	+322	+1268	+1273	+1269	− 2	+ 5	− 4
7	4	10	849	328	1170	1165	1169	−111	−104	−112
8	3	8	953	334	1282	1256	1264	− 26	− 19	−27
9	2	7	1015	340	1354	1293	1301	+ 2	+ 8	+ 1
10	1	6	993	346	1343	1305	1313	+ 4	+ 9	+ 3
11	23	5	970	352	1328	1297	1305	− 14	− 14	− 15
12	22	3	966	450	1419	1365	1372	+ 54	+ 54	+ 54
13	21	2	951	460	1415	1343	1347	+ 9	+ 7	+ 9
14	19	1	1005	470	1481	1403	1403	+ 56	+ 51	+ 56
15	18	23	1010	480	1490	1414	1409	+ 52	+ 45	+ 52
16	17	22	979	490	1464	1393	1385	+ 18	+ 11	+ 18

TABLE 30 (Contd.)

k	☋ − α	☊ + α	F_1	$D\delta$	F_2	F_3	F_4	F_5	F_6	F_7
1	2	3	4	5	6	7	8	9	10	11
					Pair 10					
17	16^h	21^h	+ 942	+500	+1438	+1373	+1369	− 7	−15	− 7
18	14	19	924	510	1433	1377	1388	+ 2	− 4	+ 3
19	13	18	928	520	1442	1395	1423	+28	+23	+29
20	12	17	893	530	1415	1377	1425	+20	+17	+21
21	10	16	833	540	1372	1343	1401	−14	−13	−13
22	9	14	722	644	1369	1366	1415	− 9	− 7	− 7
23	8	13	766	645	1418	1417	1456	+22	+25	+24
24	7	12	735	646	1389	1389	1425	−18	−13	−16
25	5	11	710	647	1365	1366	1402	−51	−44	−49
26	4	9	748	648	1402	1403	1438	−25	−17	−23
27	3	8	785	649	1438	1439	1471	− 1	+ 6	+ 2
28	1	7	792	650	1441	1443	1473	− 9	− 5	− 6
29	0	5	796	651	1445	1447	1479	−12	− 9	− 9
30	23	4	834	652	1481	1483	1517	+16	+18	+19
31	22	3	828	653	1475	1477	1516	+ 5	+ 5	+ 8
32	20	2	782	654	1431	1433	1475	−45	−49	−41
33	19	0	826	655	1477	1478	1521	− 9	−14	− 5
34	18	23	+ 856	+656	+1509	+1511	+1554	+15	+ 8	+19
					Pair 11					
0	13	19	+ 954	− 91	+ 856	+ 793	+ 763	+40	+48	+50
1	12	18	941	104	828	780	750	+27	+33	+33
2	11	16	882	117	753	719	689	−35	−33	−33
3	9	15	912	130	776	757	727	+ 3	+ 6	+ 1
4	8	14	930	143	785	775	748	+23	+23	+17
5	7	12	873	156	714	713	695	−30	−33	−40
6	6	11	962	171	782	788	784	+59	+66	+57
7	4	10	911	184	720	715	719	− 7	0	− 9
8	3	8	936	197	734	706	714	−12	− 5	−14
9	2	7	997	210	786	718	726	− 1	+ 5	− 3
10	0	6	966	223	747	705	713	−14	−12	−15
11	23	5	1035	236	805	769	777	+50	+50	+49
12	22	3	928	174	757	695	702	−26	−26	−27
13	21	2	947	176	775	691	695	−33	−35	−34
14	19	1	1020	178	848	755	755	+26	+21	+25
15	18	23	996	180	816	722	717	−12	−19	−13
16	17	22	1021	182	834	744	736	+ 7	0	+ 6
17	15	21	952	184	764	680	676	−54	−60	−55
18	14	20	946	186	759	683	694	−36	−41	−37
19	13	18	968	188	774	707	735	+ 4	− 1	+ 3
20	12	17	957	190	759	700	748	+17	+14	+16
21	10	16	867	192	674	624	682	−49	−48	−50
22	9	14	753	68	688	681	730	− 2	0	− 3
23	8	13	723	70	660	656	695	−37	−34	−37
24	7	12	763	72	699	696	732	− 1	+ 4	− 1
25	5	11	769	74	703	701	737	+ 4	+11	+ 4
26	4	9	762	76	692	691	726	− 7	+ 1	− 7
27	3	8	774	78	700	700	732	− 2	+ 5	− 2
28	1	7	765	80	684	684	714	−20	−16	−20
29	0	5	776	82	692	693	725	−10	− 7	−10
30	23	4	796	84	707	708	742	+ 7	+ 9	+ 7
31	21	3	830	86	738	739	778	+43	+40	+43
32	20	2	796	88	703	704	746	+10	+ 6	+10
33	19	0	823	90	729	730	773	+37	+32	+37
34	18	23	+ 822	− 92	+ 727	+ 728	+ 771	+34	+27	+34

TABLE 30 (Contd.)

k	$\Omega-\alpha$	$\Omega+\alpha$	F_1	$D\delta$	F_2	F_3	F_4	F_5	F_6	F_7
1	2	3	4	5	6	7	8	9	10	11
					Pair 13					
0	13^h	19^h	+ 979	+337	+1309	+1236	+1206	+ 43	+ 51	+ 47
1	12	18	1034	328	1353	1298	1268	+100	+106	+101
2	10	17	954	319	1261	1222	1192	+ 20	+ 27	+ 17
3	9	15	918	310	1222	1199	1169	− 8	− 5	− 15
4	8	14	911	301	1210	1198	1171	− 11	− 11	− 21
5	1	13	927	292	1216	1215	1197	+ 11	+ 10	− 3
6	5	11	909	277	1177	1184	1180	− 11	− 4	− 16
7	4	10	859	268	1120	1113	1117	− 78	− 71	− 83
8	3	9	949	259	1203	1168	1176	− 24	− 18	− 28
9	1	8	903	250	1152	1065	1073	− 31	− 28	− 35
10	0	6	964	241	1209	1154	1162	− 46	− 44	− 50
11	23	5	986	232	1224	1177	1185	− 28	− 28	− 31
12	21	4	932	378	1313	1230	1237	+ 19	+ 15	+ 16
13	20	2	958	382	1344	1229	1233	+ 11	+ 7	+ 9
14	19	1	938	386	1330	1198	1198	− 28	− 33	− 30
15	18	0	968	390	1358	1221	1216	− 15	− 22	− 16
16	16	23	1048	394	1437	1303	1295	+ 59	+ 52	+ 58
17	15	21	1039	398	1433	1301	1297	+ 57	+ 51	+ 56
18	14	20	949	402	1350	1226	1237	− 8	− 13	− 9
19	12	19	997	406	1397	1281	1309	+ 60	+ 59	+ 60
20	11	17	886	410	1288	1180	1228	− 26	− 26	− 25
21	10	16	884	414	1297	1199	1257	− 1	0	0
22	9	15	761	476	1240	1225	1274	+ 12	+ 15	+ 13
23	7	14	761	475	1243	1232	1271	+ 4	+ 10	+ 6
24	6	12	708	474	1190	1181	1217	− 55	− 48	− 53
25	5	11	707	473	1188	1181	1217	− 59	− 52	− 56
26	4	10	735	472	1213	1208	1243	− 37	− 30	− 34
27	2	8	780	471	1255	1251	1283	− 2	+ 3	+ 2
28	1	7	806	470	1275	1272	1302	+ 12	+ 16	+ 16
29	0	6	804	469	1271	1269	1301	+ 7	+ 9	+ 11
30	22	5	767	468	1230	1229	1263	− 35	− 38	− 30
31	21	3	883	467	1344	1343	1382	+ 79	+ 76	+ 84
32	20	2	836	466	1297	1297	1339	+ 31	+ 27	+ 37
33	18	1	780	465	1241	1241	1284	− 28	− 35	− 22
34	17	23	+ 813	+464	+1274	+1274	+1317	+ 1	− 6	+ 8
					Pair 14					
0	13	19	+ 957	+ 6	+ 959	+ 972	+ 942	+ 17	+ 22	+ 21
1	11	18	978	− 16	955	967	937	+ 33	+ 40	+ 35
2	10	17	924	38	875	884	854	− 28	− 22	− 28
3	9	16	953	60	887	893	863	+ 2	+ 6	− 1
4	8	14	885	82	800	804	777	− 62	− 61	− 67
5	6	13	934	104	825	825	807	− 11	− 10	− 18
6	5	12	960	124	827	824	820	+ 23	+ 30	+ 22
7	4	10	940	146	787	790	794	+ 19	+ 26	+ 19
8	2	9	901	168	728	746	754	0	+ 4	+ 1
9	1	8	938	190	747	796	804	+ 72	+ 75	+ 73
10	0	7	908	212	700	734	742	+ 31	+ 32	+ 33
11	23	5	813	234	585	617	625	− 65	− 65	− 62
12	21	4	955	401	557	620	627	− 41	− 45	− 38
13	20	3	876	434	446	543	547	−100	−105	− 96
14	19	1	982	467	521	642	642	+ 17	+ 12	+ 22
15	17	0	969	500	469	606	601	− 3	− 10	+ 3

TABLE 30 (Contd.)

k	$\Omega-\alpha$	$\Omega+\alpha$	F_1	$D\delta$	F_2	F_3	F_4	F_5	F_6	F_7
1	2	3	4	5	6	7	8	9	10	11
					Pair 14					
16	16^h	23^h	+970	−533	−432	+583	+575	−8	−15	−2
17	15	22	975	566	405	567	563	+2	−3	+9
18	14	20	1010	599	410	579	590	+50	+45	+57
19	12	19	924	632	286	460	488	−30	−31	−22
20	11	18	1013	665	340	518	566	+69	+70	+78
21	10	16	+888	−698	+189	+370	+428	−48	−47	−38
					Pair 15					
0	12	20	+968	+88	+1052	+1087	+1057	+57	+66	+62
1	11	18	915	72	980	1009	979	−22	−15	−19
2	10	17	905	56	950	972	942	−59	−53	−59
3	9	16	965	40	999	1013	983	−19	−15	−21
4	7	15	942	24	963	971	944	−58	−54	−62
5	6	13	969	8	972	973	955	−48	−47	−54
6	5	12	1036	+8	1035	1030	1026	+22	+29	+23
7	3	11	1019	−8	1004	1010	1014	+10	+15	+12
8	2	9	998	24	969	1001	1009	+4	+8	+6
9	1	8	1043	40	1002	1085	1093	+88	+91	+91
10	0	7	998	56	946	1003	1011	+5	+6	+9
11	22	5	1048	72	982	1034	1042	+35	+32	+40
12	21	4	925	99	829	929	936	−71	−75	−65
13	20	3	1024	116	912	1062	1066	+58	+53	+65
14	19	2	935	133	808	992	992	−16	−22	−9
15	17	0	944	150	794	999	994	−15	−22	−7
16	16	23	944	167	772	992	984	−24	−31	−15
17	15	22	987	184	799	1032	1028	+18	+13	+28
18	13	20	982	201	780	1021	1032	+21	+18	+32
19	12	19	909	218	685	930	958	−53	−54	−41
20	11	18	983	235	740	988	1036	+24	+25	+12
21	9	17	+887	−252	+634	+882	+940	−73	−67	−60
					Pair 16					
6	4	12	+955	+78	+1024	+1025	+1021	+28	+35	+29
7	3	11	934	72	999	998	1002	+10	+15	+11
8	2	10	944	66	1005	1002	1010	+20	+23	+21
9	1	8	894	60	953	948	956	−33	−30	−32
10	23	7	959	54	1017	1016	1024	+36	+34	+37
11	22	6	872	48	926	926	934	−53	−57	−52
12	21	4	904	20	927	930	937	−49	−53	−47
13	19	3	932	+10	946	955	959	−25	−32	−23
14	18	2	994	0	1000	1015	1015	+32	+24	+34
15	17	1	1004	−10	994	1016	1011	+27	+20	+29
16	16	23	942	20	917	946	938	−43	−50	−41
17	14	22	946	30	912	947	943	−37	−40	−35
18	13	21	996	40	955	996	1007	+29	+27	+31
19	12	19	930	50	874	921	949	−26	−27	−24
20	10	18	904	60	836	889	937	−39	−35	−37
21	9	17	932	−70	861	917	975	0	+6	−3
22	8	16	734	+224	961	971	1020	+46	+52	+49
23	7	14	760	210	977	986	1025	+53	+59	+56
24	5	13	763	196	967	975	1011	+40	+47	+43

TABLE 30 (Contd.)

k	☊ − α	☊ + α	F_1	$D\delta$	F_2	F_3	F_4	F_5	F_6	F_7
1	2	3	4	5	6	7	8	9	10	11
					Pair 16					
25	4^h	12^h	+ 695	+182	+ 885	+ 893	+ 929	−41	−34	−38
26	3	11	801	168	975	982	1017	+48	+53	+51
27	1	9	715	154	873	879	911	−57	−55	−53
28	0	8	768	140	907	913	943	−23	−23	−19
29	23	7	804	126	928	932	964	− 1	− 3	+ 3
30	22	5	836	112	943	947	981	+17	+14	+21
31	20	4	825	98	917	920	959	− 4	−10	0
32	19	3	790	84	869	972	1014	+52	+45	+56
33	18	1	831	70	897	899	942	−18	−25	−14
34	16	0	+ 811	+ 56	+ 864	+ 866	+ 909	−50	−57	−45
					Pair 17					
0	13	21	+ 943	+224	+1151	+1067	+1037	− 5	+ 2	+ 2
1	12	20	939	216	1147	1077	1047	+ 3	+ 9	+ 7
2	11	19	981	208	1181	1127	1097	+51	+56	+52
3	9	18	902	200	1093	1055	1025	−22	−15	−24
4	8	16	916	192	1106	1084	1054	+ 5	+ 8	0
5	7	15	892	184	1079	1068	1041	−10	− 9	−17
6	5	14	933	179	1107	1107	1090	+37	+45	+36
7	4	12	931	166	1092	1100	1097	+42	+49	+41
8	3	11	846	158	1004	996	1001	−55	−50	−56
9	2	10	909	150	1059	1017	1025	−33	−30	−34
10	0	8	989	142	1130	1034	1042	−18	−18	−18
11	23	7	947	134	1086	1029	1037	−25	−27	−25
12	22	6	911	179	1096	1041	1049	−15	−19	−15
13	20	5	952	238	1191	1092	1099	+34	+26	+34
14	19	3	957	244	1202	1063	1067	0	− 7	− 1
15	18	2	1001	250	1256	1096	1096	+27	+19	+28
16	17	1	966	256	1228	1062	1057	−14	−21	−13
17	15	23	987	262	1248	1079	1071	− 1	− 6	0
18	14	22	973	268	1238	1070	1066	− 8	−11	− 7
19	13	21	981	274	1255	1092	1105	+29	+27	+31
20	11	20	894	280	1169	1012	1042	−36	−33	−34
21	10	18	880	286	1158	1007	1057	−23	−19	−21
22	9	17	824	292	1121	980	1039	−43	−37	−41
23	8	16	687	310	1005	984	1032	−51	−45	−48
24	6	15	734	306	1048	1030	1068	−17	− 8	−14
25	5	13	735	302	1045	1031	1067	−20	−13	−17
26	4	12	729	298	1033	1022	1058	−31	−24	−28
27	2	11	814	294	1111	1102	1137	+46	+49	+49
28	1	9	834	290	1125	1118	1150	+58	+60	+62
29	0	8	838	286	1122	1116	1146	+52	+52	+56
30	23	7	801	282	1079	1075	1107	+11	+ 9	+15
31	21	6	779	278	1052	1049	1084	−12	−19	− 8
32	20	4	749	274	1019	1016	1055	−45	−51	−40
33	19	3	773	270	1039	1037	1079	−22	−29	−17
34	17	2	+ 841	+266	+1105	+1103	+1146	+43	+35	+48
					Pair 18					
0	13	22	+ 933	+132	+1052	+1041	+1011	+23	+28	+27
1	12	20	931	128	1053	1045	1015	+26	+30	+28
2	10	19	872	124	989	983	953	−36	−29	−36
3	9	18	861	120	972	969	939	−51	−44	−53

TABLE 30 (Contd.)

k	$\Omega-\alpha$	$\Omega+\alpha$	F_1	$D\delta$	F_2	F_3	F_4	F_5	F_6	F_7
1	2	3	4	5	6	7	8	9	10	11
					Pair 18					
4	8^h	16^h	+915	+116	+1028	+1027	+ 997	+ 7	+11	+ 3
5	7	15	913	112	1026	1026	999	+ 8	+11	+ 2
6	5	14	900	113	1008	1008	991	− 1	+ 7	− 2
7	4	13	913	108	1016	1016	1013	+21	+28	+20
8	3	11	842	104	946	946	951	−42	−37	−43
9	1	10	849	100	949	950	958	−25	−24	−26
10	0	9	901	96	996	1001	1009	+15	+14	+14
11	23	7	861	92	958	962	970	−25	−27	−25
12	21	6	926	69	1001	1007	1015	+20	+13	+20
13	20	5	916	44	961	974	981	−25	−33	−25
14	19	4	986	37	1024	1046	1050	+54	+46	+54
15	18	2	925	30	960	990	990	− 7	−15	− 7
16	16	1	966	23	995	1031	1026	+28	+21	+28
17	15	0	958	16	973	1015	1007	+ 9	+ 4	+10
18	14	22	911	9	917	965	961	−38	−41	−37
19	12	21	949	+ 2	951	1003	1016	+17	+18	+18
20	11	20	899	− 5	889	947	977	−23	−20	−22
21	10	18	907	12	887	948	999	− 3	+ 1	− 2
22	9	17	892	− 19	878	942	1001	0	+ 6	+ 1
23	7	16	746	+240	994	1005	1053	+51	+59	+53
24	6	15	749	230	987	997	1035	+33	+42	+35
25	5	13	701	220	929	938	974	−29	−22	−27
26	4	12	746	210	962	969	1005	+ 1	+ 8	+ 3
27	2	11	710	200	913	920	955	−49	−46	−47
28	1	10	833	190	1024	1028	1060	+55	+56	+57
29	0	8	790	180	968	973	1003	− 2	− 2	+ 1
30	22	7	792	170	958	962	994	−12	−17	− 9
31	21	6	817	160	972	976	1011	+ 4	− 3	+ 7
32	20	5	820	150	966	969	1008	+ 1	− 7	+ 4
33	19	3	803	140	939	942	984	−24	−31	−21
34	18	2	+820	+130	+ 948	+ 950	+ 993	−15	−23	−12
					Pair 19					
6	5	14	+918	+163	+1076	+1076	+1059	+26	+34	+27
7	4	13	848	162	1005	1009	1006	−36	−29	−34
8	2	12	854	161	1015	1012	1017	−34	−31	−32
9	1	10	906	160	1066	1048	1056	− 4	− 3	− 2
10	0	9	957	159	1115	1075	1083	+14	+13	+16
11	22	8	907	158	1070	1047	1055	−23	−29	−21
12	21	6	931	175	1112	1090	1098	+11	+ 4	+14
13	20	5	889	202	1092	1053	1060	−36	−44	−33
14	19	4	903	211	1115	1062	1066	−39	−47	−36
15	17	3	987	220	1212	1154	1154	+40	+31	+43
16	16	1	984	229	1219	1160	1155	+31	+24	+34
17	15	0	994	238	1231	1172	1164	+31	+26	+35
18	13	23	929	247	1173	1117	1113	−29	−30	−25
19	12	21	913	256	1169	1117	1130	21	−20	−17
20	11	20	914	265	1174	1127	1157	− 3	0	+ 1
21	10	19	979	274	1245	1203	1253	+84	+89	+88
22	8	18	843	283	1131	1091	1150	−28	−19	+24
23	7	16	706	420	1134	1129	1177	−10	− 2	− 5
24	6	15	713	420	1141	1137	1175	−21	−12	−16

TABLE 30 (Contd.)

k	☊ $-\alpha$	☊ $+\alpha$	F_1	$D\delta$	F_2	F_3	F_4	F_5	F_6	F_7
1	2	3	4	5	6	7	8	9	10	11
					Pair 19					
25	4^h	14^h	+ 741	+420	+1169	+1166	+1202	− 4	+ 4	+ 1
26	3	12	771	420	1197	1195	1231	+16	+21	+21
27	2	11	772	420	1195	1193	1228	+ 2	+ 5	+ 7
28	1	10	752	420	1173	1172	1204	−27	−26	−21
29	23	9	851	420	1269	1268	1298	+56	+52	+62
30	22	7	808	420	1224	1224	1256	+ 5	0	+11
31	21	6	765	420	1180	1180	1215	−45	−52	−39
32	19	5	811	420	1227	1227	1266	− 3	−13	+ 3
33	18	3	773	420	1189	1189	1231	−47	−56	−40
34	17	2	+ 826	+420	+1244	+1244	+1287	0	− 8	+ 7
					Pair 20					
0	12	22	+ 891	+ 5	+ 883	+ 931	+ 901	−11	− 3	− 9
1	11	21	922	10	926	969	939	+15	+ 23	+17
2	10	19	898	15	906	940	910	−27	− 20	−26
3	9	18	906	20	917	942	912	−37	− 30	−37
4	7	17	925	25	947	962	932	−30	− 22	−31
5	6	16	948	30	979	987	960	−14	− 8	−16
6	5	14	936	48	979	979	962	−24	− 16	−22
7	3	13	960	60	1015	1009	1006	+ 7	+ 12	+11
8	2	12	897	65	962	968	973	−38	− 35	−33
9	1	10	968	70	1038	1073	1081	+57	+ 58	+63
10	0	9	944	75	1018	1102	1110	+74	+ 73	+81
11	22	8	937	80	1022	1074	1082	+34	+ 28	+42
12	21	7	1013	+ 45	1064	1116	1124	+63	+ 55	+73
13	20	5	867	0	868	967	974	−99	−107	−88
14	18	4	935	− 5	931	1075	1079	− 7	− 17	+ 5
15	17	3	895	10	890	1063	1063	−35	− 44	−22
16	16	1	901	15	892	1080	1075	−35	− 42	−21
17	15	0	910	20	889	1089	1081	−42	− 47	−27
18	13	23	980	25	952	1159	1155	+20	+ 19	+36
19	12	22	927	30	897	1110	1123	−25	− 23	− 8
20	11	20	936	35	896	1109	1139	−21	− 18	− 3
21	9	19	1001	40	953	1167	1217	+45	+ 53	+64
22	8	18	+ 862	− 45	+ 822	+1034	+1093	−92	− 83	−72
					Pair 21					
0	12	22	+ 896	+102	+ 988	+ 987	+ 957	− 7	− 2	− 3
1	11	21	928	98	1022	1023	993	+29	+ 35	+32
2	10	20	884	94	972	973	943	−22	− 15	−20
3	8	18	849	90	930	931	901	−64	− 55	−63
4	7	17	916	86	998	999	969	+ 3	+ 12	+ 3
5	6	16	900	82	981	981	954	−12	− 4	−13
6	4	15	903	82	980	980	963	− 3	+ 6	− 3
7	3	13	877	78	950	949	946	−21	− 16	−21
8	2	12	859	74	933	934	939	−28	− 25	−28
9	1	11	843	70	913	917	925	−43	− 42	−43
10	23	9	903	66	968	979	987	+19	+ 15	+19
11	22	8	899	62	966	973	981	+13	+ 7	+13
12	21	7	965	37	1008	1016	1024	+55	+ 47	+55
13	19	6	918	10	929	945	952	−17	− 28	−17
14	18	4	945	+ 5	951	977	981	+11	+ 1	+11
15	17	3	983	0	988	1020	1020	+50	+ 41	+50

TABLE 30 (Contd.)

k	$\Omega-\alpha$	$\Omega+\alpha$	F_1	$D\vartheta$	F_2	F_3	F_4	F_5	F_6	F_7
1	2	3	4	5	6	7	8	9	10	11
				Pair 21						
16	16^h	2^h	+984	− 5	+985	+1021	+1016	+46	+38	+46
17	14	0	986	10	975	1015	1007	+36	+33	+36
18	13	23	967	15	949	992	988	+17	+16	+17
19	12	22	934	20	914	960	973	+ 1	+ 3	+ 1
20	10	21	957	25	907	954	984	+12	+19	+12
21	9	20	976	30	938	989	1039	+67	+76	+67
22	8	18	826	− 35	796	848	907	−66	−57	−66
23	7	17	710	+185	903	911	959	−14	− 4	−14
24	5	15	777	178	963	971	1009	+35	+44	+35
25	4	14	730	171	909	915	951	−23	−15	−23
26	3	13	705	164	875	881	917	−57	−52	−57
27	1	12	767	157	928	932	966	− 9	− 8	− 9
28	0	10	829	150	980	984	1016	+41	+39	+41
29	23	9	778	143	919	923	953	−23	−27	−23
30	22	8	799	136	931	934	966	−10	−16	−10
31	20	6	806	129	930	932	967	− 9	−18	− 9
32	19	5	833	122	951	953	992	+15	+ 5	+15
33	18	4	783	115	894	896	938	−39	−49	−39
34	16	3	+824	+108	+930	+ 932	+ 975	− 3	−12	− 3
				Pair 22						
0	12	23	−923	+ 43	+956	+ 960	+ 930	+11	+16	+ 9
1	11	21	937	32	965	969	939	+26	+32	+23
2	9	20	880	21	895	898	868	−39	−29	−43
3	8	19	913	+ 10	914	917	887	−15	− 5	−20
4	7	17	890	− 1	885	887	857	−39	−30	−44
5	6	16	902	12	889	890	863	−27	−19	−33
6	4	15	942	18	919	919	902	+18	+27	+14
7	3	13	911	28	878	877	874	− 4	+ 1	− 7
8	2	12	891	39	852	853	858	−15	−12	−18
9	1	11	927	50	877	882	890	+23	+24	+20
10	23	10	955	61	893	907	915	+54	+49	+52
11	22	8	917	72	850	859	867	+12	+ 6	+10
12	21	7	947	82	871	881	889	+40	+32	+38
13	19	6	938	94	845	864	871	+27	+16	+25
14	18	4	967	107	861	890	894	+56	+46	+55
15	17	3	870	120	755	791	791	−41	−50	−40
16	15	2	891	133	764	804	799	−27	−33	−28
17	14	1	930	146	783	827	819	− 1	− 4	− 1
18	13	23	877	159	715	763	759	−56	−57	−56
19	12	22	919	172	747	797	810	+ 1	+ 3	+ 1
20	10	21	922	185	732	784	814	+11	+18	+11
21	9	19	867	198	661	714	764	−33	−25	−32
22	8	18	864	−211	658	712	771	−20	−11	−19
23	6	17	731	+ 5	744	753	801	+15	+27	+16
24	5	16	757	− 8	757	765	803	+23	+33	+25
25	4	14	725	21	712	719	855	+81	+89	+83
26	3	13	670	34	642	648	684	−82	−77	−80
27	1	12	730	47	686	692	726	−36	−35	−34
28	0	11	790	60	731	735	767	+10	+ 8	+13
29	23	9	788	73	713	717	747	− 4	− 8	− 1
30	21	8	799	86	709	712	744	− 1	−10	+ 2

TABLE 30 (Contd.)

k	☊ − α	☊ + α	F_1	$D\delta$	F_2	F_3	F_4	F_5	F_6	F_7
1	2	3	4	5	6	7	8	9	10	11
					Pair 22					
31	20^h	7^h	+838	− 99	+ 734	+ 736	+ 771	+32	+22	+36
32	19	5	823	112	707	709	748	+15	+ 5	+19
33	18	4	797	125	668	670	712	−14	−24	−10
34	16	3	+818	−138	+ 678	+ 679	+ 722	0	− 9	+ 5
					Pair 23					
0	12	23	+891	+ 22	+ 903	+ 937	+ 907	−91	−86	−86
1	10	21	969	18	983	1013	983	+82	+91	+86
2	9	20	869	14	877	901	871	−33	−23	−30
3	8	19	911	10	912	929	899	− 8	+ 2	− 6
4	7	18	953	6	965	975	945	+35	+45	+36
5	5	16	900	2	901	906	879	−33	−25	−33
6	4	15	972	+ 2	969	969	952	+37	+46	+39
7	3	14	906	− 2	899	895	892	−26	−20	−24
8	1	12	855	6	849	853	858	−63	−62	−61
9	0	11	894	10	884	907	915	− 9	−11	− 8
10	23	10	913	14	898	953	961	+34	+29	+35
11	22	9	911	18	898	932	940	+10	+ 3	+11
12	20	7	933	41	898	932	940	+ 7	− 3	+ 8
13	19	6	892	70	823	886	893	+57	+46	+58
14	18	5	881	80	802	895	899	−40	−52	−39
15	16	3	938	90	853	962	962	+20	+11	+21
16	15	2	899	100	805	924	919	−25	−31	−24
17	14	1	939	110	828	955	947	0	− 3	+ 1
18	13	0	944	60	821	951	947	− 3	− 4	− 2
19	11	22	927	50	797	929	942	−11	− 6	−10
20	10	21	894	40	749	880	910	−46	−39	−45
21	9	20	958	30	810	941	991	+32	+41	+33
22	7	18	912	− 20	757	888	947	−15	− 4	−15
23	6	17	704	+180	892	912	960	− 5	+ 7	− 5
24	5	16	729	176	913	931	969	+ 3	+13	+ 3
25	4	15	724	172	904	919	955	−16	− 7	−16
26	2	13	734	168	908	920	956	−17	−14	−17
27	1	12	790	164	958	968	1002	+28	+29	+28
28	0	11	846	160	1007	1016	1048	+69	+67	+69
29	22	9	775	156	929	936	966	−16	−23	−16
30	21	8	766	152	914	920	952	−33	−42	−33
31	20	7	823	148	966	971	1006	+18	+ 8	+18
32	19	6	787	144	927	931	970	−21	−32	−21
33	17	4	831	140	967	971	1013	+19	+ 9	+19
34	16	3	+837	+136	+ 971	+ 974	+1017	+20	+11	+20
					Pair 24					
6	4	15	+891	+ 52	+ 938	+ 938	+ 921	−30	−21	−29
7	2	14	914	48	957	960	957	+ 9	+13	+11
8	1	13	887	44	931	928	933	−13	−12	−11
9	0	11	902	40	942	928	936	− 7	− 9	− 5
10	23	10	948	36	983	949	957	+17	+12	+19
11	21	9	946	32	983	962	970	+33	+23	+35
12	20	8	885	49	940	920	928	− 6	−17	− 3
13	19	7	855	70	926	889	896	−36	−48	−33
14	17	5	854	70	925	872	876	−53	−65	−50

TABLE 30 (Contd.)

k	$\Omega-\alpha$	$\Omega+\alpha$	F_1	$D\delta$	F_2	F_3	F_4	F_5	F_6	F_7
1	2	3	4	5	6	7	8	9	10	11
				Pair 24						
15	16^h	4^h	+ 933	+ 70	+1008	+ 946	+ 946	+20	+10	+23
16	15	2	867	70	943	876	871	−52	−58	−49
17	14	1	960	70	1029	961	953	+33	+30	+37
18	12	0	975	70	1042	973	969	+51	+53	+55
19	11	23	902	70	972	903	916	+ 1	+ 6	+ 5
20	10	21	884	70	949	880	910	− 2	+ 5	+ 2
21	8	20	865	70	927	861	911	+ 2	+13	+ 6
22	7	19	893	70	968	904	963	+57	+69	+61
23	6	18	741	135	884	874	922	+18	+31	+23
24	5	16	709	124	841	832	870	−31	−21	−26
25	3	15	761	113	882	875	911	+13	+20	+18
26	2	14	765	102	873	867	903	+ 8	+12	+13
27	1	12	409	91	862	858	892	0	+ 1	+ 5
28	23	11	771	80	852	848	880	−10	−15	− 4
29	22	10	760	69	827	824	854	−33	−41	−27
30	21	9	760	58	814	811	843	−41	−51	−35
31	20	7	782	47	824	822	857	−24	−34	−18
32	18	6	811	36	843	841	880	+ 2	−11	+ 8
33	17	5	827	25	848	847	889	+13	+ 1	+20
34	16	3	+ 819	+ 14	+ 831	+ 830	+ 873	0	− 9	+ 7
				Pair 25						
0	11	23	+ 857	+101	+ 949	+ 908	+ 878	−51	−46	−55
1	10	22	943	94	1031	996	966	+34	+42	+30
2	8	21	914	87	995	967	937	+ 2	+14	− 2
3	7	19	884	80	957	937	907	−31	−19	−34
4	6	18	932	73	1004	992	962	+21	+34	+18
5	5	17	869	66	939	934	908	−36	−24	−38
6	3	16	894	61	958	959	943	− 3	+ 5	− 5
7	2	14	873	54	929	933	931	−18	−14	−20
8	1	13	918	47	972	965	970	+18	+19	+17
9	23	12	952	40	1000	972	980	+25	+20	+24
10	22	10	1010	33	1045	958	966	+ 8	0	+ 8
11	21	9	966	26	995	960	968	+ 7	− 3	+ 7
12	20	8	908	101	1014	974	982	+18	+ 7	+18
13	18	7	961	104	1066	994	1001	+34	+20	+35
14	17	5	994	107	1102	1000	1004	+34	+22	+35
15	16	4	1022	110	1135	1016	1016	+44	+34	+46
16	14	3	941	113	1059	929	924	−51	−56	−49
17	13	1	945	116	1062	927	919	−59	−60	−57
18	12	0	954	119	1075	937	934	−47	−45	−44
19	11	23	1043	122	1168	1029	1043	+59	+64	+62
20	9	21	938	125	1062	924	956	−31	−21	−27
21	8	20	952	128	1075	937	988	− 2	+ 9	+ 2
22	7	19	904	131	1032	897	955	−38	−26	−34
23	5	18	686	220	911	890	937	−59	−46	−54
24	4	16	801	218	1023	1005	1043	+44	+54	+49
25	3	15	791	216	1010	995	1031	+29	+36	+35
26	2	14	732	214	949	936	972	−32	−28	−26
27	0	13	743	212	957	946	981	−26	−28	−19
28	23	11	782	210	993	984	1016	+ 6	+ 1	+13
29	22	10	805	208	1013	1006	1036	+23	+15	+30
30	20	9	807	206	1013	1007	1039	+23	+11	+31

TABLE 30 (Contd.)

k	$\Omega-\alpha$	$\Omega+\alpha$	F_1	$D\delta$	F_2	F_3	F_4	F_5	F_6	F_7
1	2	3	4	5	6	7	8	9	10	11
					Pair 25					
31	19^h	7^h	+780	+204	+982	+977	+1012	−7	−19	+1
32	18	6	755	202	952	948	987	−35	−48	−26
33	17	5	796	200	992	989	1031	+6	−6	+15
34	15	4	+796	+198	+991	+988	+1031	+3	−5	+12
					Pair 26					
0	11	0	+859	+220	+1073	+1040	+1010	−50	−48	−48
1	9	22	927	220	1143	1114	1084	+18	+27	+11
2	8	21	948	220	1163	1140	1110	+38	+49	+32
3	7	20	907	220	1120	1104	1074	−4	+9	−8
4	6	18	917	220	1135	1125	1095	+11	+25	+8
5	4	17	907	220	1129	1124	1098	+8	+22	+7
6	3	16	889	220	1112	1113	1097	+2	+10	−1
7	2	15	877	220	1099	1103	1101	0	+5	−3
8	0	13	896	220	1123	1117	1122	+15	+13	+13
9	23	12	933	220	1161	1137	1145	+32	+27	+30
10	22	11	1048	220	1270	1194	1202	+83	+75	+82
11	21	9	980	220	1203	1172	1180	+55	+45	+54
12	19	8	873	258	1136	1100	1108	−23	−36	−24
13	18	7	900	262	1163	1099	1106	−31	−45	−31
14	17	6	937	266	1204	1112	1116	−27	−40	−27
15	15	4	916	270	1189	1081	1081	−67	−75	−67
16	14	3	932	274	1211	1093	1088	−66	−71	−65
17	13	2	1000	278	1279	1155	1147	−13	−15	−12
18	12	0	988	282	1272	1145	1142	−24	−22	−22
19	10	23	951	286	1240	1110	1124	−48	−40	−46
20	9	22	946	290	1235	1106	1138	−40	−29	−38
21	8	21	943	294	1232	1103	1154	−30	−18	−27
22	6	19	965	298	1260	1131	1189	−1	+13	+2
23	5	18	756	450	1211	1191	1238	+42	+55	+45
24	4	17	761	448	1213	1195	1233	+31	+43	+35
25	3	15	770	446	1219	1205	1241	+33	+40	+37
26	1	14	700	444	1147	1135	1171	−42	−40	−37
27	0	13	758	442	1202	1192	1227	+8	+6	+13
28	23	12	717	440	1158	1150	1182	−43	−48	−38
29	21	10	781	438	1219	1212	1242	+11	0	+17
30	20	9	791	436	1227	1221	1253	+16	+4	+22
31	19	8	798	434	1230	1225	1260	+17	+4	+24
32	18	6	806	432	1233	1229	1268	+19	+6	+26
33	16	5	771	430	1197	1194	1236	−19	−31	−12
34	15	4	+843	+428	+1268	+1265	+1308	+47	+39	+55
					Pair 27					
6	3	16	+872	−38	+837	+836	+820	−17	−9	−16
7	1	15	878	52	828	822	820	−14	−11	−12
8	0	14	840	66	781	790	795	−35	−36	−33
9	23	12	859	80	787	822	830	+3	−2	+5
10	22	11	881	94	789	895	903	+80	+72	+82
11	20	10	944	108	839	882	890	+71	+58	+73
12	19	8	879	151	733	780	788	−28	−41	−25
13	18	7	829	174	656	740	747	−65	−79	−62
14	16	6	928	197	732	849	853	+44	+31	+47
15	15	5	828	220	611	745	745	−60	−70	−57

TABLE 30 (Contd.)

k	$\Omega-\alpha$	$\Omega+\alpha$	F_1	$D\delta$	F_2	F_3	F_4	F_5	F_6	F_7
1	2	3	4	5	6	7	8	9	10	11
					Pair 27					
16	14^h	3^h	+ 891	−243	+653	+795	+790	−11	−16	− 8
17	13	2	863	266	598	746	738	−60	−62	−57
18	11	1	958	289	671	820	817	+23	+28	+27
19	10	23	925	312	616	764	778	−13	− 5	− 9
20	9	22	978	335	642	786	818	+31	+42	+35
21	7	21	950	358	587	727	778	− 5	+ 9	− 1
22	6	20	1047	381	663	798	856	+76	+91	+80
23	5	18	739	45	699	719	766	−10	+ 3	− 5
24	4	17	800	52	752	770	808	+35	+47	+40
25	2	16	723	59	667	681	717	−52	−46	−47
26	1	14	748	66	685	697	733	−32	−30	−27
27	0	13	775	73	704	714	749	−13	−15	− 8
28	22	12	845	80	766	774	806	+48	+40	+53
29	21	11	825	87	738	744	774	+19	+ 8	+25
30	20	9	770	94	676	681	713	−38	−50	−32
31	19	8	818	101	715	719	754	+ 7	− 6	+13
32	17	7	793	108	680	683	722	−22	−36	−16
33	16	5	765	115	646	649	691	−49	−61	−43
34	15	4	+ 856	−122	+731	+733	+776	+39	+31	+46
					Pair 28					
0	10	0	+ 906	− 26	+874	+882	+852	+ 2	+ 7	− 7
1	9	23	954	34	916	922	892	+47	+56	+39
2	8	22	917	42	870	874	844	+ 4	+16	− 3
3	6	20	896	50	839	842	812	−24	− 9	−29
4	5	19	896	58	836	837	807	−24	− 9	−28
5	4	18	918	66	854	854	828	+ 2	+17	0
6	3	16	931	76	858	858	842	+21	+29	+17
7	1	15	859	84	777	777	775	−41	−38	−45
8	0	14	848	92	763	763	768	−44	−45	−47
9	23	12	880	100	788	788	796	−11	−16	−14
10	21	11	872	108	766	765	773	−29	−40	−31
11	20	10	849	116	836	835	843	+46	+33	+44
12	19	9	924	110	819	816	824	+32	+18	+31
13	17	7	910	120	791	785	792	+ 4	−10	+ 3
14	16	6	932	130	803	793	797	+14	+ 1	+13
15	15	5	919	140	782	769	769	− 9	−19	− 9
16	14	3	963	150	818	800	795	+22	+17	+22
17	12	2	936	160	777	756	748	−20	−19	−19
18	11	1	960	170	792	768	765	+ 1	+ 6	+ 2
19	10	0	929	180	752	724	738	−21	−13	−20
20	8	22	876	190	685	655	687	−67	−54	−65
21	7	21	897	200	692	660	711	−38	−24	−36
22	6	20	920	−210	707	674	732	−12	+ 3	− 9
23	5	19	733	+ 10	748	742	789	+49	+63	+52
24	3	17	759	− 8	755	750	788	+53	+63	+57
25	2	16	733	26	710	705	741	+11	+17	+15
26	1	15	775	44	734	730	766	+41	+44	+45
27	0	13	840	62	780	776	811	+91	+89	+96
28	22	12	748	80	669	666	698	−18	−26	−13
29	21	11	809	98	711	708	738	+27	+16	+33
30	20	9	771	116	655	653	685	−21	−33	−15
31	18	8	733	134	597	595	630	−71	−86	−64
32	17	7	774	152	617	615	654	−42	−56	−35
33	16	6	806	170	632	630	672	−20	−33	−13
34	14	4	+ 853	−188	+662	+661	+704	+17	+11	+25

TABLE 30 (Contd.)

k	☊ − α	☊ + α	F_1	Dδ	F_2	F_3	F_4	F_5	F_6	F_7
1	2	3	4	5	6	7	8	9	10	11
					Pair 29					
6	2^h	17^h	+ 910	+ 23	+ 936	+ 936	+ 920	+38	+46	+41
7	1	16	857	32	891	893	891	− 5	− 1	− 2
8	0	14	901	49	949	946	951	+42	+41	+45
9	22	13	895	50	953	940	948	+25	+17	+28
10	21	12	930	50	991	949	957	+20	+ 9	+23
11	20	10	935	68	1006	988	996	+45	+32	+49
12	18	9	847	76	928	906	914	−51	−67	−47
13	17	8	949	84	1034	994	1001	+23	+ 8	+27
14	16	6	943	92	1036	976	980	−12	−25	− 8
15	15	5	972	100	1075	1003	1003	− 3	−13	+ 1
16	13	4	996	108	1109	1028	1023	+ 3	− 1	+ 8
17	12	2	975	116	1092	1003	995	−39	−38	−34
18	11	1	974	124	1100	1007	1004	−43	−38	−38
19	9	0	973	132	1108	1010	1024	−37	−26	−32
20	8	23	919	140	1058	959	991	−84	−71	−79
21	7	21	979	148	1122	1020	1071	−18	− 4	−12
22	6	20	938	156	1091	987	1045	−58	−43	−52
23	4	19	743	320	1068	1052	1099	−17	− 3	−11
24	3	18	743	332	1079	1064	1102	−28	−17	−22
25	2	16	732	344	1079	1067	1103	−41	−35	−35
26	0	15	794	356	1153	1142	1178	+20	+20	+27
27	23	14	807	368	1177	1168	1203	+31	+27	+38
28	22	12	765	380	1146	1138	1170	−15	−23	− 8
29	21	11	803	392	1195	1188	1218	+19	+ 8	+26
30	19	10	823	404	1227	1221	1253	+40	+25	+47
31	18	9	810	416	1224	1220	1255	+28	+12	+36
32	17	7	759	428	1182	1178	1217	−24	−38	−16
33	15	6	806	440	1242	1239	1281	+27	+16	+35
34	14	5	+ 814	+452	+1263	+1260	+1303	+35	+27	+43

Pair 30

k	☊ − α	☊ + α	F_1	Dδ	F_2	F_3	F_4	F_5	F_6	F_7
0	10	1	+ 908	+ 92	+ 997	+1032	+1002	+23	+25	+16
1	8	23	924	88	1010	1039	1009	+30	+39	+25
2	7	22	859	84	939	961	931	−49	−36	−52
3	6	21	927	80	1000	1015	985	+ 5	+21	+ 4
4	5	19	927	76	1000	1008	978	− 2	+14	− 1
5	3	18	962	72	1034	1038	1012	+32	+47	+30
6	2	17	908	62	973	973	957	−24	−16	−24
7	1	16	902	58	962	959	957	−24	−20	−24
8	23	14	874	54	935	939	944	−37	−41	−37
9	22	13	839	50	897	912	920	−62	−70	−62
10	21	12	894	46	942	987	995	+13	+ 2	+14
11	20	10	961	42	1006	1023	1031	−51	−64	−50
12	18	9	941	21	967	985	993	+10	− 6	+11
13	17	8	902	14	917	947	954	−29	−44	−28
14	16	7	945	+ 7	953	992	996	+13	− 1	+14
15	14	5	955	0	958	1000	1000	+16	+ 8	+17
16	13	4	1044	− 7	1042	1083	1078	+94	+90	+96
17	12	3	983	14	970	1008	1000	+16	+16	+18
18	11	1	952	21	933	968	965	−19	−14	−17
19	9	0	1008	28	983	1018	1032	+47	+58	+49
20	8	23	867	35	831	859	891	+ 6	+19	+ 8
21	7	22	950	42	903	926	977	− 8	+ 7	− 6

TABLE 30 (Contd.)

k	$\Omega-\alpha$	$\Omega+\alpha$	F_1	$D\delta$	F_2	F_3	F_4	F_5	F_6	F_7
1	2	3	4	5	6	7	8	9	10	11
				Pair 30						
22	5^h	20^h	+ 945	−49	+ 893	+ 912	+ 970	−16	− 1	−13
23	4	19	722	+170	897	899	946	−40	−26	−37
24	3	18	762	168	934	935	973	−13	− 2	−10
25	2	16	781	166	950	951	987	+ 1	+ 7	+ 4
26	0	15	721	164	888	888	924	−63	−63	−60
27	23	14	762	162	926	926	961	−26	−30	−23
28	22	13	856	160	1017	1017	1049	+62	+54	+66
29	20	11	786	158	944	944	974	−14	−27	−10
30	19	10	872	156	1028	1027	1059	+71	+56	+75
31	18	9	836	154	988	987	1022	+34	+18	+38
32	17	7	794	152	941	940	979	−10	−24	− 6
33	15	6	810	150	956	955	997	+ 8	− 3	+12
34	14	5	+ 758	+148	+ 903	+ 902	+ 945	−44	−52	−39
				Pair 32						
0	9	1	+ 923	+ 21	+ 944	+ 998	+ 968	+ 4	+ 6	−11
1	8	0	1011	24	1035	1049	1079	+83	+90	+72
2	7	23	863	27	887	921	891	−77	−65	−85
3	5	21	917	30	940	963	963	−37	−21	−42
4	4	20	923	33	952	965	935	−37	−19	38
5	3	19	933	36	967	973	947	−27	− 9	−25
6	1	17	876	44	923	922	906	−70	−64	−73
7	0	16	878	46	926	930	928	−50	−49	−53
8	23	15	904	48	959	965	970	−10	−13	−13
9	22	14	888	50	946	971	979	− 3	−10	− 5
10	20	12	900	52	954	1028	1036	+52	+39	+50
11	19	11	992	+ 54	1049	1077	1085	+99	+84	+98
12	18	10	1044	− 1	1048	1079	1087	+99	+82	+98
13	16	8	914	4	911	963	970	−20	−35	−21
14	15	7	984	7	978	1048	1052	+60	+48	+60
15	14	6	919	10	912	988	988	− 6	−15	− 6
16	13	5	973	13	965	1042	1037	+41	+35	+41
17	11	3	942	16	927	1001	993	− 5	− 2	− 4
18	10	2	968	19	951	1022	1019	+19	+26	+20
19	9	1	1007	22	988	1053	1067	+65	+76	+67
20	7	23	887	25	861	921	953	−51	−36	−49
21	6	22	897	28	864	917	968	−38	−21	−36
22	5	21	886	− 31	852	900	958	50	−34	−47
23	4	20	725	+200	930	936	983	−27	12	24
24	2	18	736	200	940	945	983	−29	20	−25
25	1	17	775	200	973	981	1017	+ 3	+ 9	+ 7
26	0	16	792	200	995	997	1033	+17	+18	+21
27	22	14	795	200	997	999	1034	+16	+ 9	+21
28	21	13	787	200	988	989	1021	+ 1	10	+ 6
29	20	12	775	200	975	976	1006	−16	−29	−10
30	19	11	764	200	964	964	996	−28	−43	−22
31	17	9	765	200	963	963	998	−28	−44	−22
32	16	8	781	200	976	976	1015	−13	−28	− 6
33	15	7	812	200	1008	1008	1050	+20	+ 8	+27
34	13	5	+ 818	+200	+1015	+1015	+1058	+26	+20	+33

TABLE 30 (Contd.)

Pair 34

k	$\Omega - \alpha$	$\Omega + \alpha$	F_1	$D\delta$	F_2	F_3	F_4	F_5	F_6	F_7
1	2	3	4	5	6	7	8	9	10	11
6	1^h	18^h	+ 918	+114	+1042	+1041	+1026	35	−28	−32
7	0	17	828	126	1062	1060	1058	− 1	+ 2	+ 2
8	22	15	925	138	1076	1082	1088	+31	+25	+34
9	21	14	869	150	1031	1052	1060	+ 4	− 6	+ 7
10	20	13	804	162	971	1027	1035	−19	32	−16
11	18	11	908	174	1084	1102	1110	+58	+41	+62
12	17	10	992	83	1077	1100	1108	+57	+40	+61
13	16	9	896	72	970	1007	1014	−35	−51	−31
14	15	8	955	61	1019	1065	1068	+21	+ 8	+25
15	13	6	871	50	921	969	968	−78	−85	−74
16	12	5	929	39	969	1014	1009	−35	−38	−31
17	11	4	996	28	1026	1066	1059	+17	+19	+21
18	9	2	1003	17	1022	1057	1056	+16	+26	+21
19	8	1	973	+ 6	985	1011	1027	−12	+ 1	− 7
20	7	0	921	− 5	918	937	970	−67	−52	−62
21	6	22	921	16	903	916	968	−67	−50	−62
22	4	21	1048	− 27	1018	1024	1081	+47	+63	+52
23	3	20	715	+250	966	965	1011	−21	− 8	−16
24	2	19	757	244	997	996	1034	+ 4	+14	+ 9
25	0	17	817	238	1049	1047	1083	+55	+58	+61
26	23	16	810	232	1037	1035	1071	+44	+42	+50
27	22	15	772	226	994	992	1026	+ 1	− 5	+ 7
28	21	13	818	220	1035	1033	1065	+42	+31	+48
29	19	12	749	214	961	959	990	−32	−47	−26
30	18	11	759	208	967	965	997	−23	−40	−17
31	17	10	784	202	985	983	1018	0	−17	+ 6
32	15	8	788	196	983	981	1021	+ 4	− 9	+11
33	14	7	791	190	979	977	1019	+ 4	− 6	+11
34	13	6	+ 760	+184	+ 942	+ 941	+ 984	−29	−36	−22

Pair 35

k	$\Omega - \alpha$	$\Omega + \alpha$	F_1	$D\delta$	F_2	F_3	F_4	F_5	F_6	F_7
0	8	2	+ 892	− 41	+ 851	+ 920	+ 890	+44	+47	+34
1	7	1	883	54	828	885	855	+ 9	+18	+ 3
2	6	23	827	67	759	801	771	−75	−61	−78
3	4	22	933	80	847	876	846	0	+17	+ 1
4	3	21	918	93	821	837	807	−39	−22	−34
5	2	19	971	106	868	875	850	+ 4	+20	+12
6	1	18	965	124	851	850	835	−11	− 4	− 8
7	23	17	946	136	818	814	812	−34	−34	−31
8	22	16	946	148	811	821	827	−19	−24	−15
9	21	14	992	160	844	878	886	+40	+30	+45
10	19	13	920	172	753	846	854	+ 8	− 7	+13
11	18	12	1027	184	845	877	885	+39	+22	+45
12	17	10	942	162	782	823	831	−15	−32	− 8
13	16	9	889	168	723	790	797	−49	−65	−42
14	14	8	988	174	817	904	907	+61	+50	+69
15	13	7	881	180	701	794	793	−53	−61	−44
16	12	5	969	186	784	878	873	+27	+24	+36
17	10	4	871	192	681	770	763	−83	−78	−73
18	9	3	982	198	786	870	869	+23	+32	+34
19	8	1	978	204	780	858	874	+28	+41	+39
20	6	0	938	210	730	799	832	−14	+ 3	− 2
21	5	23	889	216	671	732	784	−62	−45	−50
22	4	22	+ 936	−222	+ 711	+ 763	+ 820	−26	− 9	−13

TABLE 30 (Contd.)

k	$\Omega-\alpha$	$\Omega+\alpha$	F_1	$D\delta$	F_2	F_3	F_4	F_5	F_6	F_7
1	2	3	4	5	6	7	8	9	10	11
					Pair 36					
0	8^h	2^h	+ 886	+ 7	+ 896	+ 894	+ 864	+ 8	+ 9	− 5
1	7	1	938	8	947	944	914	+ 56	+ 63	+ 48
2	5	0	843	9	852	848	818	− 43	− 30	− 47
3	4	22	840	10	844	840	810	− 54	− 37	− 53
4	3	21	878	11	884	881	851	− 15	+ 3	− 9
5	2	20	870	12	883	881	856	− 12	+ 7	− 2
6	0	18	839	17	866	866	851	− 20	− 16	− 17
7	23	17	797	18	823	824	822	− 52	− 52	− 49
8	22	16	832	19	864	860	866	− 10	− 15	− 6
9	20	15	831	20	863	846	854	− 24	− 35	− 20
10	19	13	907	21	933	877	885	+ 4	− 11	+ 9
11	18	12	901	22	925	903	911	+ 27	+ 10	+ 32
12	17	11	914	31	947	915	923	+ 37	+ 20	+ 43
13	15	9	989	34	1025	964	971	+ 83	+ 69	+ 89
14	14	8	985	37	1025	936	939	+ 48	+ 37	+ 55
15	13	7	941	40	981	871	870	− 24	− 32	− 17
16	11	5	945	43	989	863	858	− 38	− 38	− 30
17	10	4	1013	46	1061	923	916	+ 18	+ 23	+ 27
18	9	3	938	49	989	840	839	− 62	− 53	− 53
19	8	2	946	52	1004	846	862	− 42	− 30	− 32
20	6	0	995	55	1052	889	922	+ 16	+ 33	+ 26
21	5	23	933	58	989	819	871	− 37	− 20	− 26
22	4	22	+ 926	+ 61	+ 984	+ 809	+ 866	− 45	− 28	− 34
					Pair 37					
0	8	2	+ 899	+104	+1006	+1014	+ 984	+ 12	+ 12	0
1	7	1	912	106	1019	1024	994	+ 19	+ 26	+ 12
2	5	0	860	108	968	970	940	− 38	− 25	− 40
3	4	22	906	110	1010	1010	980	− 2	+ 15	0
4	3	21	864	112	971	970	940	− 45	− 27	− 38
5	1	20	923	114	1038	1037	1012	+ 24	+ 41	+ 36
6	0	19	886	114	1010	1010	995	+ 4	+ 9	+ 8
7	23	17	846	116	970	971	969	− 25	− 25	− 20
8	22	16	853	118	984	981	987	− 11	− 16	− 6
9	20	15	868	120	1000	989	997	− 4	− 15	+ 2
10	19	13	921	122	1048	1013	1021	+ 17	+ 2	+ 24
11	18	12	860	124	986	972	980	− 27	− 44	− 20
12	16	11	901	121	1024	1002	1010	0	− 17	+ 8
13	15	10	964	124	1090	1046	1053	+ 39	+ 24	+ 47
14	14	8	922	127	1052	984	987	− 30	− 41	− 21
15	13	7	1039	130	1169	1085	1084	+ 64	+ 56	+ 74
16	11	6	973	133	977	879	874	−149	−150	−139
17	10	4	1000	136	1138	1028	1021	− 5	0	+ 6
18	9	3	1007	139	1148	1027	1026	− 4	+ 5	+ 7
19	7	2	961	142	1109	979	995	− 38	− 24	− 26
20	6	0	935	145	1082	947	980	− 56	− 39	− 43
21	5	23	997	148	1143	1001	1053	+ 14	+ 31	+ 27
22	4	22	+1006	+151	+1154	+1006	+1063	+ 21	+ 38	+ 35
					Pair 38					
6	0	19	+ 784	−129	+ 665	+ 665	+ 650	−106	−101	−103
7	23	17	822	136	694	693	691	− 59	− 59	− 56
8	21	16	878	143	748	751	757	+ 14	+ 6	+ 17

TABLE 30 (Contd.)

k	☊ − α	☊ + α	F_1	$D\delta$	F_2	F_3	F_4	F_5	F_6	F_7
1	2	3	4	5	6	7	8	9	10	11
					Pair 38					
9	20^h	15^h	+ 917	− 150	+ 779	+ 787	+ 795	+ 59	+48	+ 62
10	19	14	862	157	710	727	735	+ 5	− 9	+ 8
11	17	12	951	164	789	793	801	+ 77	+60	+ 80
12	16	11	854	145	711	714	722	+ 5	−12	+ 8
13	15	10	894	160	736	736	743	+ 33	+18	+ 36
14	14	8	905	175	733	726	729	+ 25	+14	+ 29
15	12	7	1004	190	814	801	800	+102	+97	+106
16	11	6	870	205	866	644	639	− 52	−53	− 48
17	10	5	962	220	744	712	705	+ 21	+24	+ 25
18	8	3	979	235	746	705	704	+ 26	+37	+ 30
19	7	2	896	250	652	602	618	− 54	− 40	− 50
20	6	1	861	265	598	540	573	− 92	−75	− 86
21	5	23	872	280	590	524	576	− 82	−65	− 78
22	3	22	919	295	621	548	605	− 47	−32	− 43
23	2	21	745	105	641	629	675	+ 29	+41	+ 34
24	1	20	738	120	614	602	640	+ 1	+10	+ 6
25	23	18	777	135	636	625	661	+ 29	+30	+ 34
26	22	17	762	150	607	597	633	+ 7	+ 4	+ 12
27	21	16	772	165	603	594	628	+ 8	0	+ 13
28	20	14	813	180	630	622	654	+ 41	+29	+ 46
29	18	13	870	195	673	666	697	+ 91	+74	+ 96
30	17	12	764	210	554	548	580	− 20	−37	− 15
31	16	11	726	225	500	495	530	− 64	−81	− 58
32	14	9	788	240	547	543	583	− 4	−16	+ 2
33	13	8	838	255	581	577	619	+ 39	+30	+ 45
34	12	7	+ 746	−270	+ 474	+ 471	+ 514	− 60	−65	− 54
					Pair 39					
0	7	3	+ 859	+155	+1017	+1001	+ 971	− 3	− 2	− 14
1	6	1	918	150	1069	1053	1023	+ 45	+54	+ 38
2	5	0	862	145	1007	993	963	− 18	− 5	− 20
3	4	23	840	140	974	962	932	− 53	−36	− 50
4	2	22	910	135	1040	1033	1003	+ 15	+32	+ 22
5	1	20	904	130	1035	1031	1006	+ 14	+31	+ 26
6	0	19	875	125	1010	1010	995	− 1	+ 4	+ 4
7	22	18	843	120	971	974	972	− 27	−29	− 21
8	21	16	808	115	936	928	934	− 69	−77	− 63
9	20	15	916	110	1038	1009	1017	+ 11	0	+ 18
10	19	14	956	105	1066	976	984	− 26	−40	+ 18
11	17	13	921	100	1023	989	997	− 17	−34	− 9
12	16	11	874	222	1098	1048	1056	+ 39	+22	+ 48
13	15	10	890	228	1120	1027	1034	+ 13	− 2	+ 23
14	13	9	854	234	1091	956	959	− 65	−75	− 55
15	12	7	973	240	1213	1050	1049	+ 21	+16	+ 32
16	11	6	926	246	1173	989	984	− 48	−49	− 36
17	10	5	1022	252	1276	1077	1070	+ 35	+38	+ 47
18	8	4	943	258	1203	989	988	− 51	− 41	− 38
19	7	2	1019	264	1289	1065	1081	+ 39	+53	+ 53
20	6	1	918	270	1190	960	993	− 53	−36	− 38
21	4	0	922	276	1196	961	1013	− 37	−20	− 22
22	3	22	+ 948	+282	+1227	+ 988	+1045	− 8	+ 7	+ 8

TABLE 30 (Contd.)

k	$\Omega-\alpha$	$\Omega+\alpha$	F_1	$D\delta$	F_2	F_3	F_4	F_5	F_6	F_7
1	2	3	4	5	6	7	8	9	10	11
					Pair 40					
0	7^h	3^h	+ 845	+ 39	+ 890	+922	+892	− 33	− 35	− 47
1	6	2	907	36	946	971	941	+ 16	+ 22	+ 7
2	4	1	827	33	861	878	948	+ 24	+ 36	+ 21
3	3	23	900	30	924	935	905	− 19	− 4	− 17
4	2	22	891	27	912	917	887	− 37	− 19	− 29
5	1	21	900	24	923	925	900	− 24	− 4	− 11
6	23	19	885	29	924	924	909	− 14	− 12	− 10
7	22	18	898	26	932	931	929	+ 6	+ 4	+ 10
8	21	17	822	23	858	860	866	− 57	− 63	− 53
9	19	16	891	20	923	926	934	+ 12	0	+ 17
10	18	14	933	17	955	959	967	+ 45	+ 29	+ 50
11	17	13	969	+ 14	985	984	992	+ 70	+ 53	+ 76
12	16	12	969	− 15	956	952	960	+ 39	+ 22	+ 45
13	14	10	932	20	914	901	908	− 13	− 26	− 6
14	13	9	980	25	958	933	936	+ 15	+ 5	+ 22
15	12	8	940	30	910	872	871	− 49	− 55	− 41
16	10	7	998	35	964	915	910	− 10	− 9	− 2
17	9	5	989	40	951	890	883	− 37	− 31	− 25
18	8	4	1015	45	972	901	900	− 20	− 10	− 11
19	7	3	988	50	944	864	880	− 39	− 26	− 30
20	5	1	908	55	855	765	798	−121	−104	−111
21	4	0	1036	60	974	876	928	+ 9	+ 26	+ 14
22	3	23	+1088	− 65	+1020	+914	+971	+ 53	+ 68	+ 69
					Pair 41					
0	7	3	+ 912	− 52	+ 866	+871	+841	+ 63	+ 61	+ 50
1	5	2	883	58	829	830	800	+ 23	+ 29	+ 16
2	4	1	814	64	753	752	722	− 55	− 43	− 57
3	3	23	870	70	796	794	764	− 12	+ 3	− 9
4	2	22	844	76	762	760	731	− 44	− 26	− 35
5	0	21	865	82	784	783	758	− 16	+ 1	− 2
6	23	20	878	92	801	801	787	+ 13	+ 16	+ 18
7	22	18	860	98	773	774	773	− 0	− 2	+ 5
8	20	17	820	104	729	724	730	− 42	− 50	− 37
9	19	16	876	110	777	760	768	− 4	− 16	+ 2
10	18	14	902	116	793	750	758	− 13	− 29	− 7
11	17	13	882	122	761	748	756	− 14	− 31	− 8
12	15	12	859	77	780	745	753	− 17	− 32	− 10
13	14	11	917	78	837	772	778	+ 9	− 4	+ 16
14	13	9	971	79	889	794	797	+ 29	+ 19	+ 37
15	11	8	956	80	876	757	756	− 12	− 15	− 4
16	10	7	952	81	874	737	731	− 36	− 35	− 28
17	9	5	1019	82	939	788	781	+ 15	+ 21	+ 24
18	7	4	964	83	884	720	720	− 45	− 33	− 36
19	6	3	954	84	877	703	720	− 45	− 30	− 35
20	5	2	1017	85	940	757	792	+ 28	+ 44	+ 38
21	4	0	945	86	858	670	722	− 41	− 24	− 31
22	2	23	+1007	− 87	+ 916	+721	+777	+ 14	+ 27	+ 25
					Pair 42					
6	23	20	+ 870	−426	+ 459	+459	+445	+ 4	+ 7	+ 7
7	21	19	865	434	442	441	440	+ 11	+ 7	+ 14
8	20	17	879	442	450	452	458	+ 42	+ 34	+ 45

TABLE 30 (Contd.)

k	☊ − α	☊ + α	F_1	$D\delta$	F_2	F_3	F_4	F_5	F_6	F_7
1	2	3	4	5	6	7	8	9	10	11
					Pair 42					
9	19^h	16^h	+ 853	−450	+414	+ 419	+427	+23	+11	+26
10	18	15	835	458	384	390	398	+ 7	− 8	+10
11	16	13	881	466	416	416	424	+46	+29	+49
12	15	12	889	531	356	353	361	− 5	−20	− 2
13	14	11	955	554	399	388	394	+41	+28	+44
14	12	10	947	577	367	344	347	+ 6	− 2	+ 9
15	11	8	957	600	357	322	321	− 7	−10	− 4
16	10	7	900	623	280	233	227	−88	−87	−85
17	8	6	1041	646	397	338	331	+28	+35	+31
18	7	4	984	669	318	249	249	−41	−29	−38
19	6	3	971	692	286	206	223	−55	−40	−52
20	5	2	948	715	241	151	186	−79	−63	−76
21	3	0	997	738	258	161	213	−39	−24	−36
22	2	23	1038	761	273	167	223	−17	− 4	−14
23	1	22	747	560	183	166	211	−16	− 5	−13
24	0	21	769	574	187	171	209	− 6	+ 1	− 3
25	22	19	797	588	197	183	219	+17	+16	+20
26	21	18	838	602	224	211	247	+58	+53	+61
27	20	17	726	616	100	88	122	−55	−63	−52
28	18	16	785	630	148	138	170	+ 6	− 8	+ 9
29	17	14	776	644	128	119	150	− 2	−18	+ 1
30	16	13	834	658	176	168	201	+62	+45	+65
31	15	12	779	672	107	100	136	+10	− 5	+13
32	13	10	785	686	99	93	133	+19	+ 8	+22
33	12	9	807	700	107	102	144	+43	+36	+46
34	11	8	+ 760	−714	+ 43	+ 39	+ 82	− 7	−10	− 4
					Pair 44					
0	6	4	+ 768	+ 0	+774	+ 854	+824	−17	−18	−35
1	5	3	754	− 10	748	812	782	−64	−59	−77
2	3	1	800	20	783	830	800	−50	−40	−58
3	2	0	854	30	820	851	821	−34	−21	−36
4	1	23	921	40	875	892	863	+ 4	+20	+ 7
5	0	22	940	50	891	898	873	+ 9	+27	+17
6	22	20	914	70	859	857	−843	−26	−26	−27
7	21	19	901	80	832	829	828	−45	+49	−46
8	20	18	995	90	918	930	936	+58	+51	+57
9	18	16	951	100	862	898	906	+24	+10	+24
10	17	15	943	110	840	915	923	+36	+21	+36
11	16	14	998	120	879	898	906	+14	− 2	+14
12	15	12	982	111	869	911	919	+23	+ 8	+24
13	13	11	972	114	856	921	927	+26	+15	+27
14	12	10	1007	117	887	967	970	+65	+57	+66
15	11	9	949	120	829	913	912	+ 2	− 2	+ 4
16	9	7	1045	123	925	1005	999	+84	+88	+86
17	8	6	989	126	865	937	930	+11	+18	+13
18	7	5	962	129	836	899	899	−25	−15	−22
19	6	3	960	132	835	887	904	−24	− 9	−21
20	4	2	971	135	844	885	920	−13	+ 3	−10
21	3	1	945	138	806	836	888	−50	−35	−46
22	2	0	1028	−141	883	902	958	+16	+29	+20
23	0	22	749	+150	895	897	942	− 5	+ 3	− 5
24	23	21	752	152	896	896	934	−17	−13	−12
25	22	20	710	154	852	851	887	−69	−69	−64

TABLE 30 (Contd.)

k	☊ − α	☊ + α	F_1	$D\delta$	F_2	F_3	F_4	F_5	F_6	F_7
1	2	3	4	5	6	7	8	9	10	11
					Pair 44					
26	21^h	18^h	+ 858	+156	+1002	+1000	+1036	+75	+70	+80
27	19	17	856	158	1004	1002	1036	+71	+61	+77
28	18	16	857	160	1010	1017	1039	+69	+55	+75
29	17	15	793	162	951	948	979	+ 5	−10	+11
30	15	13	732	164	896	893	926	− 53	− 68	−46
31	14	12	714	166	880	878	914	−70	−83	−63
32	13	11	720	168	888	886	926	− 62	−73	−55
33	12	9	791	170	961	959	1001	+ 8	+ 1	+16
34	10	8	+ 759	+172	+ 928	+ 926	+ 969	− 28	− 28	−20
					Pair 47					
0	5	5	+ 895	+163	+1064	+1054	+1024	+22	+19	+11
1	4	3	859	162	1025	1014	984	− 16	−11	− 22
2	3	2	845	161	1009	998	968	−31	−22	− 32
3	1	1	855	160	1011	1002	972	−26	−15	− 21
4	0	23	855	159	1008	1002	973	−23	− 10	− 13
5	23	22	886	158	1045	1042	1017	+23	+38	+39
6	22	21	803	163	981	982	968	−25	−24	−19
7	20	20	819	162	992	994	993	+ 1	− 4	+ 7
8	19	18	800	161	974	965	971	−19	−28	−12
9	18	17	841	160	1012	982	990	+ 2	− 10	+ 9
10	16	16	874	159	1040	970	978	− 9	− 23	− 1
11	15	14	877	158	1036	1015	1023	+37	+23	+45
12	14	13	824	160	982	928	936	− 48	−61	− 39
13	13	12	946	160	1104	1007	1013	+31	+20	+40
14	11	11	972	160	1131	991	994	+13	+ 8	+22
15	10	9	1025	160	1185	1014	1013	+33	+32	+43
16	9	8	987	160	1150	958	952	− 26	− 23	− 16
17	7	7	1051	160	1213	1003	996	+20	+28	+31
18	6	5	968	160	1131	906	906	−69	−57	−58
19	5	4	982	160	1149	912	929	−45	−31	−34
20	4	3	967	160	1135	890	925	− 47	−32	−35
21	2	2	954	160	1113	862	914	−56	− 44	−44
22	1	0	+1044	+160	+1200	+ 943	+ 999	+30	+41	+43
					Pair 48					
6	21	21	+ 871	+764	+1650	+1648	+1634	−48	−50	−54
7	20	20	876	776	1663	1659	1658	− 34	−39	−39
8	19	19	847	788	1648	1662	1668	−34	−42	−38
9	17	17	914	800	1725	1767	1775	+63	+51	+59
10	16	16	791	812	1610	1696	1704	−18	−32	−21
11	15	15	800	824	1625	1647	1655	−77	−90	−79
12	14	13	937	785	1720	1770	1778	+36	+23	+35
13	12	12	836	780	1614	1691	1697	−55	−63	− 55
14	11	11	959	775	1731	1828	1831	+69	+64	+70
15	10	10	987	770	1757	1859	1858	+86	+84	+87
16	8	8	927	765	1695	1793	1787	+ 4	+ 9	+ 6
17	7	7	995	760	1757	1846	1839	+46	+54	+49
18	6	6	938	755	1696	1776	1776	−27	−16	−23
19	5	4	998	750	1755	1824	1841	+28	+42	+33
20	3	3	930	745	1683	1741	1776	−47	−34	−41
21	2	2	982	740	1721	1767	1819	−14	− 2	− 7

TABLE 30 (Contd.)

k	☊ − α	☊ + α	F_1	$D\delta$	F_2	F_3	F_4	F_5	F_6	F_7
1	2	3	4	5	6	7	8	9	10	11
Pair 48										
22	1h	1h	+1033	+ 735	+1764	+1799	+1855	+ 12	+ 23	+19
23	23	23	738	1060	1794	1798	1843	− 10	− 5	− 2
24	22	22	761	1068	1821	1823	1861	− 2	0	+ 7
25	21	21	789	1076	1853	1853	1889	+ 15	+ 13	+25
26	20	19	791	1084	1863	1862	1898	+ 14	+ 8	+25
27	18	18	771	1092	1853	1852	1886	− 8	− 19	+ 4
28	17	17	794	1100	1887	1885	1917	+ 13	+ 1	+25
29	16	16	807	1108	1911	1909	1940	+ 26	+ 12	+39
30	14	14	759	1116	1875	1873	1906	− 18	− 30	− 4
31	13	13	705	1124	1829	1827	1863	− 71	− 82	−56
32	12	12	761	1132	1893	1891	1931	− 13	− 21	+ 3
33	11	10	772	1140	1912	1910	1952	− 2	− 7	+15
34	9	9	+ 760	+1148	+1905	+1903	+1946	− 18	− 16	0
Pair 50										
0	4	5	+ 876	+ 22	+ 903	+ 943	+ 913	+ 33	+ 30	+23
1	3	4	873	18	892	922	892	+ 16	+ 18	+11
2	2	3	832	14	847	868	838	− 35	− 29	−35
3	0	2	844	10	851	864	834	− 35	− 28	−30
4	23	0	910	6	908	915	886	+ 21	+ 31	+32
5	22	23	843	+ 2	842	844	820	− 42	− 30	−26
6	21	22	847	− 8	852	851	839	− 19	− 20	−13
7	19	20	854	12	853	852	852	− 2	− 9	+ 4
8	18	19	861	16	855	859	865	+ 15	+ 5	+22
9	17	18	876	20	867	874	882	+ 35	+ 24	+42
10	15	17	848	24	831	839	847	+ 3	− 7	+10
11	14	15	865	28	839	839	847	+ 8	− 3	+15
12	13	14	781	8	772	771	779	− 57	− 67	−50
13	12	13	840	12	824	816	822	− 10	− 18	− 2
14	10	11	763	16	741	722	725	−103	−105	−95
15	9	10	932	20	908	877	875	+ 51	+ 52	+59
16	8	9	879	24	856	813	807	− 14	− 10	− 6
17	6	8	940	28	914	861	854	+ 37	+ 46	+46
18	5	6	860	32	829	764	766	− 47	− 36	−38
19	4	5	843	36	815	739	758	− 52	− 40	−43
20	3	4	890	40	861	775	812	+ 6	+ 18	+15
21	1	2	851	44	811	716	769	− 33	− 23	−24
22	0	1	+ 923	− 48	+ 875	+ 771	+ 826	+ 27	+ 35	+37
Pair 51										
0	4	6	+ 918	+ 142	+1065	+1094	+1064	+ 76	+ 72	+66
1	3	4	889	138	1028	1050	1020	+ 33	+ 35	+28
2	2	3	834	134	969	984	954	− 32	− 26	−32
3	0	2	859	130	986	994	964	− 21	− 14	−15
4	23	0	862	126	980	984	955	− 29	− 19	−18
5	22	23	871	122	990	991	967	− 15	− 3	+ 1
6	20	22	807	122	942	942	930	− 51	− 54	−45
7	19	21	816	118	945	945	945	− 35	− 41	−28
8	18	19	851	114	975	976	982	+ 3	− 7	+10
9	17	18	853	110	974	973	981	+ 3	− 8	+10
10	15	17	870	106	983	978	986	+ 9	− 1	+17
11	14	15	839	102	943	942	950	− 26	− 37	−18

TABLE 30 (Contd.)

k	$\Omega-\alpha$	$\Omega+\alpha$	F_1	$D\delta$	F_2	F_3	F_4	F_5	F_6	F_7
1	2	3	4	5	6	7	8	9	10	11
					Pair 51					
12	13^h	14^h	+825	+144	+ 968	+ 956	+ 964	−11	−21	− 3
13	11	13	835	146	977	952	958	−16	−21	− 7
14	10	12	831	148	1023	981	984	+11	+ 9	+20
15	9	10	851	150	997	939	937	−35	−34	−26
16	8	9	821	152	974	902	896	−74	−70	−65
17	6	8	959	154	1115	1030	1023	+54	+63	+64
18	5	6	886	156	1043	946	948	−20	− 9	−10
19	4	5	848	158	1014	906	925	−42	−30	−32
20	2	4	882	160	1053	935	972	+ 6	+16	+17
21	1	3	862	162	1028	901	954	−11	− 2	0
22	23	1	+893	+164	+1057	+ 922	+ 977	+13	+18	+24
					Pair 52					
6	20	22	+876	− 48	+ 841	+ 844	+ 832	+66	+63	+70
7	19	21	827	52	786	789	789	+12	+ 6	+16
8	18	20	837	56	791	811	817	+28	+19	+32
9	16	18	843	60	794	848	856	+56	+45	+60
10	15	17	857	64	800	882	890	+78	+68	+82
11	14	16	923	68	857	862	870	+46	+36	+50
12	12	14	835	90	744	811	819	−16	−23	−12
13	11	13	805	100	701	805	811	−36	−41	−32
14	10	12	837	110	721	851	854	− 4	− 6	0
15	9	11	777	120	653	792	790	−80	−79	−76
16	7	9	870	130	741	878	872	−10	− 4	− 6
17	6	8	845	140	707	839	832	−61	−52	−57
18	5	7	870	150	721	844	846	−59	−49	−55
19	3	5	889	160	737	852	871	−45	−35	−41
20	2	4	851	170	692	795	832	−96	−86	−92
21	1	3	886	180	710	801	854	−86	−77	−82
22	0	2	966	−190	776	855	910	−41	−34	−37
23	22	0	774	+145	914	924	968	+ 5	+ 7	+ 9
24	21	23	780	162	932	940	977	+ 3	+ 2	+ 7
25	20	22	742	179	907	912	948	−38	−41	−34
26	18	20	820	196	1001	1004	1040	+42	+33	+46
27	17	19	782	213	983	985	1019	+10	0	+14
28	16	18	785	230	1006	1007	1039	+18	+ 7	+22
29	15	17	778	247	1020	1020	1051	+19	+ 9	+23
30	13	15	790	264	1053	1053	1086	+42	+33	+46
31	12	14	731	281	1014	1014	1050	− 6	−13	− 2
32	11	13	763	298	1064	1063	1103	+36	+31	+40
33	9	11	794	315	1110	1109	1151	+72	+73	+76
34	8	10	+708	+332	+1040	+1039	+1082	− 8	− 5	− 4
					Pair 56					
6	19	23	+831	+ 32	+ 876	+ 874	+ 862	−33	−38	−30
7	18	22	842	28	881	880	880	− 9	−16	− 6
8	17	21	868	24	902	910	916	+33	+25	+36
9	15	19	865	20	896	916	924	+47	+39	+50
10	14	18	847	16	870	898	906	+35	+28	+38
11	13	17	887	+ 12	901	902	910	+45	+39	+48
12	11	15	831	− 14	816	835	843	−16	−19	−13
13	10	14	840	26	810	835	841	−12	−13	− 9
14	9	13	804	38	760	787	790	−57	−56	−54

TABLE 30 (Contd.)

k	$\Omega-\alpha$	$\Omega+\alpha$	F_1	$D\delta$	F_2	F_3	F_4	F_5	F_6	F_7
1	2	3	4	5	6	7	8	9	10	11
				Pair 56						
15	8^h	12^h	+885	50	+831	+852	+850	+ 8	+ 11	+ 11
16	6	10	893	62	832	846	840	+ 4	+ 11	+ 7
17	5	9	885	64	813	819	812	− 18	− 10	− 15
18	4	8	944	86	859	855	857	+ 33	+ 42	+ 36
19	2	6	846	98	756	743	762	− 56	− 49	− 54
20	1	5	781	110	682	658	695	−117	−111	−115
21	0	4	889	122	771	739	792	− 14	− 9	− 12
22	23	2	940	−134	806	767	822	+ 22	+ 26	+ 24
23	21	1	763	+ 10	768	761	805	+ 11	+ 10	+ 13
24	20	0	752	+ 4	746	738	775	− 13	− 16	− 11
25	19	23	785	− 2	769	762	798	+ 16	+ 11	+ 18
26	17	21	806	8	783	776	812	+ 35	+ 27	+ 37
27	16	20	730	14	704	698	732	− 39	− 48	− 37
28	15	19	809	20	780	774	806	+ 41	+ 33	+ 43
29	14	18	750	26	719	713	744	− 15	− 22	− 13
30	12	16	803	32	770	765	798	+ 45	+ 40	+ 47
31	11	15	752	38	716	712	748	+ 1	− 2	+ 3
32	10	14	737	44	696	692	732	− 9	− 10	− 7
33	8	12	775	50	726	723	765	+ 30	+ 33	+ 32
34	7	11	+713	− 56	+657	+654	+697	− 32	− 27	− 30
				Pair 57						
0	3	7	+835	− 70	+770	+775	+745	+ 2	− 2	− 4
1	1	6	881	80	799	801	771	+ 33	+ 30	+ 30
2	0	5	794	90	704	704	674	− 58	− 59	− 57
3	23	3	861	100	758	757	727	+ 1	+ 4	+ 6
4	21	2	887	110	768	767	738	+ 17	+ 19	+ 25
5	20	1	886	120	759	758	735	+ 19	+ 24	+ 31
6	19	23	824	130	702	703	692	− 18	− 23	− 14
7	18	22	819	140	688	688	688	− 16	− 23	− 13
8	16	21	813	150	671	665	671	− 28	− 36	− 25
9	15	19	867	160	715	699	707	+ 13	+ 5	+ 16
10	14	18	918	170	754	733	741	+ 53	+ 46	+ 55
11	12	17	867	180	688	694	702	+ 20	+ 17	+ 22
12	11	16	783	77	702	668	676	− 1	− 3	+ 1
13	10	14	833	78	750	690	696	+ 24	+ 23	+ 25
14	8	13	806	79	718	632	634	− 32	− 29	− 31
15	7	12	761	80	670	565	563	+ 3	+ 8	+ 9
16	6	10	797	81	714	592	586	− 69	− 62	− 63
17	5	9	861	82	781	647	641	− 9	− 1	− 9
18	3	8	816	83	734	589	592	− 52	− 45	− 53
19	2	7	782	84	703	550	570	− 68	− 62	− 69
20	1	5	872	85	800	640	678	+ 45	+ 51	+ 44
21	23	4	821	86	745	578	632	+ 4	+ 6	+ 2
22	22	3	+897	− 87	+812	+638	+692	+ 70	+ 70	+ 68
				Pair 58						
0	2	7	+815	− 62	+758	+837	+807	+ 10	+ 4	+ 1
1	1	6	825	68	755	819	789	− 2	− 5	− 7
2	0	5	745	74	671	718	688	− 97	− 98	− 98
3	22	3	819	80	736	766	736	− 43	− 43	− 40
4	21	2	905	86	810	827	798	+ 25	+ 27	+ 32
5	20	1	866	92	767	773	750	− 16	− 11	− 5
6	19	0	839	102	745	742	731	− 29	− 34	− 26

TABLE 30 (Contd.)

k	$\Omega-\alpha$	$\Omega+\alpha$	F_1	$D\delta$	F_2	F_3	F_4	F_5	F_6	F_7
1	2	3	4	5	6	7	8	9	10	11
					Pair 58					
7	17^h	22^h	+877	−108	+ 778	+777	+777	+ 23	+ 16	+ 26
8	16	21	842	114	736	755	761	+ 13	+ 5	+ 16
9	15	20	817	120	705	751	759	+ 17	+ 10	+ 20
10	13	18	847	126	727	776	784	+ 48	+ 43	+ 51
11	12	17	939	132	808	796	804	+ 74	+ 71	+ 77
12	11	16	832	187	641	699	707	− 17	− 19	− 14
13	10	15	814	198	611	700	706	− 12	− 12	− 9
14	8	13	843	209	625	735	737	+ 25	+ 28	+ 28
15	7	12	780	220	549	665	663	− 43	− 38	− 40
16	6	11	822	231	589	704	698	− 1	+ 6	+ 2
17	4	9	803	242	563	674	668	− 25	− 17	− 22
18	3	8	822	253	570	674	677	− 10	− 3	− 7
19	2	7	844	264	585	680	700	+ 19	+ 25	+ 22
20	1	5	768	275	506	592	630	− 45	− 39	− 42
21	23	4	823	286	547	623	677	+ 8	+ 10	+ 11
22	22	3	882	297	587	653	707	+ 44	+ 44	+ 47
23	21	2	753	115	635	643	686	+ 29	+ 27	+ 32
24	19	0	744	124	612	618	655	+ 4	− 1	+ 7
25	18	23	777	133	633	637	673	+ 29	+ 22	+ 32
26	17	22	812	142	657	660	696	+ 58	+ 51	+ 61
27	16	20	755	151	593	595	628	− 4	− 13	− 2
28	14	19	746	160	578	579	610	− 16	− 22	− 14
29	13	18	737	169	564	564	595	− 25	− 30	− 23
30	12	17	761	178	585	585	618	+ 4	+ 1	+ 6
31	10	15	747	187	565	565	601	− 7	− 7	− 5
32	9	14	710	196	522	522	562	− 40	− 38	− 38
33	8	13	729	205	531	530	572	− 24	− 21	− 22
34	7	11	+719	−214	+ 511	+510	+553	− 37	− 32	− 35
					Pair 61					
0	1	8	+840	+ 65	+ 907	+892	+862	+ 5	− 1	+ 3
1	0	7	855	70	921	907	877	+ 21	+ 16	+ 22
2	23	6	833	75	907	895	865	+ 10	+ 6	+ 14
3	22	4	840	80	917	908	878	+ 24	+ 23	+ 31
4	20	3	853	85	930	924	895	+ 42	+ 40	+ 53
5	19	2	857	90	942	940	917	+ 65	+ 65	+ 79
6	18	0	726	85	819	820	809	− 41	− 48	− 33
7	16	23	689	90	788	788	788	− 61	− 68	− 53
8	15	22	667	95	770	759	765	− 83	− 88	− 75
9	14	21	707	100	815	787	795	− 53	− 57	− 44
10	13	19	786	105	897	863	871	+ 25	+ 21	+ 34
11	11	18	765	110	876	885	893	+ 48	+ 49	+ 57
12	10	17	766	71	833	784	792	− 52	− 49	− 43
13	9	15	721	74	790	706	712	−131	−128	−122
14	7	14	814	77	882	767	769	− 73	− 67	− 63
15	6	13	868	80	937	901	899	+ 59	+ 66	+ 69
16	5	12	936	83	1017	867	861	+ 21	+ 28	+ 31
17	3	10	944	86	1032	868	862	+ 24	+ 29	+ 34
18	2	9	874	89	964	791	794	− 43	− 39	− 33
19	1	8	810	92	907	728	748	− 88	− 85	− 77
20	0	6	875	95	983	799	837	+ 2	+ 4	+ 13
21	22	5	871	98	979	791	845	+ 11	+ 8	+ 22
22	21	4	+938	+101	+1041	+851	+905	+ 72	+ 68	+ 83

TABLE 30 (Contd.)

k	$\Omega - \alpha$	$\Omega + \alpha$	F_1	$D\delta$	F_2	F_3	F_4	F_5	F_6	F_7
1	2	3	4	5	6	7	8	9	10	11
					Pair 62					
0	1^h	8^h	+848	+110	+960	+980	+950	− 4	−10	− 5
1	0	7	846	110	952	967	937	− 7	−12	− 5
2	23	6	786	110	895	905	875	−59	−63	−54
3	21	5	870	110	977	983	953	+30	+24	+38
4	20	3	862	110	964	967	938	+25	+23	+36
5	19	2	862	110	967	968	945	+42	+42	+56
6	17	1	738	100	846	846	835	−58	−65	−50
7	16	23	795	100	904	904	904	+21	+14	+29
8	15	22	772	100	880	882	888	+16	+11	+25
9	14	21	725	100	833	836	844	−18	−22	− 9
10	12	20	798	100	904	905	913	+61	+61	+70
11	11	18	716	+100	817	817	825	−17	−16	− 8
12	10	17	765	− 19	742	739	747	−85	−82	−76
13	8	16	808	26	777	768	774	−47	−41	−38
14	7	14	818	33	776	759	761	−50	−44	−41
15	6	13	853	40	802	777	775	−26	−19	−17
16	5	12	907	47	858	827	821	+30	+37	+40
17	3	11	889	54	837	799	793	+12	+17	+22
18	2	9	865	61	805	760	763	− 7	− 3	+ 3
19	1	8	821	68	758	706	726	−34	−31	−24
20	23	7	794	75	732	674	712	−38	−40	−28
21	22	5	817	82	745	682	736	− 4	− 7	+ 6
22	21	4	+857	− 89	+770	+702	+756	+26	+22	+36
					Pair 64					
0	1	9	+793	+ 11	+803	+775	+745	−58	−62	−58
1	23	8	868	+ 4	866	842	812	+10	+ 3	+12
2	22	6	849	− 3	844	825	795	− 5	−11	0
3	21	5	866	10	853	839	809	+10	+ 4	+17
4	20	4	855	17	831	823	794	− 3	− 7	+ 6
5	18	2	834	24	807	804	781	−15	−19	− 4
6	17	1	817	22	803	805	794	− 1	− 8	+ 6
7	16	0	827	28	808	809	809	+16	+ 9	+23
8	14	23	829	34	803	790	796	+ 4	+ 1	+12
9	13	21	847	40	815	780	788	− 2	− 4	+ 6
10	12	20	918	46	878	838	846	+57	+57	+65
11	11	19	857	− 52	806	817	825	+37	+39	+45
12	9	17	737	+ 55	788	731	739	−47	−41	−39
13	8	16	813	60	868	772	778	− 7	− 1	+ 1
14	7	15	811	65	867	738	740	−43	−36	−34
15	5	14	858	70	917	766	764	−18	−10	− 9
16	4	12	876	75	949	784	778	− 3	+ 4	+ 6
17	3	11	900	80	982	807	801	+22	+27	+31
18	2	10	822	85	908	724	727	−51	−48	−42
19	0	8	754	90	849	661	681	−95	−95	−85
20	23	7	887	95	995	802	840	+65	+63	+75
21	22	6	729	100	839	645	699	−75	−79	−65
22	20	5	+841	+105	+948	+753	+807	+37	+29	+47
					Pair 65 (66)					
6	17	1	+887	+ 24	+914	+915	+905	+ 3	− 4	+ 5
7	15	0	876	46	926	926	927	+27	+22	+29
8	14	23	863	68	934	927	934	+37	+34	+39
9	13	21	841	90	936	919	927	+32	+30	+34

TABLE 30 (Contd.)

k	$\Omega-\alpha$	$\Omega+\alpha$	F_1	$D\delta$	E_2	F_3	F_4	F_5	F_6	F_7
1	2	3	4	5	6	7	8	9	10	11
					Pair 65 (66)					
10	11^h	20^h	+810	+112	+ 928	+913	+921	+28	+31	+30
11	10	19	761	134	893	900	908	+17	+22	+19
12	9	18	801	102	897	866	874	−15	− 8	−13
13	8	16	772	108	874	823	829	−57	−51	−55
14	6	15	813	114	916	846	848	−36	−27	−34
15	5	14	802	120	906	824	821	−61	−53	−59
16	4	12	806	126	928	837	831	−49	−42	−47
17	2	11	895	132	1028	928	922	+44	+47	+46
18	1	10	831	138	968	862	866	− 9	− 8	− 7
19	0	9	788	144	935	825	846	−27	−28	−25
20	23	7	717	150	876	763	803	−68	−70	−66
21	21	6	743	156	911	795	849	−20	−27	−18
22	20	5	807	162	974	857	911	+44	+36	+46
23	19	3	766	85	852	834	877	+13	+ 6	+15
24	17	2	709	84	790	774	811	−51	−59	−49
25	16	1	757	83	834	821	857	− 3	−10	− 1
26	15	0	790	82	864	852	887	+29	+24	+31
27	14	22	776	81	850	840	873	+17	+14	+19
28	12	21	763	80	839	830	861	+ 8	+ 9	+10
29	11	20	737	79	816	809	840	−11	− 8	− 9
30	10	18	732	78	814	808	842	− 7	− 3	− 5
31	8	17	752	77	839	834	871	+24	+32	+26
32	7	16	731	76	819	814	855	+10	+18	+12
33	6	15	748	75	835	831	874	+32	+41	+34
34	5	13	+672	+ 74	+ 757	+754	+797	−43	−36	−41
					Pair 67 (68)					
0	0	10	+796	+ 37	+ 835	+820	+790	−26	−31	−23
1	22	8	858	28	881	868	838	+24	+16	+27
2	21	7	828	19	845	834	804	− 7	−16	− 3
3	20	6	856	10	863	856	826	+17	+ 8	+22
4	19	5	903	+ 1	886	882	853	+47	+38	+52
5	17	3	842	− 9	829	827	805	+ 1	− 6	+ 7
6	16	2	806	13	796	797	787	−15	−23	−11
7	15	1	837	22	819	819	820	+23	+18	+26
8	13	23	833	31	805	797	804	+ 7	+ 6	+10
9	12	22	835	40	800	780	788	− 6	− 4	− 3
10	11	21	846	49	803	786	794	+ 2	+ 6	+ 4
11	10	19	867	− 58	807	815	823	+33	+38	+35
12	8	18	793	+ 67	854	820	828	+41	+50	+43
13	7	17	705	68	767	713	719	−66	−56	−65
14	6	16	744	69	802	729	731	−51	−41	−50
15	4	14	741	70	795	711	708	−72	−64	−71
16	3	13	753	71	820	729	723	−55	−50	−55
17	2	12	852	72	925	827	821	+46	+49	+46
18	1	10	804	73	876	774	778	+ 5	+ 6	+ 5
19	23	9	755	74	832	728	749	−21	−25	−22
20	22	8	757	75	841	734	774	+ 6	0	+ 5
21	21	7	755	76	843	736	790	+24	+16	+23
22	19	5	770	+ 77	852	745	799	+36	+26	+34
23	18	4	777	− 30	748	732	775	+14	+ 4	+12
24	17	3	727	28	696	682	719	−39	−48	−41

TABLE 30 (Contd.)

k	☊ − α	☊ + α	F_1	$D\delta$	F_2	F_3	F_4	F_5	F_6	F_7
1	2	3	4	5	6	7	8	9	10	11
					Pair 67 (68)					
25	16^h	1^h	+748	−26	+716	+704	+740	−16	−23	−19
26	14	0	750	24	718	708	743	−11	−14	−14
27	13	23	776	22	747	738	771	+20	+19	+17
28	12	22	791	20	767	759	790	+41	+43	+37
29	10	20	732	18	714	708	739	− 7	− 1	−11
30	9	19	731	16	719	714	748	+ 4	+12	− 1
31	8	18	722	14	718	714	751	+ 9	+18	+ 4
32	6	16	667	12	667	663	704	−35	−25	−40
33	5	15	731	10	733	730	773	+36	+45	+30
34	4	14	+697	− 8	+700	+697	+740	+ 6	+14	0
					Pair 68 (69)					
6	16	2	+825	−22	+806	+806	+796	−27	−35	−30
7	15	1	842	28	818	818	819	− 3	− 8	− 6
8	13	0	830	34	799	800	807	−14	−15	−17
9	12	22	815	40	780	781	789	−31	−29	−33
10	11	21	869	46	829	829	837	+18	+22	+16
11	9	20	885	52	831	831	839	+21	+30	+19
12	8	18	840	12	822	821	829	+12	+21	+11
13	7	17	796	8	782	779	785	−31	−21	−32
14	5	16	841	− 4	826	819	821	+ 6	+16	+ 5
15	4	15	811	0	795	785	782	−32	−23	−33
16	3	13	817	+ 4	817	805	799	−14	− 9	−14
17	2	12	857	8	866	851	845	+33	+36	+33
18	0	11	853	12	864	847	851	+40	+38	+40
19	23	9	783	16	802	783	804	− 6	−10	− 5
20	22	8	752	20	781	760	800	− 9	−15	− 8
21	20	7	760	24	796	773	827	+19	+ 9	+20
22	19	6	747	28	780	755	809	+ 2	− 9	+ 3
23	18	4	721	20	742	738	781	−25	−35	−23
24	17	3	743	20	760	756	793	−12	−21	−10
25	15	2	782	20	796	793	829	+25	+19	+27
26	14	0	814	20	826	823	858	+55	+52	+58
27	13	23	803	20	816	813	846	+44	+43	+47
28	11	22	738	20	754	752	783	−18	−13	−15
29	10	21	719	20	739	737	768	−32	−25	−29
30	9	19	728	20	752	750	784	−15	− 7	−11
31	8	18	708	20	738	736	773	−23	−14	−19
32	6	16	695	20	727	726	767	−30	−20	−26
33	5	15	700	20	732	731	774	−22	−13	−17
34	4	14	+725	+20	+756	+755	+798	+ 3	+11	+ 8
					Pair 69 (70)					
6	16	2	+856	−47	+812	+811	+801	−25	−33	−23
7	14	1	861	48	817	817	818	− 4	− 7	− 2
8	13	0	822	49	776	784	791	−27	−28	−25
9	12	23	835	50	790	808	816	+ 2	+ 4	+ 4
10	10	21	869	51	824	838	846	+36	+43	+38
11	9	20	864	52	810	804	812	+ 6	+15	+ 7
12	8	19	792	42	744	768	776	−26	−16	−25
13	7	17	795	48	741	779	785	−13	− 3	−12
14	5	16	825	54	760	807	809	+15	+25	+16

TABLE 30 (Contd.)

k	☊ $-\alpha$	☊ $+\alpha$	F_1	$D\delta$	F_2	F_3	F_4	F_5	F_6	F_7
1	2	3	4	5	6	7	8	9	10	11
					Pair 69 (70)					
15	4^h	15^h	+779	− 60	+ 703	+ 754	+ 751	−39	−30	−38
16	3	14	823	66	753	807	801	+14	+20	+15
17	1	12	843	72	772	825	819	+36	+37	+37
18	0	11	799	78	720	772	776	− 3	− 5	− 2
19	23	10	753	84	672	722	743	−32	−37	−31
20	21	8	739	90	658	705	745	−26	−35	−25
21	20	7	753	96	669	715	769	+ 2	− 8	+ 3
22	19	6	768	102	671	714	768	+ 5	− 6	+ 5
23	18	5	776	15	762	768	811	+52	+40	+52
24	16	3	759	20	736	741	778	+23	+14	+23
25	15	2	741	25	710	714	750	− 2	− 8	− 2
26	14	1	769	30	731	734	769	+21	+18	+21
27	12	23	730	35	688	691	724	−20	−18	−20
28	11	22	754	40	710	712	743	+ 3	+ 8	+ 3
29	10	21	773	45	728	730	761	+25	+32	+25
30	9	19	713	50	667	668	702	−30	−22	−30
31	7	18	743	55	698	699	736	+ 8	+19	+ 8
32	6	17	724	60	676	677	718	− 6	+ 6	− 6
33	5	16	726	65	673	674	717	− 3	+ 7	− 3
34	3	14	+676	− 70	+ 617	+ 617	+ 660	−56	−50	−56
					Pair 70 (71)					
0	23	10	+843	+213	+1055	+1095	+1065	+37	+32	+44
1	22	9	843	212	1048	1081	1051	+22	+15	+28
2	21	8	774	211	982	1007	977	−53	−62	−47
3	19	6	840	210	1047	1063	1033	+ 2	− 9	+ 8
4	18	5	880	209	1082	1091	1062	+30	+18	+36
5	17	4	890	208	1095	1098	1076	+44	+34	+49
6	16	2	841	203	1047	1045	1035	+ 2	− 6	+ 7
7	14	1	861	202	1067	1067	1068	+34	+31	+39
8	13	0	802	201	1006	1020	1027	− 8	− 9	+ 4
9	12	23	724	200	929	962	970	−66	−64	−62
10	10	21	744	199	949	976	984	−53	−46	−49
11	9	20	843	198	1039	1027	1035	− 3	+ 6	0
12	8	19	815	145	954	1002	1010	−29	−19	−26
13	7	17	785	140	919	995	1001	−39	−29	+36
14	5	16	823	135	947	1043	1045	+ 4	+14	+ 7
15	4	15	823	130	937	1044	1041	− 1	+ 8	+ 1
16	3	14	790	125	911	1022	1016	−26	−20	−24
17	1	12	837	120	958	1073	1067	+24	+25	+26
18	0	11	831	115	945	1062	1066	+22	+20	+23
19	23	10	785	110	898	1012	1033	−12	−17	−11
20	21	8	764	105	878	991	1031	−15	−24	−14
21	20	7	802	100	914	1023	1077	+30	+20	+31
22	19	6	784	95	884	991	1045	− 3	−14	− 3
23	18	5	758	245	1004	1019	1062	+13	+ 1	+13
24	16	3	774	250	1021	1034	1071	+21	+12	+21
25	15	2	764	255	1013	1024	1060	+10	+ 4	+ 9
26	14	1	749	260	1001	1010	1045	− 6	− 9	− 7
27	12	23	739	265	997	1005	1038	−14	−12	−15
28	11	22	705	270	971	977	1008	−45	−40	−46
29	10	21	743	275	1018	1023	1054	0	+ 7	− 2
30	9	19	741	280	1025	1029	1063	+ 8	+16	+ 6

TABLE 30 (Contd.)

k	☊ − α	☊ + α	F_1	$D\delta$	F_2	F_3	F_4	F_5	F_6	F_7
1	2	3	4	5	6	7	8	9	10	11
					Pair 70 (71)					
31	7^h	18^h	+722	+285	+1017	+1020	+1057	+ 1	+ 12	− 1
32	6	17	721	290	1023	1026	1067	+ 10	+ 22	+ 7
33	5	16	694	295	1001	1003	1046	− 12	− 2	− 15
34	3	14	+723	+300	+1034	+1036	+1079	+ 20	+ 26	+ 17
					Pair 71 (72)					
0	23	11	+838	− 4	+833	+ 849	+ 819	+ 21	+ 16	+ 28
1	22	9	854	6	841	855	825	+ 28	+ 21	+ 35
2	20	8	789	8	778	788	758	− 37	− 48	− 31
3	19	7	846	10	833	839	809	+ 15	+ 3	+ 21
4	18	5	877	12	858	862	833	+ 40	+ 28	+ 46
5	16	4	865	14	848	849	827	+ 35	+ 25	+ 40
6	15	3	845	14	834	833	823	+ 33	+ 26	+ 38
7	14	2	836	16	824	824	825	+ 36	+ 32	+ 41
8	13	0	842	18	827	833	840	+ 52	+ 51	+ 57
9	11	23	799	20	784	797	805	+ 19	+ 24	+ 23
10	10	22	777	22	761	772	780	− 5	+ 3	− 1
11	9	20	803	24	777	772	780	− 4	+ 5	0
12	7	19	790	52	732	752	760	− 22	− 10	− 19
13	6	18	742	58	678	708	714	− 67	− 54	− 64
14	5	17	699	64	624	662	664	−116	−104	−113
15	4	15	776	70	690	733	730	− 48	− 39	− 46
16	2	14	780	76	700	745	739	− 38	− 34	− 36
17	1	13	736	82	655	702	696	− 80	− 79	− 78
18	0	11	824	88	735	783	787	+ 12	+ 10	+ 14
19	22	10	752	94	661	706	727	− 46	− 54	− 45
20	21	9	781	100	690	735	775	+ 3	− 7	+ 4
21	20	7	749	106	655	699	753	− 18	− 28	− 17
22	18	6	757	112	650	693	747	− 22	− 35	− 22
23	17	5	766	30	737	743	886	+ 18	+ 6	+ 18
24	16	4	756	26	727	732	769	+ 2	− 8	+ 2
25	15	2	720	22	692	696	732	− 34	− 40	− 35
26	13	1	791	18	765	769	804	+ 40	+ 39	+ 39
27	12	0	751	14	730	733	766	+ 3	+ 5	+ 2
28	11	22	717	10	703	706	737	− 25	− 20	− 26
29	9	21	788	6	782	784	815	+ 55	+ 65	+ 53
30	8	20	737	− 2	739	741	775	+ 16	+ 27	+ 14
31	7	19	723	+ 2	735	736	773	+ 15	+ 27	+ 13
32	6	17	691	6	709	710	751	− 5	+ 7	− 8
33	4	16	730	10	752	753	796	+ 41	+ 51	+ 38
34	3	15	+703	+ 14	+728	+ 729	+ 772	+ 18	+ 25	+ 15
					Pair 72 (73)					
0	23	11	+831	+ 68	+898	+ 930	+ 900	+ 16	+ 11	+ 24
1	21	10	854	72	919	946	916	+ 26	+ 15	+ 33
2	20	8	795	76	868	888	858	− 39	− 50	− 32
3	19	7	832	80	909	923	893	− 11	− 23	− 4
4	17	6	890	84	967	975	946	+ 36	+ 23	+ 42
5	16	4	839	88	924	927	905	− 11	− 21	− 5
6	15	3	808	98	909	907	897	− 26	− 33	− 20
7	14	2	825	102	931	931	932	+ 2	− 2	+ 7
8	12	0	828	106	937	950	957	+ 21	+ 23	+ 26
9	11	23	743	110	858	888	896	− 46	− 41	− 41

TABLE 30 (Contd.)

k	☊ − α	☊ + α	F_1	$D\delta$	F_2	F_3	F_4	F_5	F_6	F_7
1	2	3	4	5	6	7	8	9	10	11
					Pair 72 (73)					
10	10^h	22^h	+787	+114	+ 907	+ 931	+ 939	−10	− 2	− 6
11	8	21	843	118	959	948	956	0	+12	+ 4
12	7	19	823	93	910	955	963	+ 1	+13	+ 5
13	6	18	777	92	863	933	939	−29	−16	−25
14	5	17	822	91	902	992	994	+19	+31	+22
15	3	15	769	90	843	944	941	−41	34	−38
16	2	14	786	89	871	978	972	−16	−12	−13
17	1	13	847	88	936	1047	1041	+47	+48	+49
18	23	12	815	87	901	1015	1019	+18	+13	+20
19	22	10	770	86	859	973	994	−14	−22	−12
20	21	9	792	85	886	999	1039	+25	+15	+26
21	20	8	759	84	855	966	1020	0	−11	+ 1
22	18	6	741	83	829	938	992	−35	−48	−34
23	17	5	736	235	975	991	1034	0	−12	0
24	16	4	756	244	1002	1016	1053	+13	+ 3	+13
25	14	3	782	253	1035	1046	1082	+36	+31	+36
26	13	1	750	262	1010	1020	1055	+ 2	+ 1	+ 2
27	12	0	747	271	1016	1024	1057	− 3	− 1	− 4
28	11	23	754	280	1033	1040	1071	+ 5	+10	+ 4
29	10	21	736	289	1026	1031	1062	−10	− 3	−11
30	8	20	729	298	1032	1036	1070	− 9	+ 2	−11
31	7	19	713	307	1028	1032	1069	−17	− 5	−19
32	5	18	680	316	1007	1010	1051	−41	−28	−43
33	4	16	689	325	1025	1028	1071	−27	−17	−30
34	3	15	+758	+334	+1101	+1103	+1146	+41	+48	+38
					Pair 73 (74)					
0	22	11	+822	+150	+ 977	+ 972	+ 942	−13	−21	− 6
1	21	10	825	140	965	961	931	−18	−29	−11
2	20	8	821	130	952	949	919	−25	−36	−19
3	18	7	855	120	973	971	941	+ 3	−11	+ 9
4	17	6	883	110	985	984	956	+24	+11	+30
5	16	4	854	100	946	946	924	− 2	−12	+ 3
6	15	3	871	90	959	959	950	+29	+22	+34
7	13	2	881	80	959	959	961	+46	+44	+51
8	12	1	895	70	961	959	966	+57	+59	+61
9	11	23	844	60	906	903	911	+ 7	+12	+11
10	9	22	835	50	889	887	895	− 3	+ 8	+ 1
11	8	21	832	40	871	872	880	−12	0	− 9
12	7	19	828	+ 10	834	830	837	−50	−38	−47
13	6	18	869	0	863	857	862	−19	− 6	−16
14	4	17	851	− 10	833	826	828	−47	−35	−45
15	3	16	906	20	874	868	865	− 5	+ 3	− 3
16	2	14	879	30	841	835	828	−36	−32	−34
17	0	13	925	40	881	875	869	+11	+ 9	+12
18	23	12	882	50	828	824	830	−22	−27	−21
19	22	10	885	60	826	822	845	− 2	−10	− 1
20	21	9	867	70	805	801	842	+ 1	− 9	+ 1
21	19	8	849	80	778	776	831	− 4	−17	− 4
22	18	6	880	− 90	796	794	847	+17	+ 4	+17
23	17	5	741	+ 40	785	785	827	+ 3	− 9	+ 2
24	15	4	763	36	801	801	838	+20	+12	+19

TABLE 30 (Contd.)

k	$\Omega-\alpha$	$\Omega+\alpha$	F_1	$D\delta$	F_2	F_3	F_4	F_5	F_6	F_7
1	2	3	4	5	6	7	8	9	10	11
					Pair 73 (74)					
25	14^h	3^h	+756	+ 32	+788	+788	+824	+12	+ 7	+11
26	13	1	752	28	778	778	813	+ 6	+ 5	+ 4
27	12	0	718	24	740	740	773	−28	−26	−30
28	10	23	749	20	768	768	799	+ 4	+12	+ 2
29	9	21	752	16	769	769	801	+11	+21	+ 8
30	8	20	728	12	745	745	779	− 5	+ 6	− 8
31	6	19	726	8	742	742	779	+ 1	+15	− 2
32	5	18	744	+ 4	759	759	800	+27	+40	+23
33	4	16	697	0	708	708	751	−16	− 6	−20
34	3	15	+694	− 4	+699	+699	+742	−19	−12	−23
					Pair 74 (75)					
0	22	11	+833	− 70	+765	+785	+755	+12	+ 7	+21
1	21	10	841	80	759	776	746	+ 7	− 2	+15
2	20	9	800	90	710	722	692	−42	−53	−35
3	18	7	875	100	773	782	752	+22	+ 8	+27
4	17	6	879	110	762	767	739	+14	0	+18
5	16	5	870	120	744	745	723	+ 2	−12	+ 5
6	14	3	880	130	748	746	737	+20	+15	+24
7	13	2	907	140	765	765	767	+55	+53	+59
8	12	1	825	150	671	681	688	−20	−18	+16
9	10	0	837	160	679	702	710	+ 7	+15	+10
10	9	22	850	170	684	701	709	+10	+21	+13
11	8	21	817	180	636	631	639	−56	−44	−53
12	7	20	841	234	603	639	646	−44	−31	−42
13	5	18	840	246	588	644	649	−37	−24	−35
14	4	17	855	258	589	661	663	−18	− 6	−16
15	3	16	865	270	583	665	662	−15	− 7	−14
16	1	15	894	282	604	691	684	+11	+14	+12
17	0	13	918	294	620	712	706	+38	+36	+39
18	23	12	871	306	561	656	662	− 2	− 7	− 2
19	22	11	880	318	563	660	683	+24	+16	+24
20	20	9	856	330	534	630	671	+16	+ 4	+16
21	19	8	835	342	502	599	654	+ 3	−10	+ 2
22	18	7	844	354	496	593	646	0	−14	− 1
23	16	6	770	185	589	603	645	+ 3	−10	+ 2
24	15	4	759	182	579	591	628	− 9	−17	−11
25	14	3	762	179	583	593	629	− 4	− 9	− 6
26	13	2	759	176	581	589	624	− 5	− 7	− 7
27	11	0	738	173	563	570	603	−21	−16	−24
28	10	23	734	170	563	570	601	−19	−11	−22
29	9	22	745	167	579	584	616	+ 1	+12	− 2
30	7	20	707	164	548	552	586	−25	−12	−29
31	6	19	737	161	584	588	625	+18	+32	+14
32	5	18	695	158	548	551	592	−10	+ 3	−16
33	4	17	693	155	549	551	594	− 4	+ 8	− 9
34	2	15	+732	−152	+589	+591	+634	+41	+46	+36
					Pair 75 (76)					
6	14	4	+816	− 57	+757	+760	+751	+30	+24	+30
7	13	2	795	68	725	724	726	+ 4	+ 2	+ 4
8	11	1	806	79	723	708	715	− 7	− 2	− 7
9	10	0	873	90	785	753	761	+38	+46	+38

TABLE 30 (Contd.)

k	$\Omega-\alpha$	$\Omega+\alpha$	F_1	$D\delta$	F_2	F_3	F_4	F_5	F_6	F_7
1	2	3	4	5	6	7	8	9	10	11
					Pair 75 (76)					
10	9^h	23^h	+873	—101	+776	+754	+762	+ 38	+ 49	+ 38
11	8	21	804	112	691	697	705	— 20	— 8	— 20
12	6	20	804	63	737	692	699	— 27	— 12	— 27
13	5	19	739	62	671	604	609	—117	—103	—117
14	4	17	901	61	832	749	751	+ 24	+ 36	+ 24
15	2	16	833	60	761	671	668	— 60	— 54	— 61
16	1	15	868	59	801	708	701	— 28	— 25	— 29
17	0	13	928	58	866	772	766	+ 36	+ 34	+ 35
18	23	12	883	57	822	729	735	+ 5	0	+ 4
19	21	11	848	56	793	702	725	— 6	— 17	— 7
20	20	10	835	55	788	701	742	+ 10	— 3	+ 9
21	19	18	820	54	775	691	746	+ 13	0	+ 12
22	17	7	783	53	736	656	709	— 25	— 39	— 26
23	16	6	705	30	679	668	710	— 24	— 37	— 25
24	15	4	759	30	731	721	758	+ 23	+ 15	+ 22
25	14	3	791	30	761	753	789	+ 53	+ 48	+ 52
26	12	2	797	30	765	759	794	+ 57	+ 58	+ 56
27	11	1	727	30	695	690	723	— 15	— 10	— 16
28	10	23	731	30	700	696	727	— 11	— 3	— 12
29	8	22	764	30	735	732	764	+ 25	+ 38	+ 24
30	7	21	732	30	707	705	739	— 1	+ 13	— 3
31	6	19	722	30	700	698	735	— 6	+ 8	— 8
32	5	18	710	30	691	689	730	— 12	+ 1	— 14
33	3	17	678	30	659	658	701	— 41	— 31	— 43
34	2	16	+714	— 30	+693	+692	+735	— 8	— 2	— 10
					Pair 76 (77)					
0	21	12	+827	+ 10	+836	+821	+791	— 3	— 2	+ 16
1	20	11	807	0	803	792	762	— 28	— 37	— 17
2	19	9	786	— 10	775	767	737	— 56	— 68	— 48
3	18	8	825	20	803	798	768	— 28	— 43	— 22
4	16	7	899	30	863	860	832	+ 34	+ 18	+ 37
5	15	5	888	40	844	843	821	+ 21	+ 7	+ 22
6	14	4	859	50	807	808	799	— 4	— 10	+ 1
7	12	3	857	60	795	795	797	— 9	— 9	— 5
8	11	1	877	70	803	800	807	— 1	+ 4	+ 3
9	10	0	899	80	821	815	823	+ 13	+ 21	+ 16
10	9	23	902	90	816	812	820	+ 7	+ 18	+ 10
11	7	22	841	100	740	741	749	— 67	— 52	— 65
12	6	20	886	14	868	864	871	+ 53	+ 68	+ 55
13	5	19	836	16	814	808	813	— 7	+ 7	— 5
14	3	18	855	18	829	825	827	+ 4	+ 15	+ 5
15	2	16	854	20	822	820	817	— 9	— 3	— 8
16	1	15	904	22	874	876	869	+ 41	+ 44	+ 41
17	23	14	960	24	932	938	932	+102	+ 98	+102
18	22	13	885	26	855	864	870	+ 37	+ 29	+ 36
19	21	11	845	28	818	831	854	+ 18	+ 7	+ 17
20	20	10	778	30	756	771	812	— 26	— 39	— 27
21	18	9	805	32	782	801	856	+ 16	0	+ 14
22	17	7	763	— 34	735	756	809	— 34	— 48	— 36
23	16	6	746	+ 40	790	794	836	— 10	— 23	— 13
24	14	5	731	46	779	783	820	— 28	— 36	— 31
25	13	4	735	52	787	790	826	— 24	— 28	— 28
26	12	2	784	58	840	843	878	+ 25	+ 26	+ 21
27	11	1	761	64	823	826	859	+ 3	+ 8	— 1

TABLE 30 (Contd.)

k	☊ $-\alpha$	☊ $+\alpha$	F_1	$D\delta$	F_2	F_3	F_4	F_5	F_6	F_7
1	2	3	4	5	6	7	8	9	10	11
				Pair 76 (77)						
28	9^h	0^h	+740	+ 70	+809	+812	+843	−15	− 4	−20
29	8	22	743	76	820	822	854	− 6	+ 7	−11
30	7	21	726	82	813	815	849	−14	0	−20
31	5	20	731	88	827	829	866	0	+15	− 6
32	4	19	724	94	829	831	872	+ 4	+18	− 2
33	3	17	704	100	815	816	859	−11	− 1	−18
34	2	16	+706	+106	+821	+822	+865	− 8	− 2	−15
				Pair 77 (78)						
0	21	12	+801	+ 2	+802	+778	+748	−51	−56	−38
1	20	11	850	− 2	844	825	795	− 6	−15	+ 5
2	19	9	839	6	832	819	789	−15	−27	− 6
3	17	8	844	10	832	823	793	−13	−28	− 7
4	16	7	897	14	877	873	845	+36	+20	+40
5	15	6	864	18	842	841	819	+ 8	− 7	+ 9
6	13	4	874	28	844	845	836	+23	+19	+28
7	12	3	860	32	826	826	828	+12	+12	+16
8	11	2	861	36	821	814	821	+ 3	+ 7	+ 7
9	10	0	832	40	794	780	788	−33	−25	−29
10	8	23	851	44	811	802	810	−13	0	−10
11	7	22	820	48	771	773	781	−44	−29	−41
12	6	21	859	13	842	828	835	+ 7	+23	+ 9
13	4	19	841	12	823	802	807	−23	− 9	−21
14	3	18	882	11	863	840	842	+ 9	+20	+10
15	2	17	905	10	883	861	858	+23	+31	+24
16	1	15	871	9	854	835	828	− 9	− 6	− 8
17	23	14	932	8	920	905	899	+59	+55	+59
18	22	12	898	7	887	874	880	+38	+30	+38
19	21	11	834	6	829	820	843	− 2	−13	− 3
20	19	10	865	5	868	864	905	+58	+43	+57
21	18	9	796	4	801	801	856	+ 7	− 9	+ 6
22	17	8	786	− 3	789	793	846	− 6	−21	− 8
23	16	6	758	+ 55	817	818	860	+ 6	− 7	+ 4
24	14	5	761	60	823	824	861	+ 4	− 4	+ 1
25	13	4	747	65	812	813	849	−10	−14	−13
26	12	2	767	70	835	837	872	+11	+12	+ 7
27	10	1	741	75	814	815	848	−16	− 8	−20
28	9	0	715	80	794	796	827	−39	−28	−43
29	8	23	740	85	826	827	859	−10	+ 3	−15
30	7	21	724	90	819	820	854	−17	− 3	−22
31	5	20	728	95	831	832	869	− 4	+11	−10
32	4	19	738	100	849	850	891	+15	+29	+ 9
33	3	17	712	105	828	829	872	− 6	+ 4	−13
34	1	16	+698	+110	+817	+818	+861	−20	−16	−27
				Pair 78 (79)						
0	21	12	+845	+ 35	+879	+852	+822	−10	−15	+ 4
1	20	11	840	30	866	845	815	−15	−24	− 4
2	18	10	818	25	842	827	797	−32	−47	−23
3	17	8	842	20	860	851	821	− 7	−22	− 1
4	16	7	884	15	893	888	860	+34	+18	+38
5	15	6	842	10	848	847	825	+ 1	−14	+ 2
6	13	4	844	+ 5	847	849	840	+17	+13	+22

TABLE 30 (Contd.)

k	$\Omega-\alpha$	$\Omega+\alpha$	F_1	$D\delta$	F_2	F_3	F_4	F_5	F_6	F_7
1	2	3	4	5	6	7	8	9	10	11
					Pair 78 (79)					
7	12^h	3^h	+818	0	+816	+816	+818	− 4	− 4	+ 1
8	11	2	836	− 5	827	820	827	+ 7	+11	+11
9	9	1	829	10	821	806	814	− 4	+ 7	0
10	8	23	882	15	871	861	869	+ 52	+65	+55
11	7	22	793	20	772	775	783	− 33	−18	−30
12	6	21	796	25	767	752	759	− 55	−39	−52
13	4	19	873	30	837	816	821	+ 9	+23	+11
14	3	18	843	35	800	777	779	− 32	−21	−30
15	2	17	914	40	862	840	837	+ 27	+35	+28
16	0	16	910	45	857	838	831	+ 23	+24	+24
17	23	14	895	50	841	826	820	+ 14	+10	+14
18	22	13	863	55	804	793	799	− 6	−14	− 6
19	20	12	860	60	801	795	818	+ 14	+ 1	+14
20	19	10	852	65	795	793	834	+ 32	+17	+31
21	18	8	797	70	736	738	793	− 7	−23	− 8
22	17	8	856	75	787	793	846	+ 47	+32	+45
23	15	7	784	25	763	765	807	+ 9	− 3	+ 7
24	14	5	763	20	745	747	784	− 12	−20	−15
25	13	4	754	15	739	741	777	− 17	−21	−20
26	11	3	737	10	725	727	762	− 31	−28	−34
27	10	1	724	− 5	717	719	752	− 40	−32	−44
28	9	0	711	0	710	712	743	− 47	−36	−51
29	8	23	760	+ 5	766	768	800	+ 12	+25	+ 7
30	6	22	740	10	755	757	791	+ 4	+21	− 1
31	5	20	703	15	726	728	765	− 21	− 6	−27
32	4	19	698	20	729	730	771	− 13	+ 1	−19
33	2	18	718	25	754	755	798	+ 18	+27	+12
34	1	16	+736	+ 30	+775	+776	+819	+ 38	+42	+31
					Pair 80					
0	20	13	+881	+ 74	+951	+973	+943	+ 65	+61	+78
1	19	11	834	66	894	913	883	+ 16	+ 7	+27
2	18	10	797	58	853	868	838	− 18	−32	−10
3	17	9	812	50	860	871	841	− 4	−20	+ 2
4	15	8	886	42	923	929	901	+ 67	+51	+70
5	14	6	832	34	894	866	844	+ 20	+ 5	+21
6	13	5	761	34	793	791	782	− 31	−37	−24
7	11	4	755	26	779	780	782	− 20	−18	−12
8	10	2	699	18	713	728	735	− 56	−49	−48
9	9	1	683	10	695	731	739	− 41	−30	−32
10	8	0	684	+ 2	690	717	725	− 44	−31	−35
11	6	23	721	− 6	714	706	714	− 44	−27	−34
12	5	21	773	189	580	639	646	−101	−85	−91
13	4	20	789	216	567	664	669	− 67	−52	−56
14	2	19	829	243	578	705	707	− 18	− 8	− 6
15	1	17	869	270	587	732	729	+ 15	+21	+27
16	0	16	889	297	584	743	736	+ 32	+33	+45
17	23	15	892	324	564	735	729	+ 36	+33	+49
18	21	14	883	351	528	708	714	+ 32	+22	+46
19	20	12	829	378	452	636	659	− 12	−25	+ 2
20	19	11	856	405	459	646	687	+ 27	+12	+42
21	17	10	839	432	416	607	662	+ 13	− 4	+28
22	16	8	+806	−459	+353	+545	+598	− 40	−55	−24

TABLE 30 (Contd.)

k	☊ − α	☊ + α	F_1	$D\delta$	F_2	F_3	F_4	F_5	F_6	F_7
1	2	3	4	5	6	7	8	9	10	11
					Pair 82					
0	20^h	13^h	+ 821	+ 73	+895	+858	+828	−35	−39	−19
1	19	12	878	62	939	911	881	+18	+ 9	+31
2	17	10	862	51	914	895	865	+ 2	−12	+12
3	16	9	874	40	914	902	872	+10	− 6	+16
4	15	8	884	29	908	902	874	+12	− 4	+15
5	14	7	876	18	888	887	866	+ 4	−15	0
6	12	5	873	+ 3	870	872	864	+ 2	− 1	+ 7
7	11	4	881	− 8	868	867	869	+ 7	+ 9	+12
8	10	3	880	19	855	845	852	− 9	− 3	+ 5
9	8	1	850	30	820	799	807	−54	−41	−50
10	7	0	874	41	840	826	834	−27	−12	−24
11	6	23	882	52	836	833	841	−20	− 3	−17
12	5	22	904	36	869	850	857	− 4	+13	− 1
13	3	20	952	44	910	886	891	+31	+44	+33
14	2	19	991	52	937	912	913	+53	+63	+55
15	1	18	937	60	871	849	846	−14	− 7	−13
16	23	16	987	68	911	894	887	+27	+25	+28
17	22	15	935	76	853	842	837	−23	−29	−22
18	21	14	1008	84	919	815	822	−37	−47	−37
19	19	12	934	92	838	840	865	+ 6	− 9	+ 6
20	18	11	926	100	831	840	883	+24	+ 7	+23
21	17	10	897	108	798	813	869	+10	− 7	+ 9
22	16	9	921	−116	812	833	885	+26	+10	+25
23	14	7	794	+ 50	850	854	896	+38	+28	+36
24	13	6	739	50	795	799	835	−23	−30	−25
25	12	5	745	50	800	804	840	−18	−21	−21
26	10	3	767	50	820	824	859	+ 1	+ 7	− 2
27	9	2	776	50	826	830	863	+ 5	+15	+ 1
28	8	1	794	50	842	846	877	+20	+33	+16
29	7	0	743	50	792	795	827	−30	−15	−34
30	5	22	749	50	800	803	837	−20	− 3	−25
31	4	21	738	50	790	792	829	−28	−12	−33
32	3	20	788	50	844	846	887	+30	+43	+24
33	1	18	740	50	796	798	841	−15	− 8	−21
34	0	17	+ 753	+ 50	+809	+811	+854	− 2	+ 1	− 8
					Pair 83					
0	20	13	+ 853	+ 41	+895	+895	+865	− 1	− 5	+12
1	18	12	885	24	908	910	880	+17	+ 6	+28
2	17	11	877	+ 7	885	888	858	− 2	−16	+ 7
3	16	9	877	− 10	860	862	832	−26	−42	−20
4	15	8	939	27	907	909	881	+26	+10	+30
5	13	7	909	44	859	860	839	−13	−27	−12
6	12	6	903	59	838	837	829	−20	−24	−12
7	11	4	919	76	838	839	841	− 5	− 3	+ 3
8	9	3	927	93	828	836	843	− 1	+ 8	+ 8
9	8	2	943	110	833	854	862	+21	+33	+31
10	7	0	922	127	802	820	828	−10	+ 5	0
11	6	23	943	144	805	809	817	−18	− 1	− 7
12	4	22	939	172	768	807	814	−18	− 1	− 7
13	3	20	905	188	719	782	787	−43	−30	−31
14	2	19	929	204	723	807	808	−18	− 8	− 6
15	0	18	924	220	698	798	795	−29	−25	−16

TABLE 30 (Contd.)

k.	$\Omega - \alpha$	$\Omega + \alpha$	F_1	$D\delta$	F_2	F_3	F_4	F_5	F_6	F_7
1	2	3	4	5	6	7	8	9	10	11
Pair 83										
16	23^h	17^h	+939	−236	+ 695	+ 807	+ 800	− 21	−21	− 7
17	22	15	918	252	660	782	777	−41	−47	−17
18	20	14	980	268	707	839	846	+30	+18	+45
19	19	13	931	284	643	781	806	− 7	−22	+ 8
20	18	11	930	300	635	780	823	+13	− 4	+29
22	17	10	906	316	599	747	803	+ 4	−13	+29
22	15	9	+904	−332	+ 579	+ 731	+ 783	−21	−35	− 4
Pair 84										
6	12	6	+883	+178	+1055	+1058	+1050	+52	+ 48	+52
7	10	4	822	182	999	997	999	−12	− 7	−12
8	9	3	835	186	1015	999	1006	−17	− 8	−17
9	8	2	850	190	1040	1008	1016	−20	− 8	−20
10	7	1	906	194	1107	1084	1092	+44	+ 59	+44
11	5	23	814	198	1018	1014	1022	−38	− 21	−38
12	4	22	849	221	1071	1036	1043	−30	− 13	−30
13	3	21	927	224	1153	1105	1110	+25	+ 39	+25
14	1	19	912	227	1137	1083	1084	−14	− 6	−14
15	0	18	920	230	1144	1093	1090	−20	− 16	−20
16	23	17	873	233	1098	1052	1045	−77	− 77	−77
17	22	16	968	236	1198	1157	1152	+17	+ 12	+17
18	20	14	916	239	1150	1117	1124	−23	− 35	−23
19	19	13	932	242	1170	1144	1169	+ 9	− 6	+ 9
20	18	12	926	245	1176	1159	1202	+30	+ 13	+30
21	16	10	917	248	1174	1164	1220	+36	+ 19	+36
22	15	9	883	251	1141	1139	1191	− 6	− 20	− 6
23	14	8	762	410	1178	1179	1221	+12	+ 1	+12
24	13	7	745	422	1173	1175	1211	−11	− 19	−11
25	11	5	754	434	1193	1195	1231	− 3	− 3	− 3
26	10	4	723	446	1172	1174	1209	− 37	− 32	− 37
27	9	3	753	458	1211	1213	1246	− 13	− 4	− 13
28	7	1	776	470	1244	1247	1278	+ 7	+ 22	+ 7
29	6	0	776	482	1257	1259	1291	+ 7	+ 24	+ 7
30	5	23	712	494	1207	1209	1243	−53	− 36	−53
31	4	22	808	506	1316	1318	1355	+47	+ 64	+47
32	2	20	775	518	1299	1301	1342	+21	+ 32	+21
33	1	19	722	530	1258	1260	1303	− 30	− 22	− 30
34	0	18	+745	+542	+1293	+1295	+1338	− 8	− 4	− 8
Pair 85										
0	19	14	+898	− 33	+ 863	+ 830	+ 800	− 7	− 9	+11
1	18	12	893	42	848	824	794	− 2	−11	+12
2	17	11	892	51	841	824	794	+10	− 3	+19
3	15	10	833	60	773	763	733	− 40	− 55	−35
4	14	9	869	69	796	791	763	+ 1	−15	+ 2
5	13	7	848	78	766	765	744	− 6	− 22	−10
6	12	6	844	83	755	756	748	+ 9	+ 5	+13
7	10	5	851	92	754	753	755	+27	+ 30	+31
8	9	3	857	101	750	743	750	+33	+ 42	+36
9	8	2	760	110	650	638	646	− 59	− 47	−56
10	6	1	888	119	776	769	777	+83	+100	+85
11	5	23	728	128	606	605	613	−70	− 53	−68
12	4	22	911	257	655	648	655	−16	+ 1	−14

TABLE 30 (Contd.)

k	☊ − α	☊ + α	F_1	$D\delta$	F_2	F_3	F_4	F_5	F_6	F_7
1	2	3	4	5	6	7	8	9	10	11
					Pair 85					
13	3^h	21^h	+ 910	−278	+634	+630	+ 635	−25	−11	−24
14	1	20	967	299	666	668	669	+20	+29	+21
15	0	18	947	320	621	629	626	−12	− 8	−11
16	23	17	944	341	595	612	605	−21	−21	−21
17	21	16	990	362	622	648	643	+28	+20	+28
18	20	14	962	383	574	609	616	+12	0	+11
19	19	13	962	404	554	595	620	+28	+13	+27
20	18	12	949	425	529	578	621	+40	+23	+39
21	16	11	873	446	436	492	548	−22	−39	−24
22	15	9	900	467	440	504	556	− 2	−16	− 4
23	14	8	792	255	543	553	595	+48	+37	+46
24	12	7	769	266	509	519	555	+19	+14	+16
25	11	5	727	277	455	464	500	−24	−24	−27
26	10	4	767	288	482	490	525	+12	+17	+ 8
27	9	3	709	299	410	417	450	−52	−43	−56
28	7	2	765	310	453	460	491	0	+14	− 4
29	6	0	729	321	407	413	445	−34	−17	−39
30	5	23	760	332	429	434	468	0	+17	− 5
31	3	22	749	343	408	412	449	− 8	+ 7	−13
32	2	20	751	354	403	406	447	+ 2	+13	− 4
33	1	19	766	365	407	410	453	+19	+27	+13
34	23	18	+ 739	−376	+369	+372	+ 415	− 8	− 7	−15
					Pair 86					
6	11	6	+ 861	− 61	+794	+797	+ 789	− 6	− 7	− 8
7	10	5	861	64	792	790	792	−11	− 8	−13
8	9	4	857	67	784	769	776	−34	−26	−36
9	7	2	886	70	816	786	794	−24	−10	−26
10	6	1	926	73	860	839	847	+22	+39	+20
11	5	0	825	76	755	751	759	−73	−56	−75
12	4	22	876	59	818	789	796	−44	−27	−46
13	2	21	981	56	927	888	893	+46	+58	+44
14	1	20	969	53	914	873	874	+19	+28	+17
15	0	19	1006	50	950	913	910	+48	+53	+46
16	22	17	872	47	817	786	779	−90	−93	−92
17	21	16	1016	44	966	942	937	+60	+52	+58
18	20	15	932	41	886	871	878	− 6	−17	− 8
19	19	13	979	38	937	931	956	+64	+49	+62
20	17	12	905	35	875	875	918	+19	+ 2	+17
21	16	11	885	32	862	872	928	+22	+ 5	+20
22	15	10	888	− 29	866	885	937	+23	+ 8	+21
23	13	8	746	+125	877	880	922	+ 1	− 8	− 1
24	12	7	767	130	903	907	943	+14	+ 9	+12
25	11	6	799	135	939	943	979	+43	+42	+41
26	10	4	777	140	920	924	959	+16	+21	+14
27	8	3	722	145	867	871	904	−47	−36	−49
28	7	2	776	150	924	928	959	+ 1	+15	− 1
29	6	1	751	155	905	909	941	−25	− 8	−27
30	4	23	780	160	941	944	978	+ 5	+22	+ 3
31	3	22	755	165	922	925	962	−18	− 3	−20
32	2	21	792	170	968	970	1011	+23	+35	+21
33	1	19	721	175	902	904	947	−48	−40	−50
34	23	18	+ 730	+180	+916	+918	+ 961	−42	−41	−44

TABLE 30 (Contd.)

k	$\Omega-\alpha$	$\Omega+\alpha$	F^1	$D\delta$	F_2	F_3	F_4	F_5	F_6	F_7
1	2	3	4	5	6	7	8	9	10	11
					Pair 87					
0	19^h	14^h	+ 866	+ 70	+ 934	+ 919	+ 889	+ 30	+ 28	− 45
1	18	13	842	60	899	889	859	− 1	− 10	+ 11
2	16	12	869	50	919	913	883	+ 21	+ 8	+ 30
3	15	10	856	40	896	893	863	0	− 15	+ 6
4	14	9	901	30	927	926	898	+ 34	+ 18	+ 37
5	12	8	902	20	918	918	897	+ 31	+ 17	+ 30
6	11	6	802	+ 10	806	806	798	− 69	− 70	− 61
7	10	5	809	0	804	804	806	− 62	− 59	− 53
8	9	4	826	− 10	810	813	820	− 49	− 41	− 39
9	7	3	857	20	837	846	854	− 17	− 4	− 6
10	6	1	863	30	840	849	857	− 15	+ 2	− 4
11	5	0	891	40	857	859	867	− 6	+ 11	+ 6
12	3	23	890	108	783	807	814	− 61	− 46	− 48
13	2	21	928	122	808	851	856	− 20	− 8	− 6
14	1	20	954	136	816	877	878	+ 1	+ 10	+ 16
15	23	19	936	150	780	855	852	− 26	− 24	− 11
16	22	18	984	164	812	899	892	+ 12	+ 10	+ 28
17	21	16	982	178	798	896	891	+ 10	+ 2	+ 27
18	20	15	954	192	757	868	875	− 7	− 18	+ 11
19	18	14	976	206	766	885	910	+ 26	+ 10	+ 45
20	17	12	934	220	719	845	888	+ 3	− 14	+ 23
21	16	11	903	234	678	810	866	− 20	− 37	0
22	14	10	+ 903	−248	+ 662	+ 800	+ 852	− 36	− 49	− 15
					Pair 88					
0	19	14	+ 816	+178	+ 992	+1003	+ 973	+ 13	+ 11	+ 25
1	18	13	978	162	1137	1148	1118	+146	+137	+155
2	16	12	865	146	1011	1021	991	+ 8	− 5	+ 15
3	15	10	885	130	1015	1023	993	− 2	− 17	+ 3
4	13	9	936	114	1046	1051	1023	+ 17	+ 3	+ 19
5	12	8	935	98	1029	1030	1009	− 9	− 23	− 9
6	11	7	952	78	1024	1022	1014	− 16	− 18	− 6
7	10	5	971	62	1028	1029	1031	− 10	− 7	+ 2
8	8	4	933	46	973	989	996	− 57	− 47	− 44
9	7	3	791	30	821	860	868	−196	−183	−181
10	6	1	990	+ 14	1011	1043	1051	− 25	− 8	− 8
11	4	0	996	− 2	1000	1007	1015	− 73	− 56	− 55
12	3	23	905	+ 64	970	1035	1042	− 57	− 42	− 37
13	2	23	901	56	959	1064	1069	− 42	− 29	− 20
14	1	20	935	48	981	1121	1122	0	+ 9	+ 24
15	23	19	971	40	1005	1167	1164	+ 30	+ 32	+ 55
16	22	18	893	32	917	1096	1089	− 57	− 59	− 30
17	21	16	925	24	943	1136	1131	− 26	− 34	+ 3
18	19	15	1015	16	1026	1232	1239	+ 70	− 57	+100
19	18	14	936	+ 8	940	1154	1179	− 1	− 17	+ 31
20	17	13	991	0	996	1215	1258	+ 66	+ 49	+100
21	16	11	926	− 8	927	1151	1207	+ 3	− 14	+ 39
22	14	10	+ 909	− 16	+ 900	+1131	+1183	− 32	− 45	+ 5
					Pair 89					
0	18	14	+ 888	+101	+ 988	+ 991	+ 961	− 15	− 16	+ 2
1	17	13	925	94	1015	1019	989	+ 14	+ 7	+ 27
2	16	12	892	87	977	982	952	− 22	− 34	− 13

TABLE 30 (Contd.)

k	$\Omega-\alpha$	$\Omega+\alpha$	F_1	$D\delta$	F_2	F_3	F_4	F_5	F_6	F
1	2	3	4	5	6	7	8	9	10	11
					Pair 89					
3	14^h	11^h	+895	+80	+977	+981	+951	−22	−35	−17
4	13	9	907	73	977	980	952	−20	−35	−20
5	12	8	942	66	1004	1005	985	+13	−3	+9
6	11	7	926	61	977	975	969	−2	−4	+5
7	9	5	937	54	986	987	990	+20	+26	+28
8	8	4	850	47	894	907	914	−55	−45	−46
9	7	3	916	40	957	991	999	+31	+44	+41
10	5	2	877	33	917	947	955	−12	+4	−1
11	4	0	907	+26	940	957	965	−1	+16	+11
12	3	23	954	−79	882	939	946	−19	−4	−7
13	2	22	940	96	849	941	946	−18	−5	−5
14	0	20	965	113	853	972	973	+10	+16	+24
15	23	19	932	130	799	940	936	−26	−24	−11
16	22	18	899	147	744	901	894	−68	−70	−52
17	20	16	1005	164	836	1008	1003	+42	+36	+59
18	19	15	999	181	814	996	1005	+45	+32	+63
19	18	14	991	198	788	977	1003	+44	+28	+62
20	16	13	892	215	678	876	921	−37	−54	−18
21	15	11	914	232	691	894	951	−6	−21	+14
22	14	10	+917	−249	+674	+796	+847	−109	−122	−88
					Pair 90					
6	10	7	+909	−130	+769	+772	+766	−33	−32	−31
7	9	6	894	130	759	757	760	−42	−37	−40
8	8	4	907	130	774	761	768	−38	−28	−36
9	6	3	962	130	833	807	815	+5	+20	+7
10	5	2	963	130	840	822	830	+17	+33	+19
11	4	1	895	130	772	764	772	−44	−27	−42
12	3	23	937	120	824	804	811	−9	+6	−7
13	1	22	983	120	868	846	851	+27	+38	+29
14	0	21	953	120	834	816	817	−10	−3	−9
15	23	19	980	120	857	845	841	+11	+13	+12
16	21	18	1014	120	886	884	877	+43	+38	+44
17	20	17	1009	120	884	890	885	+47	−39	+48
18	19	15	933	120	809	826	835	−6	−19	−5
19	18	14	955	120	830	858	884	+40	+24	+41
20	16	13	893	120	774	810	855	+7	−10	+8
21	15	12	892	120	781	827	884	+32	+17	+33
22	14	10	829	−35	800	831	882	+27	+14	+28
23	12	9	739	+50	796	805	846	−12	−19	−11
24	11	8	760	50	819	828	864	+2	−1	+3
25	10	7	774	50	831	839	875	+9	+10	+10
26	9	5	795	50	849	857	892	+23	+29	+24
27	7	4	764	50	814	821	853	−19	−7	−18
28	6	3	790	50	835	841	871	−5	+10	−4
29	5	1	794	50	841	847	879	−1	+16	−1
30	3	0	792	50	838	843	877	−6	+9	−6
31	2	23	698	50	745	749	787	−99	−86	−99
32	1	22	759	50	809	813	854	−36	−25	−36
33	23	20	810	50	861	864	907	+13	+16	+13
34	22	19	+808	+50	+861	+864	+907	+10	+9	+10

TABLE 30 (Contd.)

k	$\Omega-\alpha$	$\Omega+\alpha$	F_1	$D\delta$	F_2	F_3	F_4	F_5	F_6	E_7
1	2	3	4	5	6	7	8	9	10	11
					Pair 91					
6	10^h	7^h	+ 932	−281	+641	+644	+638	+ 13	+ 14	+ 11
7	9	6	884	284	595	593	596	− 32	− 27	− 34
8	7	5	902	287	612	596	603	− 27	− 17	− 28
9	6	3	950	290	661	628	636	+ 3	+ 18	+ 2
10	5	2	956	293	670	647	655	+ 20	+ 36	+ 19
11	4	1	869	296	580	569	577	− 60	− 43	− 59
12	2	23	949	311	645	618	625	− 15	− 2	− 16
13	1	22	906	314	597	563	568	− 74	− 63	− 75
14	0	21	1031	317	715	682	683	+ 38	+ 45	+ 37
15	22	20	1027	320	704	676	672	+ 25	+ 25	+ 24
16	21	18	1017	323	686	667	660	+ 11	+ 6	+ 10
17	20	17	1029	326	698	689	684	+ 32	+ 24	+ 32
18	19	16	966	329	633	635	644	− 10	− 18	− 10
19	17	14	992	332	655	666	692	+ 35	+ 19	+ 35
20	16	13	945	335	611	632	677	+ 18	+ 1	+ 18
21	15	12	915	338	586	617	674	+ 13	− 2	+ 13
22	13	11	827	228	605	628	679	+ 15	+ 4	+ 15
23	12	9	783	120	670	677	718	+ 52	+ 45	+ 52
24	11	8	762	124	647	654	690	+ 21	+ 18	+ 21
25	10	7	736	128	615	622	658	− 13	− 12	− 13
26	8	5	720	132	592	598	633	− 40	− 32	− 39
27	7	4	753	136	617	623	655	− 21	− 9	− 20
28	6	3	754	140	609	615	645	− 33	− 18	− 32
29	4	2	771	144	624	629	661	− 20	− 4	− 19
30	3	0	788	148	636	641	675	− 8	+ 7	− 7
31	2	23	791	152	636	640	678	− 7	+ 6	− 6
32	1	22	787	156	631	634	675	− 13	− 2	− 12
33	23	20	805	160	646	649	692	+ 2	+ 5	+ 3
34	22	19	+ 788	+164	+627	+630	+673	− 20	− 21	− 19
					Pair 92					
0	17	14	+ 873	− 46	+826	+800	+770	− 17	− 18	− 2
1	16	13	920	64	852	834	804	+ 13	+ 6	+ 24
2	15	11	894	82	810	798	768	− 27	− 37	− 20
3	14	10	909	100	811	805	775	− 23	− 36	− 20
4	12	9	937	118	816	813	785	− 17	− 29	− 18
5	11	8	944	136	804	803	783	− 23	− 36	− 28
6	10	6	962	156	796	797	791	− 19	− 17	− 13
7	8	5	995	174	816	816	819	+ 5	+ 13	+ 12
8	7	4	1021	192	826	825	832	+ 15	+ 27	+ 23
9	6	2	1044	210	835	836	844	+ 23	+ 39	+ 32
10	5	1	1029	228	808	812	820	− 5	+ 12	+ 5
11	3	0	1039	246	800	804	812	− 17	− 2	− 6
12	2	23	980	176	811	827	834	+ 1	+ 14	+ 13
13	1	21	961	184	782	813	818	− 18	− 8	− 5
14	23	20	1020	192	829	876	877	+ 37	+ 40	+ 51
15	22	19	975	200	772	832	828	− 16	− 17	− 1
16	21	17	982	208	766	839	832	− 16	− 22	0
17	20	16	1017	216	796	882	877	+ 25	+ 15	+ 42
18	18	15	1014	224	786	884	893	+ 38	+ 23	+ 56
19	17	14	985	232	748	856	882	+ 23	+ 7	+ 41
20	16	12	913	240	674	791	836	− 27	− 44	− 8
21	14	11	921	248	682	805	862	− 5	− 18	+ 15
22	13	10	+ 849	− 256	+599	+676	+727	−144	−155	−123

TABLE 30 (Contd.)

k	$\Omega-\alpha$	$\Omega+\alpha$	F_1	$D\delta$	F_2	F_3	F_4	F_5	F_6	F_7
1	2	3	4	5	6	7	8	9	10	11
					Pair 96					
0	17^h	16^h	+ 869	+149	+1017	+ 970	+ 940	−29	−28	−10
1	15	15	932	146	1074	1039	1009	+34	+31	+47
2	14	14	922	143	1063	1039	1009	+28	+21	+36
3	13	12	873	140	1015	1001	971	−17	−28	−14
4	11	11	879	137	1013	1006	978	−16	−26	−18
5	10	10	821	134	951	949	929	−71	−83	−79
6	9	8	887	129	1006	1009	1003	− 3	0	− 1
7	7	7	876	126	997	995	998	−14	− 6	−12
8	6	6	906	123	1026	1014	1021	+ 2	+13	+ 4
9	5	5	914	120	1035	1012	1020	− 5	+ 7	− 4
10	4	3	948	117	1072	1056	1064	+33	+48	+34
11	2	2	897	114	1018	1011	1019	−18	− 6	−17
12	1	1	928	93	1028	1013	1020	−23	−12	−22
13	0	23	966	92	1063	1048	1053	+ 3	+11	+ 3
14	22	22	1003	91	1095	1086	1087	+31	+33	+31
15	21	21	972	90	1059	1059	1055	− 7	− 9	− 7
16	20	20	952	89	1033	1043	1036	−32	−37	−32
17	19	20	998	88	1081	1105	1100	+26	+19	+26
18	17	17	955	87	1038	1073	1082	+ 1	−11	0
19	16	16	972	86	1053	1098	1124	+37	+23	+36
20	15	14	949	85	1035	1090	1135	+42	+28	+41
21	13	13	885	84	978	1043	1100	+ 1	−10	0
22	12	12	884	198	1088	1131	1182	+77	+69	+75
23	11	11	732	315	1054	1066	1107	− 5	−10	− 7
24	10	9	708	318	1035	1047	1083	−35	−35	−37
25	8	8	774	321	1102	1112	1148	+24	+29	+22
26	7	7	736	324	1064	1074	1109	−21	−13	−24
27	6	5	758	327	1085	1094	1126	−10	+ 2	−13
28	4	4	777	330	1102	1110	1140	− 3	+11	− 6
29	3	3	822	333	1152	1159	1191	+42	+55	+39
30	2	2	753	336	1085	1091	1125	−30	−18	−33
31	1	0	795	339	1131	1136	1174	+13	+24	+ 9
32	23	23	761	342	1103	1107	1148	−19	−14	−23
33	22	22	782	345	1128	1132	1175	+ 1	+ 3	− 3
34	21	20	+ 721	+348	+1072	+1076	+1119	−61	−64	−65

REFERENCES

1. N.YE.ZHUKOVSKII (N.JOUKOVSKI). Zh. Russk. fiz.-khim. obshch., ch. fiz., 16, 6, 81; 7, 145; 8, 231 (1885).
2. N.I.IDEL'SON. Astronom. yezhegodnik SSSR na 1942 g., 408 (1941).
3. A.K.KOROL'. Trud. Poltavskoi gravimetr. observat. Acad. Sci. Ukrainian SSR, 3, 162 (1950).
4. K.A.KULIKOV. Astronom. zh., 26, 165 (1949).
5. K.A.KULIKOV. Fundamental Astronomical Constants (Fundamental'nyye postoyannyye astronomii) (1956).
6. P.S.MATVEYEV. Astronom. tsirkulyar, No. 143, 17. (1953).
7. M.MOLODENSKII. Trud. Geofiz. inst., No.19, (146), 3 (1953).
8. A.YA.ORLOV. Astronom. tsirkulyar, No. 116, 16 (1951).
9. A.YA.ORLOV. Astronom. tsirkulyar, No. 126, 19 (1952).
10. A.YA.ORLOV. Analysis of Pulkovo observations with the zenith-telescope: 1915-1929, in Selected Works (Izbrannyye trudy), Vol. 1, 234, Kiev (1961).
11. N.I.PANCHENKO. Astronom. tsirkulyar, No. 148, 9 (1954).
12. N.A.POPOV. Trud. Poltavskoi. gravimetr. observat., Acad. Sci. Ukrainian SSR, 4, 103 (1951).
13. N.A.POPOV. Astronom. tsirkulyar, Nos. 101/102, 8 (1950).
14. YE. P.FEDOROV. Trud. Poltavskoi gravimetr. observat., Acad. Sci. Ukrainian SSR, 2, 3 (1948).
15. YE.P.FEDOROV. Astronom. tsirkulyar, Nos. 101/102, 9 (1950)
16. YE.P.FEDOROV. Trud. Poltavskoi gravimetr. observat., Acad. Sci. Ukrainian SSR, 4, 294 (1951).
17. YE.P.FEDOROV. Dokl. Akad. nauk SSSR, 80, 569 (1951).
18. YE.P.FEDOROV. Dokl. Akad. nauk SSSR, 91, 759 (1953).
19. YE.P.FEDOROV. Proceedings of the 10th All-Union Astronomical Conference (Trudy 10-oi vsesoyuznoi astronomomicheskoi konferentsii), Leningrad, 129 (1954).
20. A.YE.FILIPPOV. Astronom. tsirkulyar, No. 168, 14 (1956).
21. H.BONDI and R.A.LYTTLETON. Proc. Cambridge Phil. Soc., 49, 498 (1953).
22. K.BULLEN. Monthly Notices Roy. Astr. Soc., Geophysical Suppl., 3, 395 (1936).
23. E.DELANO. Astronomical J., 55, 129 (1950).

24. B.WANACH and H.MANKOPF. Resultate des Intern. Breitendienstes, 1912. 0 to 1922. 7, Potsdam (1932).
25. J.FUHRICH. Statistickky Obzor, Csl. Stat. Staatsam, 471 (1933).
26. T.HATTORI. Astr. Soc. of Japan Publications, 3, 126 (1951).
27. A.R.HINKS. Monthly Notices Roy. Astr. Soc. 70, 63 (1909)
28. S.S.HOUGH. Phil. Transactions Roy. Soc., Ser. A, 186, pt. 1, 469 (1895).
29. J.JACKSON. Monthly Notices Roy. Astr. Soc., 90, 733 (1930).
30. H.JEFFREYS. Monthly Notices Roy. Astr. Soc., 108, 206 (1948).
31. H.JEFFREYS. Monthly Notices Roy. Astr. Soc., 109, 670 (1949).
32. H.MORGAN. Astronomical J., 50, 125 (1942).
33. H.MORGAN. Astronomical J., 54, 133 (1949).
34. H.MORGAN. Colloque Intern. sur les constantes fondament. de l'Astronomie, Paris (1952).
35. H.MORGAN. Astronomical J., 57, 232 (1952).
36. S.NEWCOMB. Monthly Notices Roy. Astr. Soc., 52, 336 (1892).
37. S.NEWCOMB. The Elements of the Four Inner Planets and the Fundamental Constants of Astronomy, Washington (1895).
38. T.R.OPPOLZER. Lehrbuch zur Bahnbestimmung der Kometen und Planeten, Vol. 1, Leipzig (1889).
39. H.POINCARE. Bull. astronomique, 27, 321 (1910).
40. L.W.POLLAK and A.HANEL. Meteorol. Zschr., 52, 330 (1935).
41. E.PRZYBYLLOK. Die Nutationskonstante abg. aus den Beob. des Intern. Breitendienstes, Berlin (1920).
42. Th.ALBRECHT and B.WANACH. Directors, Resultate des Intern. Breitendienstes, Bd. III, Berlin (1909).
43. Th.ALBRECHT and B.WANACH. Directors, Resultate des Intern. Breitendienstes, Bd. IV, Berlin (1911).
44. B.WANACH. Director, Resultate des Intern. Breitendienstes, Bd. V, Berlin (1916).
45. H.KIMURA. Director, Results of the Intern. Latitude Service from 1922, 7 to 1935, Mizusawa (1940).
46. ROSS F., Astr. Nachr., 192, 48 (1912).
47. W.STEKLOFF. Annales de la Faculté des Sciences de Toulouse, 3 sér., 1, 145 (1909).
48. W.SCHWEYDAR. Astr. Nachrichten, 203, 101 (1916).
49. N.SEKIGUCHI. Japanese Journal of Astr., 1, 99 (1950).
50. N.SEKIGUCHI. Astr. Soc. of Japan Publications, 1, 103 (1950).
51. N.SEKIGUCHI. Astr. Soc. of Japan Publications, 2, No.2, 74 (1950).

52. N.SEKIGUCHI. Astr. Soc. of Japan Publications, 4, 139 (1952).
53. F.SLOUDSKY. Bull. de la Societé des. Natur. de Moscou, No. 2, 285 (1895).
54. H.SPENCER JONES. Monthly Notices Roy. Astr. Soc., 98, 440 (1938).
55. H.SPENCER JONES. Monthly Notices Roy. Astr. Soc., 99, 211 (1939).
56. W.THOMSON., Philosophical Transactions Roy. Soc. 153, 573 (1863).
57. S.UEMAE. Astr., Soc. of Japan Publications, 4, 163 (1953).
58. B.WANACH. Astr. Nachrichten, 201, 225 (1915).
59. E.W.WOOLARD. Astronomical J., 58, 1 (1953).